P9-EER-765

The World's Great Folktales

Blairsville Joint School Library
Blairsville, Pa.

3045

398
Fos

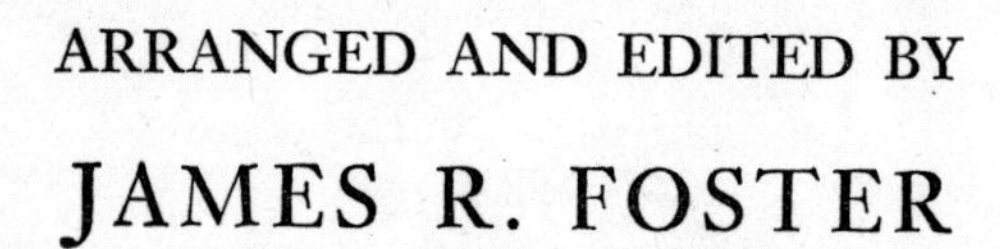

ARRANGED AND EDITED BY

JAMES R. FOSTER

Blairsville High School Library
Blairsville, Pennsylvania

THE WORLD'S GREAT
FOLKTALES

3045

HARPER & BROTHERS, NEW YORK

394

THE WORLD'S GREAT FOLKTALES

Copyright, 1953, by Harper & Brothers
Printed in the United States of America

All rights in this book are reserved. No part of the book may be used or reproduced in any manner whatsoever without written permission except in the case of brief quotations embodied in critical articles and reviews. For information address Harper & Brothers, 49 East 33rd Street, New York 16, N. Y.

FIRST EDITION

G-C

Library of Congress catalog card number: 53–7752

Contents

Preface

This book of old tales is intended to provide entertaining reading for almost everybody, and at the same time make available a goodly number of folktale "classics" until now widely scattered through many books and journals. As the same tale that charms the reader by its narrative power can also illustrate a notable folklore idea or feature, we have selected tales that are diverting and may be instructive as well. They form a diversified and representative collection which will give a good comprehensive view of the world of the folktale and help the reader, if he so wishes, to an understanding and appreciation of the popular imagination.

As better suited to this purpose, classification of the tales according to subjects instead of the usual classification according to place of origin has been adopted. How the stories are distributed geographically or whether they represent particular nations and peoples is not here considered as important as whether the stories selected can offer the reader as full a presentation of folklore themes and motifs as possible within the compass of one book.

Since the folktales of Europe have exerted the greatest influence upon European and American art and literature, these are our staple. We have had to scant the realistic tale so that we might more bountifully provide for tales in which the marvelous and supernatural play a considerable role. Actually these elements are prominent in the majority of the folktales of Europe, for most of them reflect, or are colored by, religio-magical ideas. This is not surprising since the fundamental motifs of most folktales come from story material belonging to a people whose minds run more easily down the meandering paths of associative or traditional "thinking" than along the more arduous "newfangled" roadways of logic or the new sciences. Ancient traditions, magical beliefs, rites, and myths supply the motifs of more than half of the European folktales, but dreams, drugs, optical and auditory illusions and other psychological phenomena also make important contributions. It is notable that even in tales not particularly concerned with the supernatural and magical, ideas more or less closely related to these are nearly always present somewhere in the storyteller's mind, and he assumes that they are also present in the minds of his listeners.

The editor has used the best texts available, and except for a few tales that had to be rewritten on a smaller scale, he has not altered them save when he has omitted digressions and similar extraneous material—and this he has always indicated. When he has had to translate, he has tried to make his translation literal and as plain and simple as possible. Acknowledgments to publishers who kindly gave permission to use copyrighted material have been made in the introductions of the appropriate sections.

J. R. F.

Woodmere
January, 1953

I

OTHERWORLD AND TRANSFORMED LOVERS

One of the folk muse's most fascinating themes is love between a mortal and an Otherworld or transformed being. Stories embodying it are found everywhere, and some of them are of rare excellence because of their imaginative boldness, poetic richness, and romantic charm. The belief that Otherworld beings consorted with mortals is the basis for stories about the philandering of the gods, the birth of demigods and demons, marriages of human beings with the jinn, and the love affairs of medieval knights with fairy queens, serpent women, and swan maidens. Also for tales about the diabolic commerce of witches with his Satanic Majesty, the nocturnal visits of incubus and succubus to cloister and nunnery, and the search of gnomes, sylphs, undines, and salamanders for a mortal lover, for according to the Cabalistic doctrine only by such a love can these elemental spirits win back their lost immortality. In some folktales the transformed lover is a superior being who shifts his shape of his own volition; in others the transformation is a penalty for some violated taboo or the effect of an evil spell cast by witch or wizard.

"The Serpent Woman" is from Mrs. S. G. C. Middlemore's *Spanish Legendary Tales*, 1885, and "Melusina" is the editor's condensed version based on the French romance written by Jean d'Arras in 1387. "The Forty He-goats" is the editor's translation of the tale in *Contes Populaires Inédits du Caire (Bulletin de l'Institut Egyptien*, Cairo, 1885) by S. E. Artin Pacha. The merry tale of "The Weaver Who Impersonated Vishnu" is the editor's slightly condensed version based on the story in the first book of the *Panchatantra*, and "Tannhäuser and Venus" is the abstract of the Tannhäuser story given in S. Baring-Gould's *Curious Myths of the Middle Ages*, 1884.

[1]

The Serpent Woman

There lived in the twelfth century a certain Don Juan de Amarillo, who dwelt not far from Cordova. Although not very young himself, he had a handsome young wife, whom he adored. He introduced her to all his friends; but though she made a great sensation by her beauty, wherever she appeared, yet, in some way or other, she contrived to make enemies and no friends among either sex.

No one knew where she came from, nor what her name was before she was married. All that was certain was that Don Juan had been absent from home for many years, that he had never been heard of by either friend or foe in all that time, and that he had returned as suddenly as he had departed, but bringing with him a wife.

There were many stories afloat of her origin and character. Some said that she was a strolling player, whom Don Juan had rescued from ill-treatment and persuaded to marry him for his name and position. Others said that she was a witch, and had bewitched the old Don Juan by means of love-philters and noxious herbs.

These stories were none of them true. But people repeated them to each other, and were quite satisfied in believing them. Meanwhile, Doña Pepa went about and enjoyed herself, unconscious of the tales that were told of her, but not unconscious of the terror she inspired. She was quite aware that people shunned her, and avoided her whenever they could. She was a wonderfully handsome woman, with regular features, dark eyes, and a head like that of a beautiful statue. Her figure was singularly flexible and lithe. But in spite of her beauty, people looked askance at her, and felt, without being able to say why, that there was something wrong about her. She had some curious tricks of manner which were startling. When she was pleased, she would raise her head so that it seemed really to lengthen two or three inches, and she would sway her body to and fro with delight. Whereas, if anything displeased her, or she disliked anyone, her head seemed to flatten out, and the touch of her hand was like a bite. She delighted in hearing and repeating all the ill-natured stories that she could about her neighbors, and, in short, seemed as spiteful as a woman could possibly be.

To all outward appearances, she and Don Juan got on excellently well together. But the servants of the household told a different tale. They said that at home they wrangled from morning till night, and that sometimes Don Juan was positively afraid of his wife, especially when her head flattened, for then she looked, and really was, dangerous. People said that they also had seen a look of alarm creep over the old man's face, even in company, when she showed any signs of anger.

Things went on like this for many years, but still Don Juan and his wife seemed to live in peace and harmony. To be sure, the servants, who had been in the family for years, left one after another; and when questioned as to their leaving, answered that the *señora* was a witch, and that the angel Gabriel himself could not live with her. How their master managed, they could not imagine, unless she had bewitched him.

Then it was rumored about that a favorite nephew of Don Juan was coming from Aragon to pay him a visit, and to be formally acknowledged as his heir. As he and his wife had no children he wished to leave his wealth to this nephew, the son of an only sister who was dead; and in course of time the friends and neighbors of Don Juan were invited to meet the stranger.

He was a frank, open-faced, and open-hearted young man, about twenty-seven years old, who at once won the hearts of all who saw him. He was not at all jubilant or overweening at the honors thrust upon him as his uncle's heir, but spoke quite ingenuously of his former poverty and the disadvantages as well as the pleasures of his boyhood, to his aunt's intense disgust.

Doña Pepa could not bear to hear of poor relations, much less to let the world know that Don Juan de Amarillo had any such belongings. And she gave young Don Luis such a look of mingled scorn, hatred, and disgust as made him shudder, and kept his tongue quiet for the rest of the evening. The guests tried in vain to draw him into conversation; he had received such a rebuff in Doña Pepa's glance that he became utterly silenced and wondered what sort of woman she could be. He had seen what the guests had not observed (for nobody else had at that moment noticed her), that her head had flattened, and that her eyes had grown long and narrow; that she had moistened her lips (which were white with rage) with a hissing sound, and that her tongue was forked. He had heard queer stories about his aunt, but had hitherto never paid much attention to them. Now everything he had ever heard in his life came back to his memory, and it was with the utmost effort that he forced himself to sit through the evening, and tried to appear interested in all that went on.

The more Don Luis was known, the more popular he became. Everyone liked him. His uncle worshiped him, and could hardly bear him out of his sight; for he reminded him of his dearly loved lost sister, and of his own past youth, before he became entangled in the world's wickedness and folly.

Even Doña Pepa could not withstand the freshness and charm of her innocent young nephew, and although she was continually angry with him for his careful avoidance of her, she could not retaliate upon him as she had often retaliated on others—for as time went on she had learned to love him.

He lived in constant fear of her, and tried to keep out of her way by every courteous means in his power. But she would not let him escape from her. She dogged his footsteps everywhere. If he went out for a walk, she was sure to come and meet him, and he felt certain that he was watched—not for his good, but with a jealous eye.

One evening he went to see a friend who was having a sort of reception, and stayed out rather later than usual. When he got to his uncle's house he lit his little taper and started for his room. In the hall he stumbled over what he supposed to be a coil of rope. To his horror the rope unwound itself, and proved to be a large black snake, which glided upstairs before him, and disappeared under his uncle's door. The thought instantly flashed across his mind that his uncle was in danger of his life; and without hesitation he pounded and knocked and shouted at the door for at least five minutes. They seemed to him five hours. But his uncle was old and sleepy, and it took him some time to wake up. However, at last he came to the door and demanded crossly what his nephew meant by disturbing his rest at that time of night.

"I saw a large black snake creep under this door, my dear uncle, and I was afraid that you might suffer from it before I could help you," replied his nephew.

"Nonsense!" said Don Juan, turning pale, "there is no serpent here"; and he tried to shut the door again. But Don Luis was determined to search the room. Doña Pepa was apparently asleep.

The room was carefully searched, but nothing could be found. His uncle was very angry; but as Don Luis was leaving the room, crestfallen at his failure, and wondering whether he was losing his mind, Doña Pepa opened her eyes and gave him one of her evil glances; her head flattened, and her eyes grew long and narrow. He left the room with an undefined sensation of terror; he could not sleep, and when he dozed for a few minutes, his dreams were of snakes and of loathsome reptiles.

The next morning he found only his aunt when he went down. His uncle had gone out, Doña Pepa said. Don Luis had taken such an aversion to her that he could hardly bring himself to speak to her, and she took intense delight in plying him with questions, which he felt himself obliged to answer as became a Spanish gentleman.

But at last he could bear it no longer. Doña Pepa was giving very evident signs of rage, and he was hastily beating a retreat, when she strode across the room, seized him by the arm, and said: "You shall not treat me with such disdain; you shall learn to fear me if you cannot learn to love me."

At the same moment that her hand touched his wrist, he felt a sharp sensation as if something had stung him. He threw her hand off and hurried out, thinking for the time no more about his pain. But in the course of the day his arm began to swell rapidly and to throb painfully, until at last the hand and fingers were swollen to such a degree that he could neither close them nor hold anything with them. He then became rather alarmed, and decided to go to a hermit who lived not far off, and who was renowned for his skill in the treatment of poisons, as well as for his piety.

After examining the arm the old man said, "It is a serpent's bite."

"No, it is not," interrupted Don Luis. "My aunt grasped my arm, in a frenzy of rage, and this is the result."

"Worse still," answered the hermit; "a serpent woman's bite is sometimes deadly."

"Can you do nothing for me?" cried Don Luis, in despair. "I hate her, and I have been persecuted by her for weeks."

"Yes, and you will be persecuted by her still more. She will take refuge in your room instead of on the landing. Put these leaves upon your arm, and keep wetting them when they become dry, and your arm will probably get better. As to conquering her, that will be a more difficult matter. If you can keep awake you will get the better of her. But if you sleep one minute, you will be at her mercy."

"What shall I do to her? I would do anything short of murdering her," said Don Luis excitedly.

"Take your sword, when you find her a little way from the door, and hack off a piece of the snake, and see the effect. Then come to me again."

With this advice Don Luis was obliged to be content. His arm was so much soothed by the hermit's treatment, that he determined to try the rest of his advice.

That night, when he went to his room, he undressed and was just getting into bed when he spied the snake coiled in a huge mass at the foot of it. Without a sound he drew his sword, gave a stroke at the snake, and cut off a piece of the tail. The snake reared its head and showed its fangs, preparing apparently for a spring; but Don Luis gave another blow, and another piece of the tail came off. With a hiss the snake uncoiled, dragged itself to the door, disappeared down the stairs, and crept under Don Juan's door below.

The next morning Doña Pepa did not appear. His uncle said that she had a habit of sleep-walking, and had run something sharp into her foot.

"I can guess what ails her," thought Don Luis to himself, as he condoled with his uncle, who seemed really troubled.

Don Luis had carefully preserved in a drawer the pieces of the tail which he had cut off; and on looking at them the next morning had found that they were the toes and instep of a human foot.

For some days he neither saw nor heard anything more of his aunt in any shape. But at last she reappeared and greeted him most cordially. He noticed, however, that she halted decidedly in her gait, and reported everything to the hermit.

"Have no pity for her, my son," replied the hermit, "for she intends your destruction. If you have any mercy upon her, she will have none for you. The next time strike about a foot from the head, where she cannot hide her disfigurement."

A few evenings after this conversation with the hermit, he found the snake awaiting him in the courtyard, and as usual it went upstairs before him, and coiled itself on a chest in the farthest corner of the room. All the doors in the house seemed to be constructed for harboring and helping snakes, for they were scooped away underneath for two inches.

Don Luis drew his sword and struck as nearly a foot from the head as he could. The snake made a bound to the door and disappeared, the head first and the body following and joining it outside; and it then disappeared under his uncle's door.

The next day Doña Pepa disappeared from human ken for a month. "She had a dreadful abscess on her finger," his uncle said, "which had kept her awake for many nights, and she must lie by for a time and have it lanced."

"I can guess what ails her," thought Don Luis, and went to his friend the hermit to report matters.

On the way he met an old servant who had been in his grandfather's family, and had lived with Don Juan after his marriage, but had been amongst the first to leave. The old servant stopped him and said: "I have been anxious for a long time about my master and you. Is he well? And what is going on there? I did not like to call at the house, as I left of my own accord. But I had to leave, for I could not bear to live with that horrid snake in the house, Doña Pepa."

"What do you mean by 'snake in the house,' Jorge?" asked Don Luis. "Did you ever see a snake in that house?"

"Indeed I have," replied the old servant indignantly. "It followed me all over the house, until I nearly lost my wits. If I went into the kitchen, it was there; in my room, it was there; and at last I went away because when I spoke to my master about it, he grew so angry that I saw he thought I was lying. Have you never seen the snake yourself, *señor?* for everyone else who lived there has."

"Yes, I have seen the same thing myself, if you press me so hard," answered Don Luis; "but what can I do more than I have? In snake form, I have cut off one foot and one hand. What can I do more short of murder?"

"One thing more," said old Jorge earnestly, "one thing more, and that is to watch until she is out. Go to the chest in the master's room, under the left-hand window, and open it. You will find a queer skin, striped like a serpent's, folded up in the right-hand corner. Burn that, and you will find that the snake will not torment you any more."

For his uncle's sake Don Luis bore with patience the annoying attentions of the snake as long as he could; but after a month more of torment he watched his opportunity when Don Juan and Doña Pepa were out, and went into his uncle's room. There he found the chest under the left window, just as old Jorge had said. On one side was a queer striped skin, which he immediately recognized as the snake's. He was preparing to light a fire and burn it, when he heard his uncle and Doña Pepa returning. He had only time to close the chest, slip upstairs to his room, and hide the skin, before they entered their room.

As soon as he heard them descend into the hall, he prepared and lit a fire, and took out the skin, rolling it up in his hand to make it smaller, when he heard fearful shrieks below. He rushed out to learn the cause, and was told by one of the servants that Doña Pepa had had fearful cramps, as though her body had been folded up. Then Don Luis knew that what he had heard was true; and, without giving himself time to think, he threw the skin upon the fire. In a moment it was in a blaze, and crisped and curled into nothing.

Having watched it burn to the end, he went down to his uncle. Don Juan was walking up and down the room, wringing his hands. Doña Pepa was stretched out upon a couch, looking very white and ill. The family physician was sitting beside her, holding her hand and feeling her pulse.

"What has happened?" asked Don Luis. "Is Doña Pepa ill?"

"She is dead," replied the physician solemnly; "and I cannot discover what was the matter nor what can have killed her. She was in excellent health, as far as I could make out, an hour ago, when I was called in to see her for convulsions; and now, with no bad symptoms at all she suddenly died. I cannot understand the cause at all."

Don Luis thought to himself that he perhaps could throw a good deal of light upon the subject. But he held his tongue.

When Doña Pepa was laid out for burial, the old nun who had prepared her for her last resting place, confessed that she had seen the figure of a large snake distinctly traced upon the entire length of her body.

Don Luis and Don Juan lived very happily together for years after the death of Doña Pepa. His uncle seemed like a boy again, so light-hearted and gay was he. When his friends came to see him, he would say: "I have not been so happy for many a long year."

And Don Juan's friends thought it strange, but Don Luis did not. Only the hermit and one or two others knew the secret of the Serpent Woman.

[2]

Melusina

The Earl of Poitiers, a nobleman of wealth and great virtue, had but one son, Bertrand, and when he was to be dubbed knight the earl made a great feast. He invited his brother-in-law, the Earl of Forest, who had more sons than means, to feast with him. Naturally, he accepted, and he brought three of his sons with him. After the great feast was over, the Earl of Poitiers begged him to leave his son Raymond with him, promising to provide for his future. Consent was given, and Raymond, a handsome and amiable youth, became his uncle's constant companion in hall and in the chase.

One day the Earl of Poitiers and his retinue went after a fierce boar in the forest of Colombiers. They found him, but after he had killed some of the hounds, he struck out through terrain so difficult that no one but the earl and Raymond cared about following him. Later on in the day Raymond brought the enraged animal to bay but for his pains got knocked backward. The boar again took to flight. As their horses were tiring, Raymond and the earl rested under a tree until nightfall. Suddenly they heard a fearful noise—the boar was charging directly at them. Dropping his sword, the earl seized a short spear and spitted the brute through the breast. Then Raymond struck the boar such a powerful blow that his sword broke, and part of the blade flying off pierced the earl's breast and killed him. When Raymond realized what a dreadful accident had happened, he wept and lamented piteously. After kissing the dead earl, he rode aimlessly through the forest, permitting his horse to go wherever he would.

At midnight they came to a fairy fountain. Bright moonlight shone down on it and the magnificent glade where it was. And three fair damsels were frolicking there. One of them was Melusina: the others were her sisters. The dazed Raymond did not notice these radiant maids, but his horse saw them and fled away in fright.

Melusina seemed surprised that this knight had been so uncivil as not to greet them. And she ran and caught his horse's bridle and scolded Raymond for his uncouth behavior. At first he seemed not to hear her, but suddenly rousing up, he impulsively drew his sword and laid fiercely about him. But he really came to his senses when he heard rippling laughter and a sweet voice say, "Sir vassal, with whom will you begin the battle? Your enemies are not here, and I, fair sir, am on your side." Struck by the exquisite beauty of the lady, he got down from his horse and apologized for his unseemly conduct. Soon he discovered, to his extreme surprise, that she knew his name and how the earl had met his death. Indeed, she advised him not to say anything about the accident when he returned home. "When they find the earl's body," she said, "they will see the wounds and conclude that the boar killed him." So Raymond followed her advice, and everything happened as she predicted.

And he stayed at the fountain and talked with Melusina till daybreak. Her beauty inspired him and he wished to make love to her. But she made him promise to marry her and as her husband never to try to see or visit her, or ask where she was on Saturday of each week. On her part she promised to do nothing on that day to injure his honor or that of his family. So Raymond promised he would accept her terms. Thus they plighted their troth and sealed it with a kiss. But before he said adieu, she gave him two rings—one to pro-

Blairsville Joint School Library
Blairsville, Pa.

tect him against weapons and the other to give him victory over his enemies.

After the earl's funeral, he met her again at the fountain. She advised him to ask of his kinsman Bertrand, as a gift, as much ground around this fountain as could be covered by a stag's hide. And he should have this hide cut up into thongs, for in this way much land could be covered. And so it happened, and Raymond was provided with an estate of considerable size. Melusina now made great preparations for her wedding. It was to be a gorgeous affair, and in some mysterious way she provided fit lodgings for the important noblemen and women who were guests. There were splendid tents and pavilions and a chapel ornamented with pearls and precious stones and cloth of gold. After the bishop married them, there was a splendid banquet in the pavilions and a tournament in which Raymond was the victor. And when he and Melusina retired, the bishop blessed their bed. Then the curtains were drawn and everyone took his leave.

Soon Melusina built a magnificent castle. She named it after herself, Lusinia, which has since become Lusignan. She now began to have a family—and a rather queer one it was. Her first was a son, Urian. His mouth was large, his ears enormous, and one of his eyes was red and the other green. The face of her second, a son called Gedes, was scarlet red. In thank-offering for his birth she built and endowed the convent of Malliers. And as a residence for the boy, she built the castle of Favent. A third son, Guyot, was handsome but one of his eyes was higher up in his face than the other. For him his mother built La Rochelle. Anthony, the next child, was hairy all over and had long claws. The next had only one eye. The sixth had a boar's tusk protruding from his mouth, and he was called Geoffrey with the Great Tooth. Other children she had, but all but the last two were in some way disfigured or monstrous.

Years passed and the love of Raymond for his beautiful wife never grew less. Every Saturday she left him and spent the day in strictest seclusion. Her husband never thought of intruding on her privacy. However, this was all changed when Raymond's brother, now Earl of Forest, came on a visit to them. He arrived on a Saturday, the day when Melusina was not visible, and as he and Raymond were going to dinner he inquired about his sister-in-law. And he told Raymond, when the latter made no answer, that some gossips were saying that Melusina spent her Saturdays with a paramour while others maintained that she was a fairy and had to do penance on Saturday. Now Raymond was much disturbed by what his brother said, and his mind became prey to the cruelest kind of anxiety and doubt. Resolving to find out the truth come what may, he went to that part of the castle where his wife spent her day of mystery. Finding his way barred by an iron door, he drew his sword and punched a hole in it. Looking through this hole he saw Melusina in a great marble bath which had steps leading up to it. She reclined in the water and combed her hair. Down to her navel she was shaped like a woman, but the rest of her was like a great serpent. This discovery of the awful effects of his wife's fairy origin and the expiation she was doomed to undergo struck Raymond dumb. Silently he withdrew, and anguish at the thought of losing his beautiful wife through his indiscreet curiosity made him very sad. But he was cheered when day after day passed without her giving any sign of knowing that he had broken his promise.

But one day news came that Geoffrey with the Great Tooth had set fire to the monastery of Malliers. Geoffrey had long been ashamed and angry that his brother Fromond had become a monk. So he burned Fromond's monastery, Fromond himself, and the abbot and a hundred monks. Raymond, on hearing of this terrible act, exclaimed as Melusina approached to comfort him, "Away, false serpent. You and all your children, except Fromond, came from the Devil!" This bitter speech had such an effect on Melusina that she fell to the ground in a swoon so deadly that for half an hour she did not breathe and was pulseless. When at length she recovered, she gently upbraided her husband for revealing her dual existence and putting an end to the fond dream of her life, for if she could have lived her life out with him, she could have been buried in the Church of Our Lady of Lusignan, whereas now she would have to resume her fairy shape of half-serpent half-woman, and linger about in that form until the day of judgment. After advising him what to do when she should be gone and telling him she was the daughter of King Elynas of Albany and his queen Pressyne, and that whenever she was seen hovering over Lusignan it would mean that the lord of the castle was to die shortly, with a long wail of agony she swept from the window, leaving the impression of her foot on the stone she last touched. And in her fairy serpentine form she flew three times around the castle uttering a piteous cry in the voice of a mermaid.

It is said that after this she used to come at night to visit her two infants. And their nurses saw her take them to her breast and suckle them. But at dawn she vanished.

Raymond went to Rome, where the pope heard his confession, gave him penance and the permission to retire to a hermitage. Geoffrey, whose conscience troubled him, also confessed to the pope, and promised to rebuild the abbey of Malliers and provide for one hundred and twenty monks. So he became the new earl. Some time after this he and a brother saw a strange serpentlike creature upon the battlements of the castle. The people were abashed when they heard a shrill and terrible cry, for they knew it was Melusina. And the two sons went to their father's hermitage and found him dead. And they gave him a magnificent funeral, at which were present the King and Queen of Aragon and all the nobility of the land.

[3]

The Forty He-goats

Once there was a sultan who had three daughters, each more beautiful than her sisters. When they grew up and were old enough to marry, their father, after consulting his vizier, decided that the best plan to provide suitable husbands for them was to invite all the young men who aspired to such an honor to pass on a certain day beneath the windows of the harem. So the criers made known this invitation throughout the land.

On the appointed day many young men appeared under the palace windows. The eldest princess threw down her handkerchief, and it fell upon a handsome prince. The second princess then threw hers, and it settled on the head of a great emir who was both young and attractive. Now there was a he-goat stepping along lightly through the crowd. And the handkerchief of the youngest princess descended upon his horns. The sultan commanded her to throw her handkerchief down again. And a second time, fate made it fall on the horns of the he-goat. The sultan, very angry because he did not like people to laugh at him, ordered her to try it over again. The results were the same: the kerchief, after sailing crazily through the air, settled on the goat's horns.

On seeing this example of the obstinacy of fate, the sultan declared he would never consent to his daughter's marrying a goat. He would rather see her an old maid. But the young princess wept incessantly. And she said she wished to marry the goat because that was her destiny. The older sisters, who were jealous because she was more beautiful than they, to spite her asked their father to permit this marriage. So the sultan had to yield, and he set a day for the strange wedding.

For forty days and forty nights the whole town celebrated. There were banquets, games, fireworks, music, and song. Yet amid all this, no person could help wondering how this queer union would turn out. The sultan, the vizier, the women of the palace tried one after the other to persuade the princess not to consummate her marriage. No matter what was said to her, she always gave the same response: "Can a person escape his destiny?"

When the night of the *doukhoule* came, the princess was made ready and the he-goat admitted to the nuptial chamber. Almost before the door slammed to, the goat shook himself and cast off his skin. The princess was astonished no little and pleased much more to see before her a strong, handsome young man—indeed, no one had ever seen such a handsome bridegroom. He came close and caressed her. "I am a powerful emir," he said, "but a spell has been cast upon me by some sorcerers. I have loved you long, and now am united with you. It is in your power, princess, to keep us forever from being separated!"

"And what must I do?" interrupted the princess.

"Never tell anyone that I have been transformed. Everyone must think that I am a goat. If anyone ever suspects that this is not true, I will disappear. After that day you will never see me again!" The young princess, more amazed than frightened, promised to keep the secret. So they sampled the joys of wedded bliss. They were very happy together, and the young princess kept her husband's secret well. Everyone gave up trying to understand why she loved the he-goat. The sultan, who by now had run out of arguments, concluded that since she did not complain, she was happy.

A neighboring king now declared war on the sultan. He prepared for the conflict, but as he was old, he put his two sons-in-law in command of the army, and they marched away, and the young princess's husband went with them. Soon afterward they returned victorious, and the sultan declared a three-day celebration. On the first day when the two princes marched by under the palace windows, their wives threw flowers to them. The youngest princess tossed down a rose to a very handsome young man who marched beside her brothers-in-law. When the victors passed by on the second day, she threw him a jasmine and on the third day a tamarind blossom. Her sisters welcomed this opportunity to find fault with her. "A married woman should not throw flowers to a stranger," they said. But she only laughed and mocked them. So they spoke to their father about it. The sultan became terrifically angry. The young princess was frightened out of her wits and to justify herself confessed that the young man in question was in reality her husband.

When evening came he did not appear at the palace. He had disappeared.

As each day passed, she became more and more lonesome for him. She became so sad that she considered herself the most unfortunate person in the whole world. It did no good to argue with her or recount the stories of the most illustrious and unhappy lovers. This only increased her sorrow. One day she decided to find out for herself if there was in the world an unhappier woman. She had a bath built and announced in all quarters that any woman could bathe there free if she would relate the greatest misfortune that had ever happened to her.

All the women of the town and its environs came. One told that her husband beat her. Another said her husband neglected her and ran after horrible old women and ugly Negresses. A third recounted how her spouse had divorced her and that her lover married a woman not half so good as she was.

None of these tales interested the princess—not even for an instant.

She was always sad. Finally, however, there came a poor old creature who, although she had on nothing but a riddled smock, told a tale that held her attention.

"Day before yesterday," she said, "at nightfall I went down to the river to wash my smock because I wanted to come to your bath the next morning. Not far from me there was a she-mule filling two skins with water. When the skins were full, she went a few paces further off, and striking the ground with her forefoot, sunk through a hole which opened beneath her and slid down a declivity into the interior of the earth. Forgetting to wash my smock, I followed the mule down through the subterranean passage. Soon I entered a great chamber which seemed to be the kitchen of a grand palace. The pots hung in a row over the fire. One could hear them boiling and smell the aroma of things cooking.

"As I saw no one there, neither chief-cook nor scullions, I was about to lift the lid off a pot when something struck my hand and a voice cried in my ear, "Don't touch until the mistress comes!" I was frightened and drew back. Then I saw an open bin full of fresh fine-smelling bread. I wished to taste it, but when I stretched out my hand and was about to grasp the bread, I got a blow on the back of my hand and heard the same voice in my ears crying, "Don't touch it until the mistress comes!" Becoming more frightened, I walked through the rooms. They were richly decorated: the furniture, the drapes, and the tapestry surpassed in richness, beauty, brilliance, and variety anything imaginable! Finally I came to a large chamber with a great oval pool full of water in the center. Around this pool there were forty magnificent chairs.

"No one was here either, but when I entered I heard a sound like that made by the feet of a herd of goats. Hiding behind a couch, I soon saw a number of he-goats come in and sit down in the seats. There were forty of them and the last one was riding on the next-to-last one. And the goat who rode sat down in the highest seat. For a moment they all sat motionless. Then all together they shook their sides. Their skins fell off and they became handsome young men. Their leader, of course, was the handsomest of all. He then dived into the pool and the rest followed. After their swim, they emerged and sat on their chairs, which, I observed, were covered with cloths and towels. When the youths were dry, their leader began to weep.

'O! princess of grace and beauty,' he sobbed. And his companions wept and sobbed with him. The furniture, the walls, the doors, the ceilings, the windows even—all echoed with groans and laments. It was enough to split one's soul! After they had had their cry out, the prince stood up. His companions did likewise, and each retired to the apartments where they slept."

The further the old woman progressed with her story, the more interested the princess, whose name was Sitt-el-Husna, became. She listened to every word, and when the story was ended, she was convinced that the he-goat who rode his companion was her husband. And now she thought of nothing else but going to meet him. And she offered the old woman anything she could ask for—clothes, jewels, money—if she would guide her along the subterranean passage. Of course, the woman accepted.

So early the next morning Sitt-el-Husna went to the old woman's dwelling and waited there until nightfall. Then the impatient princess asked whether it was time to set out. But she was told to wait until the moon shone on the flat roof of the bake house. She did not take her eyes off that roof until the moon appeared. Then she awakened the crone and they walked to the riverbank. The mule was there filling the water skins. When she struck the earth with her hoof, it opened and she entered the subterranean passage. The women followed her and came to the kitchen. Pots and kettles boiled cheerfully on the fire. The old woman took the lid off one pot and tasted its contents. She did the same for a second and a third—and then all of them. No blow struck her hands and no voice forbade her. Catching sight of some dainty dishes, she tasted them and forced the princess to do likewise, and the bread in the bin also let itself be eaten without protest of any kind. Every edible was fine—in fact, much better than one usually eats. Indeed the crone noticed that everything had changed since her first visit. Now joy reigned throughout this enchanted palace.

Led by her guide, the princess came to the great room with the oval pool. The women hid and saw the he-goats file in, just as they had done before, with the last goat riding one of his companions. They took stations around the pool, shook off their skins, changed into forty handsome young men, took their plunge, and the moment they emerged from the pool, the princess recognized her husband! She wished to run to him but since she did not have a veil to cover her face, modesty prevented her doing this and appearing with uncovered face before so many strange men.

Now the prince, having taken his seat as usual, began to sob and weep and call on the princess. His companions, however, did not as usual imitate him but instead began to laugh. Even the walls and doors and other parts of the great room seemed to radiate joy. Only the prince was sad. His mood now turned to uneasiness and surprise. After his joyous companions left him, he arose and was making his way toward his apartment when the princess, who no longer heeded the advice of the timorous crone and could hold back not a minute more, came out of her hiding place and approached her husband.

The sight of her filled his heart with bliss. He not only forgave her for not being able to keep his secret but did not even wish her to go to the trouble of explaining how she came to reveal it. Her perseverance and courage, said he, had broken the evil spell which had transformed him. From now on he could appear anywhere in his human shape.

When the princess brought him to the palace, the sultan greeted him amicably and was very glad to see him. But her sisters, who now recognized him as the handsome and valiant young warrior their sister had thrown the flowers to when the victors marched past, became more jealous than ever. But they pretended to be friendly with her and to be happy about what had happened. The sultan ordered a splendid seven-day celebration, and the prince and princess loved each other very much. They lived long and had many children.

[4]

The Weaver Who Impersonated Vishnu

A weaver and a wright who lived near each other had since childhood been very close friends, and they always passed their leisure hours together. One day in a temple in the place there was a great religious celebration. As the two friends were walking along among the many actors, dancers, mimes, and men from strange countries, a beautiful princess riding an elephant caught their eyes. On her were all the marks of high nobility and with her were a crowd of eunuchs and servants of the seraglio. The instant the weaver saw her he was struck by the arrow of love and fell to the ground as if poisoned or seized by a malign demon. When the wright saw him thus stricken, he was touched by pity and, lifting him up, took him home. There, thanks to some magic verses repeated in his presence and chilling draughts prescribed by the doctor, the weaver came to himself. Then the wright asked him: "Well, friend! Why did you suddenly lose consciousness? Tell me what caused it."

"Companion," responded the weaver, "lend a careful ear and I will tell you everything. O friend! if you really wished to do what would be the best for me, you would fetch wood so that I could burn myself on a pyre. But perhaps I am imposing on your friendship and causing you inconvenience. If so, please forgive me."

When the wright heard this, with his eyes full of tears and his voice shaking with emotion, he said, "Whatever it is that is causing your trouble, tell it to me so that I can remedy it, if remedy there is." "Companion," said the weaver, "nothing can cure my sickness. Therefore do not delay my death." "O friend!" cried the wright, "tell me what it is anyway, so that I also, if I believe the case hopeless, can leap into the pyre with you. I cannot stand being separated from you—I have resolved to die with you."

"Companion," said the weaver, "then listen. The instant I saw that princess riding on the elephant, the venerable god whose banner displays a fish, that is, Kama the god of love, put me in this painful condition, and I cannot stand it." When the wright heard this, he smiled and said, "If this is all there is to the affair, the remedy will be easy to find. So go to see her today." "But how can we have an interview with a young lady in her apartment which is well guarded and where no one enters but the wind?" "Companion," answered the wright, "let me show you how clever I am." And taking some wood from a vâyouda tree, he fashioned a Garuda bird which could be set in motion by turning a peg, and fabricated two arms and the discus, shell, club, and bow. And he also made the diadem and the breast jewel. Then he had the weaver mount the Garuda bird, put the signs of Vishnu upon him, showed him how to wind the peg, and said: "Companion, go in the form of Vishnu to the princess's apartment at midnight. She is alone in the top chamber of the seven-story palace. In her naïveté she will take you for Vishnu. Win her love by false and deceitful words and enjoy her."

So that very night the weaver entered the princess's chamber in the form of Vishnu and said: "Princess, are you sleeping or are you awake? For you I have come in person from the milky sea, and I have abandoned Lakshmi because I am full of love for you. Grant me, then, your favors." When the princess saw that he was mounted on Garuda, had the breast jewel, the four arms with the discus, club, and the rest, she pressed her hands together respectfully and said, "O venerable one, I am but an impure insect from among mere human beings, while you are the worthy object of adoration and the creator of the three worlds. How then can such different beings love each other?" "My well-beloved," answered the weaver, "you say true. However, the woman named Radha, born in the family of Nanda, was formerly my spouse. She has reincarnated herself in you. That is why I have come here." "O venerable one," said then the princess, "if this is true ask my father for me so that he will give me to you without hesitation." "Well-beloved," said the weaver, "I do not show myself to men, and for a still stronger reason I do not talk to them. Therefore, let us love in the fashion of the celestial musicians. But if you will not consent, I will curse you and reduce your father and all his family to ashes."

The princess was afraid to say "no," and after spending the night with her, the weaver returned home without being seen by anyone. And so each night he visited her. But one day the servants of the women's quarters saw that the red coral on the princess's lower lip was cracked, and they said to each other: "This seems to indicate the princess has been entertaining a lover. But how could she do this when her chamber is so well guarded? Let us inform the king."

So they went to the king and said: "Majesty, although the chamber of the princess is well guarded, someone enters there. Let your majesty give commands." And the king was vexed and after making some philosophical reflections about daughters, he went to the queen and said, "We must make certain that the servants of the women's quarters have told the truth. The god of death is incensed against the person who committed this sin." When the queen heard this, she was troubled. She went straight to the princess's apartment, and she saw that her daughter's lips were cracked and the skin on parts of her body scratched. And she said: "Ah! wayward one, why have you dishonored your family and destroyed your virtue? Who is the person who visits you and is sought by the god of death? Tell me the truth."

As the queen spoke thus with a great deal of warmth, the princess, lowering her head in fear and shame, said: "Mother, Vishnu, mounted on Garuda, comes to me each night. If you don't believe me, let a woman hide in my apartment tonight and she will see that venerable spouse of Kama." Now when the queen had heard this, she went to the king and with a smiling face said, "Majesty, your happiness increases. In the middle of each night the venerable Vishnu comes to our daughter. He has married her after the manner of the celestial musicians. Tonight you and I will go to the window and look for him."

The king was happy when he heard this, and he could hardly wait for darkness to come. Then in the night while he hid at the window with his wife, he saw Vishnu descend through the sky, and he rode Garuda and carried the discus, the shell, the club, and the bow in his four hands. Then the king felt like a man who swam in a pool of nectar, and he said to his wife: "My dear, no one in the world is happier than we, for the venerable Vishnu loves our child. So all the wishes of our hearts are answered. Now through the power of my son-in-law I will conquer the whole world."

Having taken this resolution, he provoked by unjust acts all the kings whose countries bordered on his, and when they saw this, they united and made war on him. While this was going on, he had the queen say to her daughter: "My child, while you are my daughter and the venerable Vishnu my son-in-law, is it fitting that all the kings should make war on us? You must tell your husband to destroy our enemies."

Therefore when the weaver made his visit, the princess humbly said, "O venerable one, it is not fitting that my father should be conquered by his enemies, seeing that you are his son-in-law. Show, then, your gracious power and cause our enemies to perish." "Well-beloved," answered the weaver, "the enemies of your father amount to nothing at all! Do not be alarmed! With my discus I will break them into little bits." However, within a very short time, the enemy conquered nearly all of the realm. The king kept sending the false Vishnu camphor, alms, musk, and other kinds of choice perfumes as well as various kinds of clothes, flowers, foods, and drinks. And he had his daughter tell him, "O venerable one, at dawn this city will certainly be taken. And there are no woods or crops left. And all my soldiers are either wounded so badly they cannot fight or have been killed. Since you know this, do now what is fitting."

And the weaver thought it over. "If the city is taken," he reflected, "I will die with the rest, and I will be separated from her. Consequently I am going to mount the Garuda bird and show myself all armed high in the sky. Perhaps our enemies will take me for Vishnu and, seized by fear, will perish under the blows of the king's warriors. And if, in flying through the air to protect the city, I am killed, that will be more beautiful still, for it is said that the person who sacrifices his life for a cow, a brahman, his master, his wife, or his city wins the eternal worlds."

Having made this resolve, he cleaned his teeth and said to the princess: "Well-beloved, when all the enemies will have been killed, I will eat and drink. Indeed, I will not make love to you until after that has happened. Now tell your father that at dawn he must lead out a great army and they must fight. As for me, I will hover in the air and cause the enemy to lose their strength. After that, they will be killed easily. If, however, I kill the soldiers of the enemy myself, these sinners will go to paradise. Consequently, they must be killed while fleeing so that they will not go there."

In the meanwhile the real Vishnu, who knows the past, the future, and the present, smiled and said to the real Garuda, "Hear, volatile one! Do you know that a weaver who impersonates me and rides about on a wooden Garuda is carrying on an affair with the king's daughter?" "Indeed," answered the latter, "I know all about it. What ought we to do now?" "Today," said Vishnu, "the weaver, having resolved to die, made a vow and has gone forth to fight. Wounded by the arrows of the bravest warriors, he will surely meet death. When he will have been slain, everyone will say that a great number of warriors came together and slew Vishnu and Garuda. After that the men of the world will no longer worship us. Therefore go quickly and enter that wooden Garuda, and I will enter the

Blairsville Joint School Library
Blairsville, Pa.

body of the weaver so that he can destroy the enemy. Our prestige and grandeur will be enhanced by the massacre of these warriors."

So Garuda went into the wooden bird and Vishnu into the weaver's body. Then through the might of the venerable one, the weaver—who rode aloft on Garuda and carried the shell, discus, club, and bow—was enabled as by magic to take away the strength of the hostile warriors. Then the king with his army vanquished them in battle and slew them. And word of this massacre spread through the world. It was said that the king had been able to destroy his enemies because he had Vishnu for a son-in-law.

As soon as the weaver observed that his enemies were dead, he came down to the ground with a happy heart. And then the king's minister and the inhabitants of the city saw that the supposed Vishnu was in reality their fellow citizen, the weaver. And when they asked for an explanation, he told them everything. The king, who had acquired glory in destroying his enemies, suddenly felt a great affection for the weaver, and he solemnly gave him the princess in marriage before the whole world. He also gave him lands, and the weaver and the princess passed the time on them very happily, eating, drinking, and loving.

[5]

Tannhäuser and Venus

A French knight was riding over the beauteous meadows in the Hörsel vale on his way to Wartburg, where the Landgrave Hermann was holding a gathering of minstrels who were to contend in song for a prize.

Tannhäuser was a famous minnesinger, and all his lays were of love and of women, for his heart was full of passion, and that not of the purest and noblest description.

It was toward dusk that he passed the cliff in which is the Hörselloch, and as he rode by, he saw a white glimmering figure of matchless beauty standing before him, and beckoning him to her. He

Blairsville High School Library
Blairsville, Pennsylvania

knew her at once by her attributes and by her superhuman perfection to be none other than Venus. As she spoke to him, the sweetest strains of music floated in the air, a soft roseate light glowed around her, and nymphs of exquisite loveliness scattered roses at her feet. A thrill of passion ran through the veins of the minnesinger; and, leaving his horse, he followed the apparition. It led him up the mountain to the cave, and as it went flowers bloomed upon the soil, and a radiant track was left for Tannhäuser to follow. He entered the cavern and descended to the palace of Venus in the heart of the mountain.

Seven years of revelry and debauch were passed, and the minstrel's heart began to feel a strange void. The beauty, the magnificence, the variety of the scenes in the pagan goddess's home, and all its heathenish pleasures palled upon him, and he yearned for the pure fresh breezes of earth, one look up at the dark night sky spangled with stars, one glimpse of simple mountain flowers, one tinkle of sheep bells. At the same time his conscience began to reproach him, and he longed to make his peace with God. In vain did he entreat Venus to permit him to depart, and it was only when, in the bitterness of his grief, he called upon the Virgin Mother, that a rift in the mountain side appeared to him, and he stood again above ground.

How sweet was the morning air, balmy with the scent of hay, as it rolled up the mountain to him and fanned his haggard cheek! How delightful to him was the cushion of moss and scanty grass after the downy couches of the palace of revelry below! He plucked the little heather bells and held them before him; the tears rolled from his eyes and moistened his thin and wasted hands. He looked up at the soft blue sky and the newly risen sun, and his heart overflowed. What were the golden, jewel-incrusted, lamp-lit vaults beneath to that pure dome of God's building?

The chime of a village church struck sweetly on his ear, satiated with Bacchanalian songs; and he hurried down the mountain to the church which called him. There he made his confession; but the priest, horror-struck at his recital, dared not give him absolution, but passed him on to another. And so he went from one to another till at last he was referred to the pope himself. To the pope he went. Urban IV (1261–4) then occupied the chair of St. Peter. To him Tannhäuser related the sickening story of his guilt and prayed for absolution. Urban was a hard and stern man, and shocked at the immensity of the sin, he thrust the penitent indignantly from him, exclaiming, "Guilt such as thine can never, never be remitted. Sooner shall this staff in my hand grow green and blossom than that God should pardon thee!"

Then Tannhäuser, full of despair, and with his soul darkened, went away, and returned to the only asylum open to him, the Venusberg. But lo! three days after he had gone, Urban discovered that his pastoral staff had put forth buds, and had burst into flower. Then he sent messengers after Tannhäuser, and they reached the Hörsel vale to hear that a wayworn man, with haggard brow and bowed head, had just entered the Hörselloch. Since then Tannhäuser has not been seen.

II

BIRTH

There is perhaps no more common situation in folk literature than the husband and wife who desire children but cannot have them. For help they usually appeal first to the Deity and the saints, and give many alms to the poor. If this does no good, they then beg the magician, or even the Devil, to aid them. Often the child is promised to the being who seemingly caused it to be born. There are many tales which indicate that formerly people entertained many queer ideas about how children were begot. In "The Juniper Tree" pregnancy is caused by just standing under a tree and wishing for a child. Dreaming of a baby, holding a doll in the lap, sunlight, water from a summer shower or in Lake Fakone in Japan, the mere suggestion of a husband, fruit, or a fish, or the vapor rising from a cooked fish, the moon, the foam of the ocean, and the like can in a folktale cause pregnancy. And generally the birth of twins is considered decidedly irregular and evidence that the mother has been unfaithful to her spouse. Of course, if a god was the father of both children, or even of one of them, as was the case of Hercules, the mother is not thought so culpable.

"The Apple Tree," a Tuscan folktale, is from C. G. Leland's *Etruscan Roman Remains*, 1892. The curious "Legend of Margaret, Countess of Henneberg" is from *An Itinerary* by Fynes Moryson ed. 1617. "The Girl Born with a Serpent around Her Neck" is translated from F. M. Luzel's *Contes Populaires de Basse-Bretagne*, 1887, and "The Beast with Seven Heads" from Emmanuel Cosquin's *Contes Populaires de Lorraine*, 1886. "Hercules Is Born" is the editor's version of the story of Alcmena and Galanthis in the ninth book of Ovid's *Metamorphoses*.

[1]

The Apple Tree

Once there was a beautiful lady who married a wealthy and handsome lord. And the great desire of his heart was to have an heir, but as his wife bore no children he became almost mad with disappointment and rage, threatening her with the worst ill-usage and torture unless she became a mother. And she spent all her time in prayer and all her money on the poor, but in vain. Then her husband hated her altogether, and took a maidservant in her place. And finding her one day giving a piece of bread to some poor person, he had her hands cut off, so that she could no more give alms. And she lived among the lowest servants in great distress.

One day there came to the castle a friar, who begged for something in charity of her; and she replied that she had nothing to give, and that if she had aught she could not give it, being without hands. When he heard her story, he looked a long time at her in silence, considering her extreme misery and goodness. Then he told her to embrace an apple tree in the garden and say:

> Apple tree, fair apple tree!
> With my love I come to thee.
> I would be tonight in bed
> With my husband as when wed:
> May I so become a mother.
> Grant this favor; and another
> Still I earnestly implore—
> May he love me as before!

"And when you have done this," the friar continued, "take from the tree two apples and eat them. And go to your husband and he will love you and take you to his bed, and you will in time bear two beautiful babes."

And so it came to pass, and the husband bitterly regretted his cruelty and the loss of her hands. And she bore the two children. But the girl who had been a servant and his mistress persuaded him that his wife had been unfaithful, and that they were not his. Then he took a donkey—on it were two panniers—and he put a babe into each and sat her in the middle and bade her ride away.

So she rode on in utter grief and sorrow, hardly able with her stumps of arms to manage the children or to drive. But at last she came to a well and stooped to drink. And lo! as soon as she did this her hands grew again, for it was the fountain which renews youth and life. Then her heart grew light, for she felt that fortune had not left her. And, indeed, all went well, for she came to a castle where no one was to be seen. And she entered and found food on the tables, and wine and all she required everywhere. And when she and the children had eaten, at the next meal there was food again. Now this castle belonged to fairies, who, seeing her there, pitied her and cared for her in this manner.

And considering her case, they sent a dream to her husband. And the dream came to him by night and told him all the truth, how his wife had been true to him, and how evilly he had done. Then he rode forth and sought far for the castle till he found it. And he took her and the children home. And as they came near the gate, they saw before it a statue which had never been there. Now the wicked servant had said, "May I be turned to stone if this be not true which I have said of thy wife." And the words were remembered by the fairies, for they hear all things. And the statue was the figure of the girl turned to stone. But the husband and wife lived together happily ever after.

[2]

Legend of Margaret, Countess of Henneberg

While I stayed at The Hague, I walked out in half an hour's space to the village of Lausdune, where I saw a wonderful monument, the history whereof printed in a paper, the Earl of Leicester (as they said) had carried with him into England, leaving only the same in written hand, the copy whereof I will set down, first remembering that two basins of brass hanged on the wall, in which the children (whereof I shall speak) were baptized.

The manuscript was in Latin, and is thus Englished:

So strange and monstrous thing I tell,
As from the world's frame ne'er befell:
He parts amazed that marks it well.

Margaret, wife of Hermanuus, Count of Henneberg, daughter to Florence, Count of Holland and Zealand, sister to William, King of the Romans, and Cæsar, or Governor of the Empire. This most noble countess, being about forty-two years old, the very day of preparation called Parascene, about nine of the clock in the year 1276 brought forth at one birth 365 children, which being baptized in two basins of brass, by Guido, suffragan of Utrecht, all the males were called John and all the females Elizabeth; but all of them together with the mother died in one and the same day, and lie buried here in the church of Lausdune. And this happened to her, in that a poor woman bearing in her arms two twins, the countess, wondering at it, said she could not have them both by one man, and so rejected her with scorn; whereupon the woman, sore troubled, wished that the countess might have as many children at a birth, as there be days in the whole year; which, besides the course of nature, by miracle fell out, as in this table is briefly set down for perpetual memory, out of old chronicles, as well written as printed. Almighty God must be in this beheld and honored, and extolled with praises forever and ever. Amen.

[3]

The Girl Born with a Serpent Around Her Neck

A married couple who had lived together many years were very unhappy because they had no children. Neither prayers nor pilgrimages to Folgoët, to Sainte-Anne-d'Auray, or other holy places did any good.

One spring day while returning from one of these pilgrimages, they saw in the fields and woods broods of little birds, toads, serpents, and all kinds of animals created by God, and they could not help saying, "God gives young ones even to the toads and serpents!" "If he would only give us an infant," said the woman, "even though it were born with a toad or serpent, I would be satisfied!"

Nine months after this she gave birth to a girl baby, and strange to relate, there was a little serpent around her neck. The little serpent uncoiled itself and fled into the garden where it hid in the vegetation. But a red mark, exactly the shape of the serpent, remained about the baby's neck. The infant was baptized and received the name of Joy, because of the happiness she had brought to her parents. She grew up full of health and beauty. One day when she was twelve, she entered her father's garden alone and was startled to hear a little voice say, "Good day, my sister, my pretty little sister!" And a graceful serpent came from under a bush toward her.

At first the girl was frightened, but the snake said, "Do not be afraid. I will not harm you. Quite the contrary, for you are my sister, my dear little sister."

"O Lord! a serpent my sister!" exclaimed Joy.

"Yes, for your mother is also mine," said the serpent.

"How could that be?"

"This is how it was. Our mother said one day, as she was returning from a pilgrimage, that if God would give her a child, even though it were born with a toad or snake, she would be happy. God granted her wish, and in due time, you were born—and I came with you coiled around your neck, which still bears the mark. You are going to be married soon—"

"Oh! no," interrupted Joy, "I have no wish to marry."

"You will marry soon," insisted the serpent; "however, it would be better for you if it was not so. That red mark around your neck—I am the only one in the world who can remove it."

"How can you do that?"

"Bring me a bowl full of sweet milk and a white piece of cloth and you will see how."

Joy ran to the house and brought back a wooden bowl of sweet milk and a napkin. She set the bowl on the grass near the serpent. It got into the bowl, rolled around in the milk, and then coiled around Joy's neck, touching every part of the mark. Then gliding from the girl's neck, the snake said, "Now wipe your neck with the napkin." She did this and the red mark vanished.

"Do not tell your mother," said the serpent, "how you got rid of the mark." And then it glided off into the vegetation.

Just then the mother entered the garden. Joy ran to her crying, "See, mother, the red circle has disappeared from my neck," and she was very happy.

"What did you do to make it go away?" asked her mother.

"I don't know—unless it was through the grace of God."

Her father also came and said, "If you can tell me who did it, I will give him much money. And I would give you everything you want."

"I can't tell you anything about it, father, unless it was done by the grace of God."

The parents did not press her further.

Each day Joy became more beautiful, and the most eligible beaux thereabouts asked for her hand in marriage. But she refused them all, saying that she was still too young to marry; and this vexed her parents very much.

One day a fine gentleman from a distant country came to ask her to marry him. No one knew him. However, Joy liked him and they were soon married, and there were great feasts and wonderful celebrations on the occasion. Then Joy departed with her husband to go to his country. He lived in a magnificent castle far, far away. When he was absent from home, which was very often, he left Joy all the keys of the castle save one which opened a room he had forbidden her to enter. There were many rooms in the castle and all contained riches and treasures of all sorts. The young woman derived much pleasure from going from room to room examining and admiring the beautiful things. But after a while the forbidden room began to stimulate her curiosity—so much that she scarcely thought of anything else. Her husband, observing that she was more thoughtful and dreamy than usual, one day asked her, "My dear, what is your heart's desire? Tell me and I will get it for you immediately."

"All I want," she answered, "is a sea crab."

And her husband went to the seashore and brought back a crab. But the forbidden room was always in her mind and would not let her rest. One day while her husband was gone, she pointed to the forbidden room and asked her maid what was in it. The maid had never seen the door to that chamber opened and therefore did not know what was in it.

Finally Joy could restrain herself no longer. She unlocked that door and looked in—then she fainted and fell upon the threshold. She had seen a horrible thing—from a great beam hung eleven pregnant women, each dangling from an iron hook inserted under the chin.

When Joy regained consciousness, she hastily wrote a letter and tied it with a black ribbon to the neck of a little dog which had come along with her from her father's house. Then she told the dog to carry the letter to her parents, whom she begged to come and get her, for she was in danger of her life. The faithful little dog did what she had asked him to. When he arrived, Joy's father and mother were walking in the garden. When they saw the dog they cried, "Some news from Joy!" But when they read the letter, they cried out in anguish. Then a serpent emerged from a near-by bush and spoke.

"Go quickly and order all the men of the house to go with you, for Joy is in danger of her life." Having said this, the serpent disappeared in the bush.

So Joy's parents, the dog, and the men of the house rushed to her rescue. At the very moment they entered the courtyard of their daughter's husband, this monster was dragging Joy along by the hair, and he had raised his sword ready to strike her. Just then an angry serpent, coming up like a flash of lightning, bit him on the heel. He gave a cry, fell to the ground, and instantly swelled up like a barrel. The serpent, leaping upon him, snatched out his eyes, and he died.

This serpent was no other than Joy's sister. Joy, who was with child and whose time had arrived, gave birth on the spot to a son.

A great crowd gathered to see the master of the château dead, for he was the terror of the countryside and no one regretted his demise—quite the contrary. And they besought Joy's father not to have the child baptized but to kill it immediately. Naturally they feared that if they let the infant live, he would be like his father. So he was killed.

When this was done, the people cried, "The serpent which killed the tyrant ought to be baptized, for there must have been some magic or witchcraft mixed up in what she did." But the priests refused to give baptism to a serpent.

If the master of the château had slain Joy, as was his intention, that would have been his twelfth; and in slaying twelve, he would have slain twenty-four, for all were with child. Then he would have become a sorcerer, but God did not permit it.

[4]

The Beast with Seven Heads

Once there was a fisherman. One day he caught a large fish. "If you will let me go," said the fish, "I will bring you a great number of little fishes." The fisherman then threw it back into the water and soon a large number of little fishes filled his nets. When he had enough of them, he returned home and told his wife what had happened. "You should not have thrown back the big one," said she, "because it is so large and knows how to talk so well. You must try to catch it again."

The fisherman was not particularly interested, but his wife insisted and he returned to the river. Throwing in his net, he caught the large fish again. "Since you must have me," said the fish, "I am going to tell you what you ought to do. When you kill me, give three drops of my blood to your wife, three to your mare, and three to your little bitch. Besides put three drops in a glass and keep my gills."

The fisherman did just as the fish had directed: he gave three drops of its blood to his wife, three to his mare, and three to his little bitch. He preserved the fish's gills and three drops of its blood in a glass. When some time had passed, his wife gave birth to three fine boys, his mare had three handsome colts, and the bitch three pretty pups. He found three fine lances in the spot where he had put the gills. And the blood in the glass would begin to boil if any of the boys were harmed or in danger.

When the fisherman's sons had become strong handsome youths, the eldest one day mounted his horse, took his lance, whistled up his dog, and left his father's house. He came to a fine castle all shining with silver and gold. "Who owns this fine castle?" he asked some of the natives. "Don't go in it," they answered; "it's the dwelling of an old witch with seven heads. No one who went in there ever came out. She transformed them all into toads." "I am not afraid," said the cavalier; "I will enter it." So he went into the castle and saluted the witch: "Good day, my good woman." She shook her seven heads and cried, "You poor earthworm, what are you going to do here?" And as she spoke, she struck him with her baton, and instantly he became a toad, like his predecessors.

That instant his brothers at home saw the blood in the glass begin to boil. "Our brother is in trouble," said the second brother, "and I wish to find out what happened to him." So he mounted his horse and taking his dog and lance rode until he came to the castle. "Did you see a rider with a spear and a dog pass here?" he asked a woman who stood there. "He left three days ago and some accident must have happened to him." "Doubtless he was punished for his curiosity," she answered. "He must have entered the castle of the beast with the seven heads and been changed into a toad." "I am not afraid of the beast with the seven heads," cried the young man. "I will cut off the seven heads with my lance." Entering the castle grounds, he saw a horse in the stable and a dog in the kitchen. "My brother is here," thought he. He greeted the witch. "Good day, my good woman." "Poor earthworm, what are you going to do here?" And without giving him time to brandish his lance, she struck him with her baton and changed him into a toad.

Again the blood began to boil in the glass. Seeing this, the fisherman's youngest son started out to find his two brothers. As he was crossing a wide river, the river spoke to him. "You pass but you will not pass again." "That is a bad omen," thought the young man, "but it does not matter." And he pursued his way. Meeting some men, he asked, "Did you see two horsemen pass?" One of them replied, "We saw one; he was looking for his brother." And on approaching the castle, the youngest brother heard rumors about the witch. Stopping a charcoal-burner who was coming out of the woods, he said, "Some kind old people have told me of a beast with seven heads. They say she turns all who enter her castle into toads." "Oh," answered the charcoal-burner, "I fear nothing. I will enter with you and together we will set things aright."

So together they entered the castle, and the young man caught sight of his brothers' horses, lances, and dogs. As soon as he saw the witch, he began to shout, "Old witch, give me my brothers or I will cut off all your heads." "What did you come here to do, earthworm?" she shouted. Just as she raised her baton, the young man cut off one of her heads with a blow of his lance. As he asked, "Old witch, where are my brothers?" he severed another head. Each time she raised her baton, the young man and the charcoal-burner cut off a head. At the fifth one, the witch began to cry, "Wait, wait, I will give you back your brothers." Taking her baton, she rubbed it with grease and struck the cellar door several times. Instantly all the toads there resumed the shapes they formerly had. The witch thought that she would be pardoned, but the charcoal-burner said to her, "You have been doing these evil things to men long enough." So he cut off the last two heads.

Now it was said that the person who killed the beast with the seven heads would possess the castle and marry the daughter of the king. To prove that he had killed the beast, he had to show the seven tongues. The fisherman's youngest son took the tongues and wrapped them in a silk handkerchief. The charcoal-burner, who also had cut off some of the beast's heads, had not thought of taking out the tongues. But afterward, realizing their importance, he killed the fisherman's son and took them away from him. Showing the tongues to the king, the evil charcoal-burner was rewarded with the hand of the princess.

[5]

Hercules Is Born

And so to her daughter-in-law Iole, Alcmena told this story of the birth of Hercules:

"O may the gods be merciful and give you swift deliverance when you are about to become a mother and appeal to Lucina for help, her whom Juno bribed and turned against me. Before the natal hour of Hercules, destined for so many toils, arrived, the sun had traversed the tenth sign of the Zodiac, and the one I bore had become so large that it was quite obvious that mighty Jupiter had begot the child.

"Even now as I am speaking, the memory of what I next endured makes a cold shudder run through my limbs. When my time had come, the malign influence of Juno caused my pains to be drawn out seven days. Extending my arms toward heaven, with loud cries I invoked both Lucina and the Nixian deities of birth. Lucina came but she had been corrupted and had now resolved to give my life to the vengeful Juno. Seating herself upon the altar before my door, the goddess crossed her legs, clasped her knees, and interlocked her fingers. She thus retarded my delivery, and the charms which she now uttered in a low voice were for the same purpose.

"In my anguish I said foolish things. I railed at Jupiter and called him ungrateful. I complained in words that should have moved the insensate rocks, and I wished to die. But the matrons of Cadmus tried to raise my spirits. They spoke encouraging words and offered up vows in my behalf. And in constant attendance upon me was my beloved handmaid Galanthis, honey-haired and quick of mind. As she went in and out the door, she noticed how stiffly Lucina was perched on the altar, and she observed the crossed knees and clasped hands. She suspected that something unusual was going on and guessed that the jealous Juno was at the bottom of it. So the wily maid suddenly shouted at Lucina, 'Whoever you are, you must now congratulate my mistress, for her wishes have been fulfilled and her child is born.' Lucina, too, much surprised to use her wits, unclenched her hands, uncrossed her legs and leaped to her feet. The instant those bonds were loosened, I could feel an inward slackening, and my child was born.

"It is said that Galanthis laughed with glee when she saw that she had tricked Lucina. Thereupon the angry goddess caught the maid by the hair and dragged her along the ground. And the vixen would not let the girl rise to her feet but changed her into a weasel. Although her maiden form had gone, Galanthis still loved to dwell in the home, was still agile, and still took pride in her glorious honey-colored tresses."

III

ADVENTURES OF THE SOUL

Some very curious ideas about the soul can be found in folktales. The belief in the "double" or other soul, e.g. the Egyptian *Ka*, the Iranian *hamzád*, and the Scottish *wraith*, is world-wide. The soul-animal or soul-bird is similar. These are co-existent doubles of the human being, and the fate of one is bound up with that of the other. A related idea is that of the life-token or life-index, which is some object, plant, or animal chosen by or born with a person, and which indicates in some way that the person is well, or in danger, sick or dead, e.g. a lighted candle that goes out or a life-tree which withers when the person is in great danger or dying. Another wide-spread belief is that of the separable soul, i.e., that a giant, or the like, can deposit his soul (life, strength, heart, etc.) for safekeeping in a secret part of his body or in some object outside it.

According to tradition, the soul often leaves the body temporarily to go on its travels, some of which are experienced as dreams. If for some reason the soul does not return, its owner becomes sick or insane, falls into a trance and finally dies. And the soul's wanderings are perilous. Sometimes evil medicine men snare it and will not return it to its owner until ransom is paid. Sometimes when it takes the form of a shadow, it is nailed under a coffin lid or sealed into a cornerstone. If it is a reflection, a demon might pull it down into watery depths. As the blood is often thought to be the seat of the soul, the soul is lost if the blood is all spilled. Usually a person has little or no control over his soul's comings and goings, but it is believed that a magician can conjure the soul out of his body and into that of a person or animal whose soul is away—an idea obviously related to vampirism. And, of course, the necromancer can force the soul of a dead person to appear and speak.

"The Egyptian Brothers" is the editor's version of the famous Egyptian story known as "Two Brothers" or "Anpu and Bata." "The King Who Lost His Body" is based on Theodore Benfey's translation in his *Panchatantra*, 1859. "The Giant Whose Life Was Hidden in an Egg" is a Lapland tale and is translated from the German as found in *Germania*, 1870. "The Young King of Easaidh Ruadh" is from J. F. Campbell's *Popular Tales of the West Highlands*, 1860, and "Chundun Rajah" is an Indian tale from Mary Frere's *Old Deccan Days*, 1881. "The Pretty Witch's Lover" is a Tuscan tale from C. G. Leland's *Etruscan Roman Remains*, 1892. "Godfather Death" and "The Singing Bone" are from Margaret Hunt's translation of the Grimms' *Household Tales*, 1884.

[1]

The Egyptian Brothers

Once there were two brothers. Anpu was the name of the elder and Bata the name of the younger. Anpu had a wife and a house and a farm. Bata lived with him and worked in the fields. He ploughed, he harvested the corn, and he followed behind the oxen. Bata was clever and strong and an excellent worker: there was not his equal in the whole land. The spirit of a god was in him. Every evening he returned from the fields laden with wood, milk, fodder, and vegetables. And he put them down before his brother, who was usually sitting with his wife. After his supper he lay down in the stable with his cattle. At dawn he took bread which he had baked and laid it before Anpu. And he took along food for his midday meal as he drove his cattle to pasture. As he walked behind them, his cattle would say to him, "The pasturage in such-and-such a place is fine." He would listen to them and take them to the good place they had in mind. And they became fat and multiplied.

Now at the time of ploughing Anpu said to him, "Let us make ready a good yoke of oxen for the plow, for the land has come out from the water and is fit for tillage. And bring corn to the field, for we begin to plow tomorrow morning." And Bata did all his brother asked him. When morning came, the brothers went to the fields, and their hearts were glad when they set to work. And they used up all the seed grain they had brought out. So Anpu sent his brother to the house for more. And Bata found his brother's wife sitting and tiring her hair. He said to her, "Arise and give me some grain to take to the field, for Anpu does not wish to wait. Do not delay." She answered, "Go, open the seed bin and take as much as you need. I don't wish to drop my locks of hair while I dress them."

Bata went to the granary and took a large measure, for he needed much seed, and filling it with wheat and barley, carried it out.

"How much grain are you carrying on your shoulder?" asked his brother's wife.

"Three bushels of barley and two of wheat."

"You are very strong," said she, "and every day I see proofs of your strength." And her heart beat faster because of him. She wished to embrace him. "Come," said she, "let us lie together for an hour. If you will, I promise to make you two fine garments."

But this wicked invitation made Bata as angry as an enraged cheetah and he said, "Never say this evil thing to me again. You are to me as a mother and your husband is to me as a father. It is he who shelters me and gives me my livelihood. But do not be afraid, for I promise never to tell anyone what has happened today." Then, taking up the measure of grain, he returned to the fields. And he and his brother went on with their work.

That evening Anpu returned home before his brother, who, loading himself with fodder, followed after the oxen. And he put them in the stable and made them lie down. Now Anpu's wife was afraid because of the words she had uttered to Bata. So she took a lump of fat and discolored her face so that it appeared as if she had been badly beaten. She planned to accuse Bata of beating her. When Anpu came in and saw her, she looked as if she had been assaulted. She did not pour water on his hands, as was her custom, nor make a light to brighten the house. She was lying very sick.

"Who has spoken to you?" he asked.

"No one has spoken to me except your younger brother," she answered. "He found me alone when he came for the seed, and he said to me, 'Come, let us lie together; tie up your hair.' But I would not listen to him and I told him, 'Am I not as your mother, and your brother as your father?' And he became afraid and beat me to stop me from telling you. If you let him live, I will die. He is returning soon. I complain of his wicked words, for he would have done this even in daylight."

Anpu became like an angry cheetah. He sharpened his knife and taking it in his hand, stood behind the stable door to kill his brother.

When Bata's foremost cow entered the stable, she said to him, "Look! there's your brother standing before you with his knife to slay you. Flee away!" Bata heard this, and the next cow that came in said the same thing. So, looking beneath the stable door, he saw his brother's feet. Bata threw his load to the ground and fled away. The brother pursued him. Then Bata cried out to Ra Harakhti, "My good Lord! Thou art he who divides the evil from the good." And Ra stood and heard his appeal. Then Ra made a wide water between him and his brother and filled it with crocodiles. Anpu was on one bank and Bata on the other. And the first smote twice on his hands because he had failed to slay the second. And Bata called to him and said, "Stand there until dawn, and when Ra arises, I will plead my case and he will be my judge, for he can distinguish between good and bad. But never again will I live in your home; I shall go to the valley of the acacia."

Now when Ra Harakhti made it day, the brothers could see each other. And Bata asked, "Why did you try to slay me craftily without listening to what I would say in defense of myself? Am I not in truth your brother and are you not like a father to me? And is not your wife like a mother to me? The truth is that it was your wife who spoke the wickedness. She asked me to lie with her, but she told you just the reverse." Anpu understood what had happened, and Bata swore an oath by Ra Harakhti, saying, "Your coming to slay me by deceit with your knife was an abomination." Then he cut off a bit of his flesh, cast it into the water, and the fish swallowed it. He became weak and faint. Anpu saw this and stood weeping for his brother afar off and cursing his own heart. Because of the crocodiles he could not come where Bata was. And Bata called to him saying, "Since you devised an evil scheme, will you not now devise a good thing, such as I would do for you? When you return home, take care of the cattle, for I will not come there. And I ask you to do this for me: come and seek after me when you are notified that something is happening to me. I am going to the valley of the acacia and shall draw out my heart and put it upon the top of the flowers of the acacia. It will happen that when the acacia is cut down, my heart will fall to the ground. Come, then, and search for it, and do not give up even though you do not find it before seven years have passed. You will find it. When you do, put it in a cup of cold water and I shall live again so that I may right what has been done wrong. You will know that things are happening to me when a cup of beer in your hand shall become troubled. When this comes about, do not tarry."

Bata went to the valley of the acacia and Anpu returned home. He cast dust on his head, and he killed his wife and threw her to the dogs. And he sat mourning for his younger brother.

Now many days afterward Bata lived all alone in the valley of the acacia. He passed the time hunting the beasts of the wilderness and at night he slept under the acacia which bore his heart upon the topmost flower. And later on he built a tower here and filled it with good things and made himself a home. And he went out from his tower one day and met the Nine Gods, who were walking about to look over the country. The Nine Gods talked to one another, and they addressed Bata, saying, "Ho! Bata, bull of the Nine Gods, do you live alone? Because of your brother's wife, you left your village. Know that she has been killed. You have given him an answer to his sins against you." And they felt compassion for Bata. Ra Harakhti said to Khnumu, "Create a woman for him that he may not live alone." And Khnumu framed a mate for Bata. She was shaped more beautifully than any woman in the whole land. The essence of every god was in her. When they saw her, the seven Hathors said with one mouth, "She will die a sharp death."

Bata loved her exceedingly, and she lived in his tower. When he killed any beasts in his hunting, he brought them in and laid them before her. He gave her this advice: "Do not go outside lest the sea seize hold of you. I cannot rescue you from it, for I am a woman like you. My heart is placed on the crest of the acacia flower, and if another find it, I must fight with him." And he told her everything.

One day while he was out hunting, the girl went walking under the acacia tree, which was at the side of the tower. And the sea saw her and threw up its waves after her. She fled and got into the tower. And the sea called to the acacia, saying, "Oh, would that I could seize her!" The acacia brought a lock from her hair and the sea carried it to Egypt, dropping it where the fullers of Pharaoh's linen worked. The aroma of the lock permeated Pharaoh's clothes. And the fullers were scolded. "The smell of ointment is in Pharaoh's clothing," cried those who examined it, and they rebuked the chief fuller time and again. One day while he was trying to think what to do, he saw the lock of hair floating on the water and had a servant fetch it. Discovering that an exquisite aroma came from it, he took it to Pharaoh. And the scribes and wise men were summoned. They said to Pharaoh, "This lock of hair belongs to a daughter of Ra Harakhti. The essence of every god is in her, and it is a tribute to you from another land. Let messengers be sent abroad to seek her: and as for the messenger who shall go to the valley of the acacia, let many men go with him to bring her." Then said Pharaoh, "Your words are excellent." And men set out. After many days some returned to report to the king, but those who had gone to the valley of the acacia did not come back, for Bata had slain them all except one. He was spared to report to Pharaoh. His majesty now sent many men and soldiers, as well as horsemen, to bring her. Amongst them there was a woman and she was provided with beautiful ornaments such as women love. And she brought Bata's wife back with her, and they rejoiced over her in the whole land.

And his majesty loved her very much and raised her to high estate. When he asked her about her husband, she said, "Let the acacia be cut down and chopped up." So men and soldiers with their weapons were sent to cut down the acacia. And they cut the flower upon which was the heart of Bata, and he immediately fell dead.

The next day when Anpu entered his house and washed his hands, and one gave him a cup of beer, it became troubled. And one gave him another of wine, and the smell of it was bad. Then he took his staff, and his sandals, and likewise his clothes and weapons of war and started for the valley of the acacia. Entering Bata's tower, he found his brother lying dead upon his mat. And he wept and went out to look for Bata's heart under the acacia tree. For three years he searched but in vain. When he began the fourth year, he yearned to return to Egypt, and said, "I will go tomorrow."

The next morning he looked again under the acacia but saw nothing. But in the afternoon, he found a seed and brought it in. It contained Bata's heart. Casting the seed into a cup of cold water, he sat down to watch what would happen. When the night came, Bata's heart sucked up the water. Bata shuddered in all his limbs and looked up at his older brother. Then Anpu handed the cup of cold water to Bata and Bata drank it. His heart stood again in its place, and he became as he had been. The brothers embraced each other and then talked together.

"Oh, brother," said Bata, "I am to become as a great bull which bears every good mark. No one knows its history, and you must sit upon my back. When the sun rises I shall be where my wife is, that I may settle accounts with her. You must take me to the king. For all good things shall be done for you. For bringing me to Pharaoh, you will be laden with silver and gold. I shall become a great marvel and because of me all in the land shall rejoice and you shall go to your village."

In the morning twilight Bata came in the form of a bull. And Anpu sat upon his back until dawn. He came to the place where the king was and he was shown to his majesty. Pharaoh was delighted and made him great offerings, saying, "This is a great wonder which has come to pass." All the land rejoiced. They gave him silver and gold for his brother, who went and stayed in his village. They gave to the bull many men and many things, and Pharaoh prized him above all that was in his land.

After many days the bull entered the purified place. He stood near the princess, his former wife, and spoke to her. "Look at me! I am alive indeed." And she said to him, "And pray, who are you?" And he answered, "I am Bata! When you caused Pharaoh to destroy the acacia, which was my abode, I perceived that I would not be permitted to live. But see, I am alive. I am in the form of a bull." These words made the princess terribly afraid. And Bata left the purified place.

And Pharaoh was sitting, passing the time joyously with her. She was at his table and pleased him greatly. And she said to him, "Swear to me by the gods, saying, 'Whatever you command, I will obey for your sake.' " And he did as she wished. Then she said, "Let me eat of the bull's liver, for he is good for nothing." These words grieved Pharaoh greatly. Nevertheless, when the next day appeared, they proclaimed a great feast with offerings to the bull. And the king sent one of the chief butchers to sacrifice the bull. And when he was sacrificed, as he was upon the shoulders of the people, he shook his neck and threw two drops of blood over against the two doors of the palace. One fell upon one side, in the great door of Pharaoh, and the other upon the other door. They grew as two great avocado trees, and each one was exceedingly fine.

And a man went to tell his majesty. "Two great avocado trees have grown, as a great marvel of his majesty, in the night by the side of the great gate." There was rejoicing over these trees throughout the land and offerings were made to them.

Many days afterward his majesty was adorned with the blue crown, with garlands of flowers on his neck, and he rode in the chariot of pale gold and went out from the palace to look at the avocado trees. The princess followed him. And he sat beneath one of the trees and it spoke thus to his wife: "Oh, you deceitful woman, I am Bata. I have been evilly dealt with, but I am alive. I know who caused my acacia to be cut down. I then became a bull and you had me killed again."

Not long after this the princess stood at Pharaoh's table and the king was greatly pleased with her. So she asked him to swear he would do anything she requested. When he agreed he would, she asked him to command that the two avocado trees be cut down and made into beams. He gave orders and sent skillful craftsmen to fell the avocado trees. The princess stood looking on as the work was being done. And a chip flew up and entered her mouth. She swallowed the chip, and after many days gave birth to a boy baby. And one went to tell Pharaoh, "There is born to you a son." They brought the child and gave him servants and a nurse: all the land rejoiced. As they were about naming the child, the king felt a great affection for the boy and raised him to the royal son of Kush.

Later on the king made the boy heir of all the land. Some time after this, when the king died and flew up to heaven, the boy said, "Let the great nobles be assembled." When these had gathered, he ordered that the king's widow be summoned. When she came he cried, "Know, Oh wicked woman, that I, who came from an avocado chip, am Bata. And I still live in spite of your evil attempts to kill me." And he told those assembled there how she had caused the acacia to be felled, the bull to be slaughtered, and the avocado trees to be chopped down. Then he ordered that she be led out and slain. And the nobles all agreed that he had done the just thing.

Then Bata summoned his brother Anpu and made him hereditary prince in all this land. Bata was King of Egypt for thirty years, and after he died Anpu occupied the throne.

[2]

The King Who Lost His Body

As King Makunda, who resided in the northern city of Lilavati, was returning from an expedition to his hunting preserves, he saw a humpbacked jester entertaining a crowd of people gathered in the center of town. And the king was so pleased by the fellow's drollery, he brought him to the palace, where he often joked with him. Indeed, he would hardly permit the jester to leave his side. One day the minister wished to discuss confidential matters with the king and thought it best that the hunchback be sent from the room. So he said, "O king, it is said by the wise, 'What six ears have heard is soon spread abroad.' " However the king, who did not wish to part even for a moment with his jester, replied, "Except when two of them are the hunchback's."

Now one day a fakir entered the palace and set himself down by the King Makunda. The latter, who knew that this was a very wise man and wishing to learn something rare from him, took him aside and talked with him. And the fakir taught him the magic secret of causing one's soul to enter into the body of a person who had died. After he had imparted this knowledge, the fakir vanished. And the king made himself thoroughly familiar with the formula of this incantation. Moreover, he taught it to his jester. Soon after, the king and his jester went hunting. King Makunda, happening to look into a great thicket, discovered there the body of a Brahman who had died of thirst. And the desire to test the efficacy of his magic incantation came to the king. So he asked his jester if he remembered the magic formula, but the latter had evil thoughts and lied, saying, "O king! I have forgotten it!" Thereupon the king, throwing his horse's bridle reins to his jester, gave his soul to deep meditation, and when he murmured the mysterious incantation his soul parted from his body and entered that of the dead Brahman. But the evil hunchback did not let the opportunity escape. At the same instant he repeated the magic formula and sent his soul into the corpse of the king, left soulless but a second before. Quickly mounting the king's horse, he said to the king, "You may go wherever you wish, but I am king now and will rule the country." As soon as he had said this, he rode quickly to the city, and arriving at the palace, seized the royal power. The king, whose soul now tenanted the corpse of the Brahman, remembered the verse of the old minister, bewailed his fate, and thought, "Alas! What a foolish thing I have done! Shall I go to the city and tell the queen and the minister about the strange accident that has happened to me? Certainly not: that would be silly, for they would not believe a word of it. They would not believe it was I, and even if they did they would not understand why or how I changed form." And with such gloomy thoughts whirling in his head, he took a road that led away from the city.

Now the hunchback, although he wore the king's body, did not always say what the king would have been likely to say. He made strange observations and said incongruous things. After observing this, the queen became suspicious. Taking the old minister aside, she said, "O father! This person cannot possibly be the king. He does not know how to speak to the point." The minister told her he was of the same opinion and was trying to think of a way to find the real king. Soon after this he hit on the device of offering food to all strangers passing through the city. After serving them food and washing their feet, he would repeat the following verse and ask each guest to complete it.

> What six ears have heard is soon spread abroad;
> Except when two of them are the hunchback's.

Now as word of this proceeding got about, King Makunda in the body of the Brahman heard of it and, thinking it over, left the place where he was living and wandered sorrowfully back toward his own city. And he said to himself, "Certainly my wife has thought of this device to find me again." Late one evening he entered the house where the minister played host to the travelers. Finding the minister himself in the place, King Makunda said, "Dear sir! I am a Brahman from a distant land. As I am hungry, I am certain food will be given me even though mealtime has long since passed by." When the minister saw his guest was a Brahman, he stayed, although he then wished to return home. So he washed King Makunda's feet and as usual recited the verse. Then the king, seizing his opportunity, completed it, saying:

> The hunchback became king; the king became
> beggar and vagabond.

And the minister was full of joy because he had found the true king. Learning from him what had happened, the minister took him home, honored him as was befitting, and spoke: "O royal master! See the might of my wisdom! I will make you king again as soon as you regain possession of your own body." After these words he went directly to the queen and found her holding a dead parrot in her hands and mourning over it. And he said to her, "What a fortunate event! This dead parrot will be of great use to us. Now call the false king and say, 'Is there a magician in the city who can make the parrot speak?' When you have said this, the false king will be glad of this opportunity to show off what he can do with the magic incantation, and he will send his soul into the dead parrot to make it speak. At the same instant, the real king, who will be standing behind me, can enter his own body."

And this was exactly what happened. The minister then took the parrot, now tenanted by the hunchback, and killed it. King Makunda, restored to his old body, reigned again over his people.

[3]

The Giant Whose Life Was Hidden in an Egg

A woman once had a husband who had carried on a feud with a giant for seven years. This giant was passionately fond of the woman and wished to kill her mate so that he could marry her himself. After seven years he finally succeeded in slaying the husband. However, the dead man had a grown son, and he resolved to take vengeance on the giant who had slain his father and now was living with his mother. But the young man found it impossible to kill the giant either with fire or sword. No matter how he tried to slay him, his attempts failed. Indeed, there appeared to be no soul in the giant's body.

"Dear mother," the young man asked her one day, "do you know where the giant keeps his life?" His mother knew nothing about this, but she promised to try to trick the giant into giving her some information on this subject. She waited until he was in a good mood and then asked him, among other things, where his life was.

"Why do you want to know this?" asked the giant.

"Because," she said, "if either one of us ever is in great need or danger, it would be so consoling to know that your life at least is in a well-guarded safe place."

The giant, who saw no reason to be suspicious, then told her where he had hidden his life. "Far out on a burning sea," said he, "there is an island. And on the island there is a cask, and in the cask there is a sheep, and in the sheep a hen, and in the hen an egg, and in that egg resides my life."

The next day when her son visited her, she said, "Now, dear son, I know where the giant's life is. He told me that it is at a great distance from here." And she told him all the giant had said. Then spoke her son: "I must now look about and find some helpful companions to go with me over the burning sea." So he got a bear, a wolf, a hawk, and a diving bird to go along, and they all set out in a boat. He himself sat under an iron tent in the center of the vessel, and he had with him the sea diver and the hawk so that their feathers would not be singed. He let the bear and the wolf do the rowing. That is the reason that the bear has dark-brown hair and the wolf dark-brown patches on his coat. Both had made a trip over the burning sea, whose waves rise up like flames.

They reached the island where the giant's soul was said to be. And they found the cask. The bear smashed it in with his mighty paws and out sprang a sheep. But the wolf caught it, sunk his teeth into its haunch and tore the animal to bits. A hen then flew out of the sheep. The hawk darted upon the hen and tore her open with his claws. And an egg fell out of the hen, dropped into the sea, and sank out of sight. Then the sea diver flew out and dived into the waves after the egg. The bird remained under the water a long time.

When he could not stay down any longer, he came up to the surface to get his breath. Then he dived under again, and although staying down longer than the first time, he did not find the egg. Finally at the third attempt he found the egg resting on the bottom of the sea. He brought it up to the surface and gave it to the young man, who was very happy to get it. Immediately he kindled a great fire on the shore and when the flames leaped up, he placed the egg right in the middle of them. Then without delay he rowed back over the sea. As soon as he touched the land, he hurried by the shortest route to the giant's home and when he saw the giant, he noticed that he was just as much burned as the egg on the island. That they had overcome the giant made the mother as happy as it made her son. There was still a little life in the monster, and when he saw their joy, he began to speak. "I was a fool to let myself be beguiled by the old, evil woman into disclosing where my life resided!" Suddenly he seized the iron tube which he used to suck men's blood. However, the woman had thrust the end of the tube into the burning hearth and he sucked in glowing coals, ashes, and fire. So he was burned as much on the inside as on the outside. Then the fire died out, and as it did so, the life of the giant came to an end.

[4]

The Young King of Easaidh Ruadh

The young King of Easaidh Ruadh, after he got the heirship to himself, was at much merrymaking, looking out what would suit him, and what would come into his humor. There was a Gruagach near his dwelling who was called the brown curly long-haired Gruagach. The king thought to himself that he would go to play a game with him. He went to the soothsayer and said to him, "I am made up that I will go to game with the brown curly long-haired Gruagach." "Aha!" said the soothsayer, "art thou such a man? Art thou so insolent that thou art going to play a game against the brown curly long-haired one? 'Twere my advice to thee to change thy nature and not to go there." "I won't do that," said he. " 'Twere my advice to thee, if thou shouldst win of the Gruagach, to get the cropped rough-skinned maid that is behind the door for the worth of thy gaming, and many a turn will he put off before thou gettest her."

He lay down that night, and if it was early that the day came, 'twas earlier than that that the king arose to hold gaming against the Gruagach. He reached the Gruagach, he blessed the Gruagach, and the Gruagach blessed him. Said the Gruagach to him, "Oh young King of Easaidh Ruadh, what brought thee to me today? Wilt thou game with me?"

They began and they played the game. The king won. "Lift the stake of thy gaming so that I may get leave to be moving." "The stake of my gaming is to give me the cropped rough-skinned girl thou hast behind the door." "Many a fair woman have I within besides her," said the Gruagach. "I will take none but that one." "Blessing to thee and cursing to thy teacher of learning."

They went to the house of the Gruagach and he set in order twenty young girls. "Lift now thy choice from amongst these." One was coming out after another, and every one that would come out would say, "I am she; art thou not silly that art not taking me with thee?" But the soothsayer had asked him to take none but the last one that would come out. When the last one came out, he said, "This is mine." He went with her, and when they were a bit from the house, her form altered, and she was the loveliest woman that was on earth. The king was going home full of joy at getting such a charming woman.

He reached the house, and he went to rest. If it was early that the day arose, it was earlier than that that the king arose to go to game with the Gruagach. "I must absolutely go to game against the Gruagach today," said he to his wife. "Oh!" said she, "that's my father, and if thou goest to game with him, take nothing for the stake of thy play but the dun shaggy filly that has the stick saddle on her."

The king went to encounter the Gruagach, and surely the blessing of the two to each other was not beyond what it was before. "Yes!" said the Gruagach, "how did thy young bride please thee yesterday?" "She pleased fully." "Hast thou come to game with me today?" "I came." They began at the gaming, and the king won from the Gruagach on that day. "Lift the stake of thy gaming, and be sharp about it." "The stake of my gaming is the dun shaggy filly on which is the stick saddle."

They went away together. They reached the dun shaggy filly. He took her out from the stable, and the king put his leg over her and she was the swift heroine! He went home. His wife had her hands spread before him, and they were cheery together that night. "I would rather myself," said his wife, "that thou shouldest not go to game with the Gruagach any more, for if he wins he will put trouble on thy head." "I won't do that," said he; "I *will* go to play with him today."

He went to play with the Gruagach. When he arrived, he thought the Gruagach was seized with joy. "Hast thou come," he said. "I came." They played the game, and, as a cursed victory for the king, the Gruagach won that day. "Lift the stake of thy game," said the young King of Easaidh Ruadh, "and be not heavy on me, for I cannot stand to it." "The stake of my play is," said he, "that I lay it as crosses and as spells on thee, and as the defect of the year, that the cropped rough-skinned creature, more uncouth and unworthy than thou thyself, should take thy head, and thy neck, and thy life's look off, if thou dost not get for me the GLAIVE OF LIGHT of the King of the oak windows." The king went home, heavily, poorly, gloomily. The young queen came meeting him, and said to him, "*Mohrooai!* my pity! there is nothing with thee tonight." Her face and her splendor gave some pleasure to the king when he looked on her brow, but when he sat on a chair to draw her toward him, his heart was so heavy that the chair broke under him.

"What ails thee, or what should ail thee, that thou mightest not tell it to me?" said the queen. The king told her how it happened. "Ha!" said she, "what should'st thou mind, and that thou hast the best wife in Erin, and the second best horse in Erin. If thou takest my advice, thou wilt come well out of all these things yet."

It was early that the day came, it was earlier than that that the queen arose, and she set order in everything, for the king was about to go on his journey. She set in order the dun shaggy filly, on which was the stick saddle, and though he saw it as wood, it was full of sparklings with gold and silver. He got on it; the queen kissed him, and she wished him victory of battlefields. "I need not be telling thee anything. Take thou the advice of thine own she comrade, the filly, and she will tell thee what thou shouldest do." He set out on his journey, and it was not dreary to be on the dun steed.

She would catch the swift March wind that would be before, and the swift March wind would not catch her. They came at the mouth of dusk and lateness, to the court and castle of the King of the oak windows.

Said the dun shaggy filly to him, "We are at the end of the journey, and we have not to go any further; take my advice, and I will take thee where the sword of the King of the oak windows is, and if it comes with thee without scrape or creak, it is a good mark on our journey. The king is now at his dinner, and the sword of light is in his own chamber. There is a knob on its end, and when thou catchest the sword, draw it softly out of the window 'case.'" He came to the window where the sword was. He caught the sword and it came with him softly till it was at its point, and then it gave a sort of a "sgread." "We will now be going," said the filly. "It is no stopping time for us. I know the king has felt us taking the sword out." He kept the sword in his hand, and they went away, and when they were a bit forward, the filly said, "We will stop now, and look thou whom thou seest behind thee." "I see," said he, "a swarm of brown horses coming madly." "We are swifter ourselves than these yet," said the filly. They went, and when they were at a good distance forward, "Look now," said she; "whom seest thou coming?" "I see a swarm of black horses, and one white-faced black horse, and he is coming and coming in madness, and a man on him." "That is the best horse in Erin; it is my brother, and he got three months more nursing than I, and he will come past me with a whir, and try if thou wilt be so ready, that when he comes past me, thou wilt take the head off the man who is on him; for in the time of passing he will look at thee, and there is no sword in his court will take off his head but the very sword that is in thy hand." When this man was going past, he gave his head a turn to look at him; he drew the sword and he took his head off, and the shaggy dun filly caught it in her mouth.

This was the King of the oak windows. "Leap on the black

horse," said she, "and leave the carcass there, and be going home as fast as he will take thee home, and I will be coming as best I may after thee." He leaped on the black horse, and "*Moirë!*" he was the swift hero, and they reached the house long before day. The queen was without rest till he arrived. They raised music, and they laid down woe. On the morrow he said, "I am obliged to go to see the Gruagach today, to try if my spells will be loose." "Mind that it is not as usual the Gruagach will meet thee. He will meet thee furiously, wildly, and he will say to thee, didst thou get the sword? And say thou that thou hast got it; he will say, how didst thou get it? And thou shalt say, if it were not the knob that was on its end I had not got it. He will ask thee again, how didst thou get the sword? And thou wilt say, if it were not the knob that was on its end, I had not got it. Then he will give himself a lift to look what knob is on the sword, and thou wilt see a mole on the right side of his neck, and stab the point of the sword in the mole; and if thou dost not hit the mole, thou and I are done. His brother was the King of the oak windows, and he knows that till the other had lost his life, he would not part with the sword. The death of the two is in the sword, but there is no other sword that will touch them but it." The queen kissed him, and she called on victory of battlefields to be with him, and he went away.

The Gruagach met him in the very same place where he was before. "Didst thou get the sword?" "I got the sword." "How didst thou get the sword?" "If it were not the knob that was on its end I had not got it," said he. "Let me see the sword." "It was not laid on me to let thee see it." "How didst thou get the sword?" "If it were not the knob that was on its end, I got it not." The Gruagach gave his head a lift to look at the sword; he saw the mole; he was sharp and quick, and he thrust the sword into the mole, and the Gruagach fell down dead.

He returned home, and when he returned home, he found his set of keepers and watchers tied back to back, without wife, or horse, or sweetheart of his, but was taken away.

When he loosed them, they said to him, "A great giant came and he took away thy wife and thy two horses." "Sleep will not come on mine eyes nor rest on mine head till I get my wife and my two horses back." In saying this, he went on his journey. He took the side that the track of the horses was, and he followed them diligently. The dusk and lateness were coming on him, and no stop did he make until he reached the side of the green wood. He saw where there was the forming of the site of a fire, and he thought that he would put fire upon it, and thus he would put the night past there.

He was not long here at the fire, when the slim dog of the greenwood came on him. He blessed the dog, and the dog blessed him.

"Oov! oov!" said the dog. "Bad was the plight of thy wife and thy two horses here last night with the big giant." "It is that which has set me so pained and pitiful on their track tonight; but there is no help for it." "Oh! king," said the dog, "thou must not be without meat." The dog went into the wood. He brought out creatures, and they made them meat contentedly. "I rather think myself," said the king, "that I may turn home; that I cannot go near that giant." "Don't do that," said the dog. "There's no fear of thee, king. Thy matter will grow with thee. Thou must not be here without sleeping." "Fear will not let me sleep without a warranty." "Sleep thou," said the dog, "and I will warrant thee." The king let himself down, stretched out at the side of the fire, and he slept. When the watch broke, the dog said to him, "Rise up, king, till thou gettest a morsel of meat that will strengthen thee, till thou wilt be going on thy journey. Now," said the dog, "if hardship or difficulty comes on thee, ask my aid, and I will be with thee in an instant." They left a blessing with each other, and he went away. In the time of dusk and lateness, he came to a great precipice of rock, and there was the forming of the site of a fire.

He thought he would gather dry fuel, and that he would set on fire. He began to warm himself, and he was not long thus when the hoary hawk of the gray rock came on him. "Oov! oov!" said she. "Bad was the plight of thy wife and thy two horses last night with the big giant." "There is no help for it," said he. "I have got much of their trouble and little of their benefit myself." "Catch courage," said she. "Thou wilt get something of their benefit yet. Thou must not be without meat here," said she. "There is no contrivance for getting meat," said he. "We will not be long getting meat," said the falcon. She went, and she was not long when she came with three ducks and eight blackcocks in her mouth. They set their meat in order, and they took it. "Thou must not be without sleep," said the falcon. "How shall I sleep without a warranty over me, to keep me from any one evil that is here?" "Sleep thou, king, and I will warrant thee." He let himself down, stretched out, and he slept.

In the morning, the falcon set him on foot. "Hardship or difficulty that comes on thee, mind, at any time, that thou wilt get my help." He went swiftly, sturdily. The night was coming, and the little birds of the forest of branching bushy trees were talking about the brier roots and the twig tops; and if they were, it was stillness, not peace for him, till he came to the side of the great river that was there, and at the bank of the river there was the forming of the site of a fire. The king blew a heavy, little spark of fire. He was not long here when there came as company for him the brown otter of the river. "Och! och!" said the otter. "Bad was the plight of thy wife and thy two horses last night with the giant." "There is no help for it. I got much of their trouble and little of their benefit." "Catch courage, before midday tomorrow thou wilt see thy wife. Oh! king, thou must not be without meat," said the otter. "How is meat to be got here?" said the king. The otter went through the river, and she came and three salmon with her, that were splendid. They made meat, and they took it. Said the otter to the king, "Thou must sleep." "How can I sleep without any warranty over me?" "Sleep thou, and I will warrant thee." The king slept. In the morning the otter said to him, "Thou wilt be this night in the presence of thy wife." He left blessing with the otter. "Now," said the otter, "if difficulty be on thee, ask my aid and thou shalt get it."

The king went until he reached a rock, and he looked down into a chasm that was in the rock, and at the bottom he saw his wife and his two horses, and he did not know how he should get where they were. He went round till he came to the foot of the rock, and there was a fine road for going in. He went in, and if he went it was then she began crying. "Ud! ud!" said he, "this is bad! If thou art crying now when I myself have got so much trouble coming about thee." "Oo!" said the horses, "set him in front of us, and there is no fear for him till we leave this." She made meat for him, and she set him to rights, and when they were a while together, she put him in front of the horses.

When the giant came, he said, "The smell of the stranger is

within." Says she, "My treasure! My joy and my cattle! There is nothing but the smell of the litter of the horses." At the end of a while he went to give meat to the horses, and the horses began at him, and they all but killed him, and he hardly crawled from them.

"Dear thing," said she, "they are like to kill thee."

"If I myself had my soul to keep, it's long since they had killed me," said he.

"Where, dear, is thy soul? By the books I will take care of it."

"It is," said he, "in the Bonnach stone."

When he went on the morrow, she set the Bonnach stone in order exceedingly. In the time of dusk and lateness, the giant came home. She set her man in front of the horses. The giant went to give the horses meat and they mangled him more and more.

"What made thee set the Bonnach stone in order like that?" said he.

"Because thy soul is in it."

"I perceive that if thou didst know where my soul is, thou wouldst give it much respect."

"I would give that," said she.

"It is not there," said he, "my soul is; it is in the threshold."

She set in order the threshold finely on the morrow. When the giant returned, he went to give meat to the horses, and the horses mangled him more and more.

"What brought thee to set the threshold in order like that?"

"Because thy soul is in it."

"I perceive if thou knewest where my soul is, that thou wouldst take care of it."

"I would take that," said she.

"It is not there that my soul is," said he. "There is a great flagstone under the threshold. There is a wether under the flag. There is a duck in the wether's belly, and an egg in the belly of the duck, and it is in the egg that my soul is."

When the giant went away on the morrow's day, they raised the flagstone and out went the wether. "If I had the slim dog of the greenwood, he would not be long bringing the wether to me." The slim dog of the greenwood came with the wether in his mouth. When they opened the wether, out was the duck on the wing with the other ducks. "If I had the hoary hawk of the gray rock, she would not be long bringing the duck to me." The hoary hawk of the gray rock came with the duck in her mouth; when they split the duck to take the egg from her belly, out went the egg into the depths of the ocean. "If I had the brown otter of the river, he would not be long bringing the egg to me." The brown otter came and the egg in her mouth, and the queen caught the egg, and she crushed it between her two hands. The giant was coming in the lateness, and when she crushed the egg, he fell down dead and he has never moved out of that.

They took with them a great deal of his gold and silver. They passed a cheery night with the brown otter of the river, a night with the hoary falcon of the gray rock, and a night with the slim dog of the greenwood. They came home and they set in order a hearty hero's feast, and they were lucky and well pleased after that.

[5]

Chundun Rajah

Once upon a time a rajah and ranee died, leaving seven sons and one daughter. All these seven sons were married, and the wives of the six eldest used to be very unkind to their poor little sister-in-law; but the wife of the seventh brother loved her dearly, and always took her part against the others. She would say, "Poor little thing, her life is sad. Her mother wished so long for a daughter, and then the girl was born and the mother died and never saw her poor child, or was able to ask anyone to take care of her." At which the wives of the six elder brothers would answer, "You only take such notice of the girl in order to vex us." Then, while their husbands were away, they invented wicked stories against their sister-in-law, which they told them on their return home; and their husbands believed them rather than her, and were very angry with her, and ordered her to be turned out of the house. But the wife of the seventh brother did not believe what the six others said, and was very kind to the little princess, and sent her secretly as much food as she could spare from her own dinner. But as they drove her from their door, the six wives of the elder brothers cried out, "Go away, wicked girl, go away, and never let us see your face again until you marry Chundun Rajah (King Sandalwood). When you invite us to the wedding, and give us six eldest six common wooden stools to sit on, but the seventh sister (who always takes your part) a fine emerald chair, we will believe you innocent of all the evil deeds of which you are accused, but not till then!" This they said scornfully, railing at her; for Chundun Rajah, of whom they spoke (who was the great rajah of a neighboring country) had been dead many months.

So, sad at heart, the princess wandered forth into the jungle; and when she had gone through it, she came upon another, still denser than the first. The trees grew so thickly overhead that she could scarcely see the sky, and there was no village nor house of living creature near. The food her youngest sister-in-law had given her was nearly exhausted, and she did not know where to get more. At last, however, after journeying on for many days, she came upon a large tank, beside which was a fine house that belonged to a rakshas. Being very tired, she sat down on the edge of the tank to eat some of the parched rice that remained of her store of provisions; and as she did so she thought, "This house belongs doubtless to a rakshas, who, perhaps, will see me and kill and eat me; but since no one cares for me, and I have neither home nor friends, I hold life cheap enough." It happened, however, that the rakshas was then out, and there was no one in his house but a little cat and dog, who were his servants.

The dog's duty was to take care of the saffron with which the rakshas colored his face on high days and holidays, and the cat had charge of the antimony with which he blackened his eyelids. Before the princess had been long by the tank, the little cat spied her out, and running to her said, "O sister, sister, I am so hungry, pray give me some of your dinner." The princess answered, "I have very little rice left; when it is all gone I shall starve. If I give you some, what have you to give me in exchange?" The cat said, "I have charge of the antimony with which my rakshas blackens his eyelids, I will give you some of it"; and running to the house she fetched a nice little pot full of antimony, which she gave to the princess in exchange for the rice. When the little dog saw this, he also ran down to the tank, and said, "Lady, lady, give me some rice, I pray you; for I, too, am very hungry." But she answered, "I have very little rice left, and when it is all gone I shall starve. If I give you some of my dinner, what will you give me in exchange?" The dog said, "I have charge of my rakshas' saffron, with which he colors his face. I will give you some of it." So he ran to the house and fetched a quantity of saffron and gave it to the princess, and she gave him also some of the rice. Then, tying the antimony and saffron up in her sari, she said good-by to the dog and cat and went on her way.

Three or four days after this, she found she had nearly reached the other side of the jungle. The wood was not so thick, and in the distance she saw a large building that looked like a great tomb. The princess determined to go and see what it was, and whether she could find anyone there to give her any food, for she had eaten all the rice and felt very hungry, and it was getting toward night.

Now the place toward which the princess went was the tomb of the Chundun Rajah, but this she did not know.

Chundun Rajah had died many months before, and his father and mother and sisters, who loved him very dearly, could not bear the idea of his being buried under the cold ground; so they had built a beautiful tomb, and inside it they had placed the body on a bed under a canopy, and it had never decayed, but continued as fair and perfect as when first put there. Every day Chundun Rajah's mother and sisters would come to the place to weep and lament from sunrise to sunset; but each evening they returned to their own homes. Hard by was a shrine and small hut where a Brahman lived, who had charge of the place; and from far and near people used to come to visit the tomb of their lost rajah, and see the great miracle, how the body of him who had been dead so many months remained perfect and undecayed; but none knew why this was. When the princess got near the place a violent storm came on. The rain beat upon her and wetted her, and it grew so dark she could hardly see where she was going. She would have been afraid to go into the tomb had she known about Chundun Rajah; but, as it was, the storm being so violent and night approaching, she ran in there for shelter as fast as she could, and sat down shivering in one corner. By the light of an oil lamp that burnt dimly in a niche in the wall, she saw in front of her the body of the rajah lying under the canopy, with the heavy jeweled coverlet over him, and the rich hangings all round. He looked as if he were only asleep, and she did not feel frightened. But at twelve o'clock, to her great surprise, as she was watching and waiting, the rajah came to life; and when he saw her sitting shivering in the corner, he fetched a light and came toward her and said, "Who are you?" She answered, "I am a poor lonely girl. I only came here for shelter from the storm. I am dying of cold and hunger." And then she told him all her story—how that her sisters-in-law had falsely accused her, and driven her from among them into the jungle, bidding her see their faces no more until she married the Chundun Rajah, who had been dead so many months; and how the youngest had been kind to her and sent her food, which had prevented her from starving by the way.

The rajah listened to the princess's words, and was certain that they were true, and she no common beggar from the jungles. For, for all her ragged clothes, she looked a royal lady, and shone like a star in the darkness. Moreover, her eyelids were darkened with antimony, and her beautiful face painted with saffron, like the face of a princess. Then he felt a great pity for her, and said, "Lady, have no fear, for I will take care of you," and dragging the rich coverlet off his bed he threw it over her to keep her warm, and going to the Brahman's house, which was close by, fetched some rice, which he gave her to eat. Then he said, "I am the Chundun Rajah of whom you have heard. I die every day, but every night I come to life for a little while." She cried, "Do none of your family know of this? And if so, why do you stay here in a dismal tomb?" He answered, "None know it but the Brahman who has charge of this place. Since my life is thus maimed, what would it avail to tell my family? It would but grieve them more than to think me dead. Therefore, I have forbidden him to let them know; and as my parents only come here by day, they have never found it out. Maybe I shall sometime wholly recover, and till then I will be silent about my existence." Then he called the Brahman who had charge of the tomb and the shrine (and who daily placed an offering of food upon it for the rajah to eat when he came to life) and said to him, "Henceforth, place a double quantity of food upon the shrine, and take care of this lady. If I ever recover, she shall be my ranee." And having said these words he died again. Then the Brahman took the princess to his little hut, and bade his wife see that she wanted for nothing, and all the next day she rested in that place.

Very early in the morning Chundun Rajah's mother and sisters came to visit the tomb, but they did not see the princess; and in the evening, when the sun was setting, they went away. That night when the Chundun Rajah came to life he called the Brahman, and said to him, "Is the princess still here?" "Yes," he answered; "for she is weary with her journey, and she has no home to go to." The rajah said, "Since she has neither home nor friends, if she be willing, you shall marry me to her, and she shall wander no further in search of shelter." So the Brahman fetched his shastra [sacred books] and called all his family as witnesses, and married the rajah to the little princess, reading prayers over them, and scattering rice and flowers upon their heads. And there the Chundun Ranee lived for some time. She was very happy; she wanted for nothing, and the Brahman and his wife took as much care of her as if she had been their daughter. Every day she would wait outside the tomb, but at sunset she always returned to it and watched for her husband to come to life. One night she said to him, "Husband, I am happier to be your wife, and hold your hand and talk to you for two or three hours every evening, than were I married to some great living rajah for a hundred years. But oh! what joy it would be if you could come wholly to life again! Do you know what is the cause of your daily death? and what it is that brings you to life each night at twelve o'clock?"

"Yes," he said, "it is because I have lost my Chundun Har [sandalwood necklace], the sacred necklace that held my soul. A Peri stole it. I was in the palace garden one day, when many of those winged ladies flew over my head, and one of them, when she saw me, loved me, and asked me to marry her. But I said no, I would not; and at that she was angry, and tore the Chundun Har off my neck, and flew away with it. That instant I fell down dead, and my father and mother caused me to be placed in this tomb; but every night the Peri comes here and takes my necklace off her neck, and when she takes it off I come to life again, and she asks me to come away with her, and marry her, and she does not put on the necklace again for two or three hours, waiting to see if I will consent. During that time I live. But when she finds I will not, she puts on the necklace again, and flies away, and as soon as she puts it on, I die." "Cannot the Peri be caught?" asked the Chundun Ranee; but her husband answered, "No, I have often tried to seize back my necklace—for if I could regain it I should come wholly to life again—but the Peri can at will render herself invisible and fly away with it, so that it is impossible for any mortal man to get it." At this news the Chundun Ranee was sad at heart, for she saw no hope of the rajah's being restored to life; and grieving over this she became so ill and unhappy, that even when she had a little baby boy born, it did not much cheer her, for she did nothing but think, "My poor child will grow up in this desolate place and have no kind father day by day to teach him and help him as other children have, but only see him for a little while by night; and we are all at the mercy of the Peri, who may any day fly quite away with the necklace and not return." The Brahman, seeing how ill she was, said to the Chundun Rajah, "The ranee will die unless she can be somewhere where much care will be taken of her, for in my poor home my wife and I can do but little for her comfort. Your mother and sisters are good and charitable; let her go to the palace, where they will only need to see she is ill to take care of her."

Now it happened that in the palace courtyard there was a great slab of white marble, on which the Chundun Rajah had been wont to rest on the hot summer days; and because he used to be so fond of it, when he died his father and mother ordered that it should be taken great care of, and no one was allowed to so much as touch it. Knowing this, Chundun Rajah said to his wife, "You are ill; I should like you to go to the palace, where my mother and sisters will take the greatest care of you. Do this, therefore—take our child and sit down with him upon the great slab of marble in the palace courtyard. I used to be very fond of it; and so now for my sake it is kept with the greatest care, and no one is allowed to so much as touch it. They will most likely see you there and order you to go away; but if you tell them you are ill, they will, I know, have pity on you and befriend you." The Chundun Ranee did as her husband told her; placing her little boy on the great slab of white marble in the palace courtyard and sitting down herself beside him. Chundun Rajah's sister, who was looking out of the window, saw her and cried, "Mother, there are a woman and her child resting on my brother's marble slab; let us tell them to go away." So she ran down to the place; but when she saw Chundun Ranee and the little boy she was quite astonished. The Chundun Ranee was so fair and lovable-looking, and the baby was the image of her dead brother. Then returning to her mother, she said, "Mother, she who sits upon the marble stone is the prettiest little lady I ever saw; and do not let us blame the poor thing, she says she is ill and weary; and the baby (I know not if it is fancy, or the seeing him on that stone) seems to me the image of my lost brother."

At this the old ranee and the rest of the family went out, and when they saw the Chundun Ranee they all took such a fancy to her and to the child that they brought her into the palace, and were very kind to her, and took great care of her; so that in a while she got well and strong again, and much less unhappy; and they all made a great pet of the little boy, for they were struck with his strange likeness to the dead rajah; and after a time they gave his mother a small house to live in, close to the palace, where they often used to go and visit her. There also the Chundun Rajah would go each night when he came to life, to laugh and talk with his wife, and play with his boy, although he still refused to tell his father and mother of his existence. One day it happened, however, that the little child told one of the princesses (Chundun Rajah's sister) how every evening someone who came to the house used to laugh and talk with his mother and play with him, and then go away. The princess also heard the sound of voices in the Chundun Ranee's house, and saw lights flickering about there when they were supposed to be fast asleep. Of this she told her mother, saying, "Let us go down tomorrow night and see what this means; perhaps the woman we thought so poor, and befriended thus, is nothing but a cheat, and entertains all her friends every night at our expense."

So the next evening they went down softly, softly to the place, when they saw—not the strangers they had expected, but their long-lost Chundun Rajah! Then, since he could not escape he told them all. How that every night for an hour or two he came to life, but was dead all day. And they rejoiced greatly to see him again, and reproached him for not letting them know he ever lived, though for

Blairsville Junior High School
Blairsville, Pennsylvania

so short a time. He then told them how he had married the Chundun Ranee, and thanked them for all their loving care of her.

After this he used to come every night and sit and talk with them; but still each day, to their great sorrow, he died; nor could they divine any means for getting back his Chundun Har, which the Peri wore round her neck.

At last one evening, when they were all laughing and chatting together, seven Peris flew into the room unobserved by them, and one of the seven was the very Peri who had stolen Chundun Rajah's necklace, and she held it in her hand.

All the young Peris were very fond of the Chundun Rajah and Chundun Ranee's boy, and used often to come and play with him, for he was the image of his father's and mother's loveliness, and as fair as the morning; and he used to laugh and clap his little hands when he saw them coming; for though men and women cannot see Peris, little children can.

Chundun Rajah was tossing the child up in the air when the Peris flew into the room, and the little boy was laughing merrily. The winged ladies fluttered round the rajah and the child, and she that had the necklace hovered over his head. Then the boy, seeing the glittering necklace which the Peri held, stretched out his little arms and caught hold of it; and, as he seized it, the string broke, and all the beads fell upon the floor. At this the seven Peris were frightened, and flew away, and the Chundun Ranee, collecting the beads, strung them, and hung them round the rajah's neck; and there was great joy amongst those that loved him, because he had recovered the sacred necklace, and that the spell which doomed him to death was broken.

The glad news was soon known throughout the kingdom, and all the people were happy and proud to hear it, crying, "We have lost our young rajah for such a long, long time, and now one little child has brought him back to life." And the old rajah and ranee (Chundun Rajah's father and mother) determined that he should be married again to the Chundun Ranee with great pomp and splendor, and they sent letters into all the kingdoms of the world, saying, "Our son the Chundun Rajah has come to life again, and we pray you come to his wedding."

Then, among those who accepted the invitation were the Chundun

Ranee's seven brothers and their seven wives; and for her six sisters-in-law, who had been so cruel to her, and caused her to be driven out into the jungle, the Chundun Ranee prepared six common wooden stools; but for the seventh, who had been kind to her, she made ready an emerald throne, and a footstool adorned with emeralds.

When all the ranees were taken to their places, the six eldest complained, saying, "How is this? Six of us are given only common wooden stools to sit upon, but the seventh has an emerald chair?" Then the Chundun Ranee stood up, and before the assembled guests told them her story, reminding her six elder sisters-in-law of their former taunts, and how they had forbidden her to see them again until the day of her marriage with the Chundun Rajah, and she explained how unjustly they had accused her to her brothers. When the ranees heard this they were struck dumb with fear and shame, and were unable to answer a word; and all their husbands, being much enraged to learn how they had conspired to kill their sister-in-law, commanded that these wicked women should instantly be hanged, which was accordingly done. Then, on the same day that the Chundun Rajah remarried their sister, the six elder brothers were married to six beautiful ladies of the court, amid great and unheard-of rejoicings, and from that day they all lived together in perfect peace and harmony unto their lives' end.

Blairsville Joint School Library
Blairsville, Pa.

[6]

The Pretty Witch's Lover

There were two witches, mother and daughter, who lived by the seaside, and the younger was a beautiful girl who had a lover, and they were soon to be married. But it began to be reported that the women were given to sorcery and had wild ways; and someone told the young man of it, and that he should not take such a wife. So he resolved to see for himself by going to their house, but intending to remain till midnight, when, he knew, if they were witches they could not remain longer at home. And he went and made love, and sat till it was after eleven, and when they bade him go home, he replied, "Let me sit a little longer"; and so again, till they were out of patience.

Then seeing that he would not go, they cast him by their witchcraft into a deep sleep, and with a small tube sucked all his blood from his veins, and made it into a blood pudding or sausage, which they carried with them. And this gave them the power to be invisible till they should return.

But there was another man on the lookout for them that night, and that was the brother of the youth whom they had put to sleep; for he had long suspected them, and it was he who had warned his brother. Now he had a boat, and as he observed for some time every morning that it had been untied and used by someone in the night, he concluded it was done by these witches. So he hid himself on board carefully, and waited and watched well.

At midnight the two witches came. They wished to go to Jerusalem to get clove gilly flowers. And when they got into the boat the mother said, "Boat, boat, go for two!" But the boat did not move. Then the mother said to the daughter, "Perhaps you are with child—that would make three." But the daughter denied it. Then the mother cried again, "Boat, boat, go for two!" Still it did not move, so the mother cried again, "Go for two or three, or still for four—as many as you will!" Then the boat shot away like an arrow, like lightning, like thought, and they soon came to Jerusalem, where they gathered their flowers, and, re-entering the boat, returned.

Then the boatman was well satisfied that the women were witches and went home to tell his brother, whom he found nearly dead and almost out of his mind. So he went to the witches and threatened them till they gave the youth the blood sausage. And when he had eaten it, all his blood and life returned, and he was well as before. But the witches flew away as he arose, over the housetops and over the hill; and unless they have stopped they are flying still.

[7]

Godfather Death

A poor man had twelve children and was forced to work night and day to give them even bread. When therefore the thirteenth came into the world, he knew not what to do in his trouble, but ran out into the great highway, and resolved to ask the first person whom he met to be godfather. The first to meet him was the good God who already knew what filled his heart, and said to him, "Poor man, I pity thee. I will hold thy child at its christening, and will take charge of it and make it happy on earth." The man said, "Who art thou?" "I am God." "Then I do not desire to have thee for a godfather," said the man; "thou givest to the rich, and leavest the poor to hunger." Thus spake the man, for he did not know how wisely God apportions riches and poverty. He turned therefore away from the Lord, and went farther. Then the Devil came to him and said, "What seekest thou? If thou wilt take me as a godfather for thy child, I will give him gold in plenty and all the joys of the world as well." The man asked, "Who art thou?" "I am the Devil." "Then I do not desire to have thee for godfather," said the man; "thou deceivest men and leadest them astray." He went onward, and then came Death striding up to him with withered legs, and said, "Take me as godfather." The man asked, "Who art thou?" "I am Death, and I make all equal." Then said the man, "Thou art the right one, thou takest the rich as well as the poor, without distinction; thou shalt be godfather." Death answered, "I will make thy child rich and famous, for he who has me for a friend can lack nothing." The man said, "Next Sunday is the christening; be there at the right time." Death appeared as he had promised, and stood godfather quite in the usual way.

When the boy had grown up, his godfather one day appeared and bade him go with him. He led him forth into a forest, and showed him an herb which grew there, and said, "Now shalt thou receive thy godfather's present. I make thee a celebrated physician. When thou art called to a patient, I will always appear to thee. If I stand by the head of the sick man, thou mayst say with confidence that thou wilt make him well again, and if thou givest him of this herb he will recover; but if I stand by the patient's feet, he is mine, and thou must say that all remedies are in vain, and that no physician in the world could save him. But beware of using the herb against my will, or it might fare ill with thee."

It was not long before the youth was the most famous physician in the whole world. "He had only to look at the patient and he knew his condition at once, and if he would recover, or must needs die." So they said of him, and from far and wide people came to him, sent for him when they had anyone ill, and gave him so much money that he soon became a rich man. Now it so befell that the king became ill, and the physician was summoned, and was to say if recovery were possible. But when he came to the bed, Death was standing by the feet of the sick man, and the herb did not grow which could save him. "If I could but cheat Death for once," thought the physician,"he is sure to take it ill if I do, but, as I am his godson, he will shut one eye; I will risk it." He therefore took up the sick man, and laid him the other way, so that now Death was standing by his head. Then he gave the king some of the herb, and he recovered and grew healthy again. But Death came to the physician, looking very black and angry, threatened him with his finger, and said, "Thou hast overreached me; this time I will pardon it, as thou art my godson; but if thou venturest it again, it will cost thee thy neck, for I will take thee thyself away with me."

Soon afterward the king's daughter fell into a severe illness. She was his only child, and he wept day and night, so that he began to lose the sight of his eyes, and he caused it to be made known that whosoever rescued her from death should be her husband and inherit the crown. When the physician came to the sick girl's bed, he saw Death by her feet. He ought to have remembered the warning given by his godfather, but he was so infatuated by the great beauty of the king's daughter, and the happiness of becoming her husband, that he flung all thought to the winds. He did not see that Death was casting angry glances on him, that he was raising his hand in the air, and threatening him with his withered fist. He raised up the sick girl, and placed her head where her feet had lain. Then he gave her some of the herb, and instantly her cheeks flushed red, and life stirred afresh in her.

When Death saw that for a second time he was defrauded of his own property, he walked up to the physician with long strides, and said, "All is over with thee, and now the lot falls on thee," and seized him so firmly with his ice-cold hand that he could not resist, and led him into a cave below the earth. There he saw how thousands and thousands of candles were burning in countless rows, some large, others half-sized, others small. Every instant some were extinguished, and others again burnt up, so that the flames seemed to leap hither and thither in perpetual change. "See," said Death, "these are the lights of men's lives. The large ones belong to children, the half-sized ones to married people in their prime, the little ones belong to old people; but children and young folks likewise have often only a tiny candle." "Show me the light of my life," said the physician, and he thought that it would be still very tall. Death pointed to a little end which was just threatening to go out, and said, "Behold, it is there." "Ah, dear godfather," said the horrified physician, "light a new one for me; do it for love of me, that I may enjoy my life, be king, and the husband of the king's beautiful daughter." "I cannot," answered Death; "one must go out before a new one is lighted." "Then place the old one on a new one; that will go on burning at once when the old one has come to an end," pleaded the physician. Death behaved as if he were going to fulfill his wish, and took hold of a tall new candle; but as he desired to revenge himself, he purposely made a mistake in fixing it, and the little piece fell down and was extinguished. Immediately the physician fell on the ground, and now he himself was in the hands of Death.

[8]

The Singing Bone

In a certain country there was once great lamentation over a wild boar that laid waste the farmers' fields, killed the cattle, and ripped up people's bodies with his tusks. The king promised a large reward to anyone who would free the land from this plague; but the beast was so big and strong that no one dared to go near the forest in which it lived. At last the king gave notice that whosoever should capture or kill the wild boar should have his only daughter to wife.

Now there lived in the country two brothers, sons of a poor man, who declared themselves willing to undertake the hazardous enterprise; the elder, who was crafty and shrewd, out of pride; the younger, who was innocent and simple, from a kind heart. The king said, "In order that you may be the more sure of finding the beast, you must go into the forest from opposite sides." So the elder went in on the west side, and the younger on the east.

When the younger had gone a short way, a little man stepped up to him. He held in his hand a black spear and said, "I give you this spear because your heart is pure and good; with this you can boldly attack the wild boar, and it will do you no harm."

He thanked the little man, shouldered the spear, and went on fearlessly.

Before long he saw the beast, which rushed at him; but he held the spear toward it, and in its blind fury it ran so swiftly against it that its heart was cloven in twain. Then he took the monster on his back and went homeward with it to the king.

As he came out at the other side of the wood, there stood at the entrance a house where people were making merry with wine and dancing. His elder brother had gone in here and, thinking that after all the boar would not run away from him, was going to drink until he felt brave. But when he saw his young brother coming out of the wood laden with his booty, his envious, evil heart gave him no peace. He called out to him, "Come in, dear brother, rest and refresh yourself with a cup of wine."

The youth, who suspected no evil, went in and told him about the good little man who had given him the spear wherewith he had slain the boar.

The elder brother kept him there until the evening, and then they went away together, and when in the darkness they came to a bridge over a brook, the elder brother let the other go first; and when he was halfway across he gave him such a blow from behind that he fell down dead. He buried him beneath the bridge, took the boar, and carried it to the king, pretending that he had killed it; whereupon he obtained the king's daughter in marriage. And when his younger brother did not come back he said, "The boar must have killed him," and everyone believed it.

But as nothing remains hidden from God, so this black deed also was to come to light.

Years afterward a shepherd was driving his herd across the bridge, and saw, lying in the sand beneath, a snow-white little bone. He thought it would make a good mouthpiece, so he clambered down, picked it up, and cut out of it a mouthpiece for his horn. But when he blew through it for the first time, to his great astonishment, the bone began of its own accord to sing:

> Ah, friend, thou blowest upon my bone!
> Long have I lain beside the water;
> My brother slew me for the boar,
> And took for his wife the king's young daughter.

"What a wonderful horn!" said the shepherd; "it sings by itself; I must take it to my lord the king." And when he came with it to the king the horn again began to sing its little song. The king understood it all, and caused the ground below the bridge to be dug up, and then the whole skeleton of the murdered man came to light. The wicked brother could not deny the deed, and was sewn up in a sack and drowned. But the bones of the murdered man were laid to rest in a beautiful tomb in the churchyard.

IV

FAIRIES, OGRES, AND THE LIKE

Fairies are a motley crew. There are small ones and some of human size. Some are ugly and some beautiful. Some are benevolent but others are mischievous and even harmful, abducting human infants, wasting crops, and shooting fairy darts at the cattle. Some are chaste but some rather wanton. Some are ideal lovers or mistresses but others resemble witches. They originated in various ways, but a great many of them were formerly pagan gods and demigods of grot, field, home, stream, and forest. Thus the pagan Otherworld becomes the subterranean Fairyland, Venus becomes a fay, and Pluto the king of the fairies. The kind fairy godmother is one type and another is represented by the household familiars—brownies, billies, kobolds, and dwarfs. Dwarfs and undines are sometimes called elves, a class of beings somewhat similar to fairies and including pixies, mermaids, mermen, incubi, and succubi. The nix is a siren or water fairy. The swan maiden, half mortal and half supernatural, becomes human in form when her lover steals her enchanted feather covering, or her ring or crown. But if he violates a taboo or she finds her feather envelope, she becomes a swan again and disappears. The Scandinavian trolls are usually huge ogres but sometimes dwarfish skrattels.

The following stories illustrate some of the commoner traits of these beings, and fairies appear again in other tales in this book. "The Green Children" is from *Fairy Gold*, 1907, and is printed by permission of E. P. Dutton and Company, Inc. and J. M. Dent & Sons (Canada) Limited. "Fairy Ointment" and "Childe Rowland" are from Joseph Jacobs' *English Fairy Tales*, 1892. "On Fairy Time" and "The Nix of the Millpond" are from the Grimms' *Household Tales*, Margaret Hunt's translation, 1884. "A Fairy's Child" is from W. Branch Johnson's *Folktales of Brittany*, 1927, and is printed by permission of Methuen and Company, Ltd. "The Elfin Millers" is from Hugh Miller's *Scenes and Legends of the North of Scotland*, 1874. "Pipi Menou and the Flying Women" is translated from F. M. Luzel's *Contes Populaires de Basse-Bretagne*, 1887. "The Black Rock Mermaid" is from John Ashton's *Chap-books of the Eighteenth Century*, 1882, and "The Cat on the Dovrefell" is from G. W. Dasent's *Popular Tales from the Norse*, 1877.

[1]

The Green Children

That was a wonderful thing that happened at St. Mary's of the Wolf-pits. A boy and his sister were found by the country folk of that place near the mouth of the pit, who had limbs like those of men; but the color of their skin wholly differed from that of you and me and the people of our upper world, for it was tinged all of a green color.

No one could understand the speech of the Green Children. When they were brought to the house of a certain knight, Sir Richard de Calne, they wept bitterly. Bread and honey and milk were set before them, but they would not touch any of these, though they were tormented by great hunger. At length, some beans fresh-cut were brought, stalks and all, into the house, and the children made signs, with great avidity, that the green food should be given to them. Thereupon they seized on it, and opened the beanstalks instead of the pods, thinking the beans were in the hollow of the stem; and not finding anything of the kind there, they began to weep anew. When the pods were opened and the naked beans offered to them, they fed on these with great delight, and for a long time they would taste no other food.

The people of their country, they said, and all that was to be seen in that country were of a green color. Neither did any sun shine there; but instead of it they enjoyed a softer light like that which shines after sunset. Being asked how they came into the upper world, they said that as they were following their green flocks, they came to a great cavern; and on entering it they heard a delightful sound of bells. Ravished by its sweetness, they went for a long time wandering on and on through the cavern until they came to its mouth. When they came out of it, they were struck senseless by the glaring light of the sun, and the sudden warmth of the air; and they thus lay for a long time; then, being awaked, they were terrified by the noise of those who had come upon them; they wished to fly, but they could not find again the entrance of the cavern, and so they were caught.

If you ask what became of the Green Children, I cannot tell you, for no one seems to know right clearly. Perchance they found their cave, and went back again to the Green Country, as the mermaid goes back at last to the sea.

[2]

Fairy Ointment

Dame Goody was a nurse that looked after sick people and minded babies. One night she was waked up about midnight, and when she went downstairs, she saw a strange, squinny-eyed, little ugly old fellow who asked her to come to his wife who was too ill to mind her baby. Dame Goody didn't like the look of the old fellow, but business is business; so she popped on her things and went down to him. And when she got down to him, he whisked her up on to a large coal-black horse with fiery eyes, that stood at the door; and soon they were going a rare pace, Dame Goody holding on to the old fellow like grim death.

They rode and they rode till at last they stopped before a cottage door. So they got down and went in and found the good woman abed with the children playing about; and the babe, a fine bouncing boy, beside her.

Dame Goody took the babe, which was as fine a baby boy as you'd wish to see. The mother, when she handed the baby to Dame Goody to mind, gave her a box of ointment, and told her to stroke the baby's eyes with it as soon as it opened them. After a while it began to open its eyes. Dame Goody saw that it had squinny eyes just like its father. So she took the box of ointment and stroked its two eyelids with it. But she couldn't help wondering what it was for, as she had never seen such a thing done before. So she looked to see if the others were looking, and, when they were not noticing, she stroked her own right eyelid with the ointment.

No sooner had she done so than everything seemed changed about her. The cottage became elegantly furnished. The mother in the bed was a beautiful lady, dressed up in white silk. The little baby was still more beautiful than before, and its clothes were made of a sort of silvery gauze. Its little brothers and sisters around the bed were flat-nosed imps with pointed ears, who made faces at one another, and scratched their polls. Sometimes they would pull the sick lady's ears with their long and hairy paws. In fact, they were up to all kinds of mischief; and Dame Goody knew that she had got into a house of pixies. But she said nothing to nobody, and as soon as the lady was well enough to mind the baby, she asked the old fellow to take her back home. So he came around to the door with the coal-black horse with eyes of fire, and off they went as fast as before, or perhaps a little faster, till they came to Dame Goody's cottage, where the squinny-eyed old fellow lifted her down and left her, thanking her civilly enough, and paying her more than she had ever been paid before for such service.

Now next day happened to be market day, and as Dame Goody had been away from home, she wanted many things in the house, and trudged off to get them at the market. As she was buying the things she wanted, who should she see but the squinny-eyed old fellow who had taken her on the coal-black horse. And what do you think he was doing? Why he went about from stall to stall taking up things from each, here some fruit, and there again some eggs, and so on. And no one seemed to take any notice.

Now Dame Goody did not think it her business to interfere, but she thought she ought not to let so good a customer pass without speaking. So she ups to him and bobs a curtsy and said: "Gooden, sir, I hopes as how your good lady and the little one are as well as—"

But she couldn't finish what she was a-saying, for the funny old fellow started back in surprise, and he says to her, says he: "What! do you see me today?"

"See you," says she, "why, of course I do, as plain as the sun in the skies, and what's more," says she, "I see you are busy too, into the bargain."

"Ah, you see too much," said he; "now, pray, with which eye do you see all this?"

"With my right eye to be sure," said she, as proud as can be to find him out.

"The ointment! The ointment!" cried the old pixy thief. "Take that for meddling with what don't concern you. You shall see no more." And with that he struck her on her right eye, and she couldn't see him any more; and, what was worse, she was blind on the right side from that hour till the day of her death.

[3]

A Fairy's Child

Catherine Cloär [of Le Drennec in Brittany], in her hurry to fetch a bucket of water, had left her baby boy unguarded. The *poulpican* [elf] who lived in the fountain, waiting until her back was turned, whipped into the house and changed Catherine's bonny child for her own ugly little brat.

The mother could not at first notice the change, for the *poulpican* had cast a spell over her eyes; but when the brat began to grow up it was plain to the whole world that he did not belong to honest Catherine and her husband. If he were put to tend the cows he would tie holly to their tails and laugh at their caperings: if he were told to fetch water he would throw mud into it: if he were left to mind the fire it was a wonder the cottage was not burned down. In every piece of mischief he took unbounded delight.

"The child cannot be ours," declared Catherine in her sorrow. "His body is too small and his wits too sharp."

The family sat in the cottage one evening when a neighboring butcher tapped at the window. The butcher had slung a calf, tied by the legs, before him on his horse, so that man, horse, and calf looked like one strange beast in the half-darkness. The Cloär boy, when he saw it, jumped his own puny height into the air and exclaimed in terror:

> I saw the acorn before the oak
> But this is neither sense nor joke.

All present were astonished at such words from a child; and Catherine's suspicion increased that some impish trick had been played upon her.

A few days later, therefore, she bought a hundred eggs from a farmer and breaking them in half made a huge procession of shells round the fireplace, so that they looked like a procession of priests. Then, hearing the boy approaching, she hid behind the door.

As soon as he entered the room the young *poulpican* saw the strange line of eggshells. He jumped his own puny height into the air and exclaimed in terror:

> I saw the acorn before the oak
> But this is neither sense nor joke.

Catherine's mind was made up; calling her husband, she told him what had happened and said, "Husband, this is not our child. This brat is a demon whom we must in honor kill."

The husband agreed and seized the child by the scruff of its neck, drawing a knife meanwhile.

But just at that moment the *poulpican* entered the door bearing a fine healthy lad.

"Give me back my child," she said. "Here is your own. I have brought him up in a dolmen and fed him on cinders and roots. Oh, he is healthy enough, I'll warrant you."

And snatching the unfortunate changeling out of the grasp of the husband, she disappeared.

[4]

On Fairy Time

There was once a poor servant girl who was industrious and cleanly and swept the house every day, and emptied her sweepings on the great heap in front of the door. One morning, when she was just going back to her work, she found a letter on this heap, and as she could not read, she put her broom in the corner and took the letter to her employers; and behold it was an invitation from the elves, who asked the girl to hold a child for them at its christening. The girl did not know what to do, but at length, after much persuasion—and as they told her that it was not right to refuse an invitation of this kind—she consented.

Then three elves came and conducted her to a hollow mountain where the little folks lived. Everything there was small, but more elegant and beautiful than can be described. The baby's mother lay in a bed of black ebony ornamented with pearls, the covers were embroidered with gold, the cradle was ivory, the bathtub of gold. The girl stood as godmother, and then wanted to go home again, but the little elves urgently entreated her to stay three days with them. So she stayed and passed the time in pleasure and gaiety, and the little folks did all they could to make her happy. At last she set out on her way home. But first they filled her pockets quite full of money, and then they led her out of the mountain again.

When she got home, she wanted to begin her work, and took the broom, which was still standing in the corner, in her hand and began to sweep. Then some strangers came out of the house, who asked her who she was, and what business she had there. And she had not, as she thought, been three days with the little men in the mountains, but seven years, and in the meantime her former masters had died.

[5]

Childe Rowland

Childe Rowland and his brothers twain
Were playing at the ball,
And there was their sister Burd Ellen
In the midst, among them all.

Childe Rowland kicked it with his foot
And caught it with his knee;
At last he plunged among them all
O'er the church he made it flee.

Burd Ellen round about the aisle
To seek the ball is gone,
But long they waited, and longer still,
And she came not back again.

They sought her east, they sought her west,
They sought her up and down,
And woe were the hearts of those brethren,
For she was not to be found.

So at last her eldest brother went to the Warlock Merlin and told him all the case, and asked him if he knew where Burd Ellen was. "The fair Burd Ellen," said the Warlock Merlin, "must have been carried off by the fairies, because she went round the church 'widershins'—the opposite way to the sun. She is now in the Dark Tower of the King of Elfland; it would take the boldest knight in Christendom to bring her back."

"If it is possible to bring her back," said her brother, "I'll do it or perish in the attempt."

"Possible it is," said the Warlock Merlin, "but woe to the man or mother's son that attempts it, if he is not well taught beforehand what he is to do."

The eldest brother of Burd Ellen was not to be put off, by any fear of danger, from attempting to get her back, so he begged the

Warlock Merlin to tell him what he should do, and what he should not do, in going to seek his sister. And after he had been taught, and had repeated his lesson, he set out for Elfland.

> But long they waited, and longer still,
> With doubt and muckle pain,
> But woe were the hearts of his brethren,
> For he came not back again.

Then the second brother got tired and tired of waiting, and he went to the Warlock Merlin and asked him the same as his brother. So he set out to find Burd Ellen.

> But long they waited, and longer still,
> With muckle doubt and pain,
> And woe were his mother's and brother's heart,
> For he came not back again.

And when they had waited and waited a good long time, Childe Rowland, the youngest of Burd Ellen's brothers, wished to go, and went to his mother, the good queen, to ask her to let him go. But she would not at first, for he was the last and the dearest of her children, and if he was lost, all would be lost. But he begged and he begged, till at last the good queen let him go, and gave him his father's good brand that never struck in vain. And as he girt it round his waist, she said the spell that would give it victory.

So Childe Rowland said good-by to the good queen, his mother, and went to the cave of the Warlock Merlin. "Once more, and but once more," he said to the Warlock, "tell how man or mother's son may rescue Burd Ellen and her brothers twain."

"Well, my son," said the Warlock Merlin, "there are but two things, simple they may seem, but hard they are to do. One thing to do, and one thing not to do. And the thing to do is this: after you have entered the land of Fairy, whoever speaks to you, till you meet the Burd Ellen, you must out with your father's brand and off with his head. And what you've not to do is this: bite no bit and drink no drop, however hungry or thirsty you be; drink a drop or bite a bit, while in Elfland you be, and never will you see the Middle Earth again."

So Childe Rowland said the two things over and over again till he knew them by heart, and he thanked the Warlock Merlin and went on his way. And he went along, and along, and along and still farther along, till he came to the horseherd of the King of Elfland feeding his horses. These he knew by their fiery eyes, and knew that he was at last in the land of Fairy. "Canst thou tell me," said Childe Rowland to the horseherd, "where the King of Elfland's Dark Tower is?" "I cannot tell thee," said the horseherd, "but go on a little farther and thou wilt come to the cowherd, and he, maybe, can tell thee."

Then, without a word more, Childe Rowland drew the good brand that never struck in vain, and off went the horseherd's head, and Childe Rowland went on farther, till he came to the cowherd, and asked him the same question. "I can't tell thee," said he, "but go on a little farther, and thou wilt come to the henwife, and she is sure to know." Then Childe Rowland out with his good brand, that never struck in vain, and off went the cowherd's head. And he went on a little farther, till he came to an old woman in a gray cloak, and he asked her if she knew where the Dark Tower of the King of Elfland was. "Go on a little farther," said the henwife, "till you come to a round green hill, surrounded with terrace rings, from the bottom to the top; go round it three times, widershins, and each time say:

Open, door! open, door!
And let me come in.

And the third time the door will open, and you may go in." And Childe Rowland was just going on, when he remembered what he had to do; so he out with the good brand, that never struck in vain, and off went the henwife's head.

Then he went on, and on, and on, till he came to the round green hill with the terrace rings from top to bottom, and he went round it three times, widershins, saying each time:

Open, door! open, door!
And let me come in.

And the third time the door did open, and he went in, and it closed with a click, and Childe Rowland was left in the dark.

It was not exactly dark, but a kind of twilight or gloaming. There were neither windows nor candles, and he could not make out where the twilight came from, if not through the walls and roof. These were rough arches made of transparent rock, incrusted with sheepsilver and rock spar, and other bright stones. But though it was rock, the air was quite warm, as it always is in Elfland. So he went through this passage till at last he came to two wide and high folding doors which stood ajar. And when he opened them, there he saw a most wonderful and glorious sight. A large and spacious hall, so large that it seemed to be as long and as broad as the green hill itself. The roof was supported by five pillars, so large and lofty, that the pillars of a cathedral were as nothing to them. They were all of gold and silver, with freted work, and between them and around them wreaths of flowers, composed of what do you think? Why, of diamonds and emeralds, and all manner of precious stones. And the very keystones of the arches had for ornaments clusters of diamonds and rubies, and pearls, and other precious stones. And all these arches met in the middle of the roof, and just there, hung by a gold chain, an immense lamp made out of one big pearl hollowed out and quite transparent. And in the middle of this was a big, huge carbuncle, which kept spinning round and round, and this was what gave light by its rays to the whole hall, which seemed as if the setting sun were shining on it.

The hall was furnished in a manner equally grand, and at one end of it was a glorious couch of velvet, silk, and gold, and there sate Burd Elen, combing her golden hair with a silver comb. And when she saw Childe Rowland she stood up and said:

God pity ye, poor luckless fool,
What have ye here to do?
Hear ye this, my youngest brother,
Why didn't ye bide at home?
Had ye a hundred thousand lives
Ye couldn't spare any a one.
But sit ye down; but woe, O woe,
That ever ye were born.
For come the King of Elfland in,
Your fortune is forlorn.

Then they sate down together, and Childe Rowland told her all that he had done, and she told him how their two brothers had reached the Dark Tower, but had been enchanted by the King of Elfland, and lay there entombed as if dead. And then after they had talked a little longer Childe Rowland began to feel hungry from his long travels, and told his sister Burd Ellen how hungry he was and asked for some food, forgetting all about the Warlock Merlin's warning.

Burd Ellen looked at Childe Rowland sadly, and shook her head, but she was under a spell and could not warn him. So she rose up, and went out, and soon brought back a golden basin full of bread and milk. Childe Rowland was just going to raise it to his lips, when he looked at his sister and remembered why he had come all that way. So he dashed the bowl to the ground, and said, "Not a sup will I swallow, not a bit will I bite, till Burd Ellen is set free."

Just at that moment they heard the voice of someone approaching, and a loud voice was heard saying:

Fee, fi, fo, fum,
I smell the blood of a Christian man,
Be he dead, be he living, with my brand
I'll dash his brains from his brain pan.

And then the folding doors of the hall were burst open, and the King of Elfland rushed in.

"Strike then, bogle, if thou darest," shouted out Childe Rowland, and rushed to meet him with his good brand that never yet did fail. They fought, and they fought, and they fought, till Childe Rowland beat the King of Elfland down on to his knees and caused him to yield and beg for mercy. "I grant thee mercy," said Childe Rowland, "release my sister from thy spells and raise my brothers to life, and let us all go free, and thou shalt be spared." "I agree," said the Elfin King, and rising up he went to a chest from which he took a phial filled with a blood-red liquor. With this he anointed the ears, eyelids, nostrils, lips, and finger tips of the two brothers, and they sprang at once to life, and declared that their souls had been away but had now returned. The Elfin King then said some words to Burd Ellen, and she was disenchanted, and they all four passed out of the hall, through the long passage, and turned their back on the Dark Tower, never to return again. So they reached home and the good queen their mother; and Burd Ellen never went round a church widershins again.

[6]

The Elfin Millers

The meal mill was a small and very rude erection, with an old-fashioned horizontal water wheel, such as may still be met with in some places of the remote Highlands; and so inconsiderable was the power of the machinery that a burly farmer of the parish, whose bonnet a waggish neighbor had thrown between the stones, succeeded in arresting the whole with his shoulder until he had rescued his Kilmarnock. But the mill of Eathie was a celebrated mill notwithstanding. No one resided near it, nor were there many men in the country who would venture to approach it an hour after sunset; and there were nights when, though deserted by the miller, its wheels would be heard revolving as busily as ever they had done by day, and when one who had courage enough to reconnoiter it from the edge of the dell might see little twinkling lights crossing and recrossing the windows in irregular but hasty succession, as if a busy multitude were employed within. On one occasion the miller, who had remained in it rather later than usual, was surprised to hear outside the neighing and champing of horses and the rattling of carts, and on going to the door he saw a long train of basket-woven vehicles laden with sacks, and drawn by shaggy little ponies of every diversity of form and color. The attendants were slim unearthly-looking creatures, about three feet in height, attired in gray, with red caps; and the whole seemed to have come out of a square opening in the opposite precipice. Strange to relate, the nearer figures seemed to be as much frightened at seeing the miller as the miller was at seeing them; but, on one of them uttering a shrill scream, the carts moved backward into the opening, which shut over them like the curtain of a theater as the last disappeared.

There lived in the adjoining parish of Rosemarkie, when the fame of the mill was at its highest, a wild unsettled fellow, named M'Kechan. Had he been born among the aristocracy of the country, he might have passed for nothing worse than a young man of spirit; and after sowing his wild oats among gentlemen of the turf and of the fancy, he would naturally have settled down into the shrewd political landlord, who, if no builder of churches himself, would be willing enough to exert the privilege of giving clergymen, exclusively of his own choosing, to such churches as had been built already. As a poor man, however, and the son of a poor man, Tam M'Kechan seemed to bid pretty fair for the gallows; nor could he plead ignorance that such was the general opinion. He had been told so when a herdboy; for it was no unusual matter for his master, a farmer of the parish, to find him stealing pease in the corner of one field, when the whole of his charge were ravaging the crops of another. He had been told so too when a sailor, ere he had broken his indentures and run away, when once caught among the casks and packages in the hold, ascertaining where the Geneva and the sweetmeats were stowed. And now that he was a drover and a horse jockey, people, though they no longer told him so, for Tam had become dangerous, seemed as certain of the fact as ever. With all his roguery, however, when not much in liquor he was by no means a very disagreeable companion; few could match him at a song or the bagpipe, and though rather noisy in his cups, and somewhat quarrelsome, his company was a good deal courted by the bolder spirits of the parish, and among the rest by the miller. Tam had heard of the piebald horses and their ghostly attendants; but without more knowledge than fell to the share of his neighbors, he was a much greater skeptic, and after rallying the miller on his ingenuity and the prettiness of his fancy, he volunteered to spend the night at the mill, with no other companion than his pipes.

Preparatory to the trial the miller invited one of his neighbors, the young farmer of Eathie, that they might pass the early part of the evening with Tam; but when, after an hour's hard drinking, they rose to leave the cottage, the farmer, a kindhearted lad, who was besides warmly attached to the jockey's only sister, would fain have dissuaded him from the undertaking. "I've been thinking, Tam," he said, "that flyte wi' the miller as ye may, ye would better let the good people alone; or stay, sin' ye are sae bent on playing the fule, I'll e'en play it wi' you; rax me my plaid; we'll trim up the fire in the killogie thegether; an' you will keep me in music." "Na,

Jock Hossack," said Tam; "I maun keep my good music for the good people, it's rather late to flinch now; but come to the burn-edge wi' me the night, an' to the mill as early in the morning as ye may; an' hark ye, tak' a double caulker wi' you." He wrapt himself up closely in his plaid, took the pipes under his arm, and, accompanied by Jock and the miller, set out for the dell, into which, however, he insisted on descending alone. Before leaving the bank, his companions could see that he had succeeded in lighting up a fire in the mill, which gleamed through every bore and opening, and could hear the shrill notes of a pibroch mingling with the dash of the cascade.

The sun had risen high enough to look aslant into the dell, when Jock and the miller descended to the mill, and found the door lying wide open. All was silent within; the fire had sunk into a heap of white ashes, though there was a bundle of fagots untouched beside it, and the stool on which Tam had been seated lay overturned in front. But there were no traces of Tam, except that the miller picked up, beside the stool, a little flat-edged instrument, used by the unfortunate jockey in concealing the age of his horses by effacing the marks on their teeth, and that Jock Hossack found one of the drones of his pipes among the extinguished embers. Weeks passed away and there was still nothing heard of Tam; and as everyone seemed to think it would be in vain to seek him anywhere but in the place where he had been lost, Jock Hossack, whose marriage was vexatiously delayed in consequence of his strange disappearance, came to the resolution of unraveling the mystery, if possible, by passing a night in the mill.

For the first few hours he found the evening wear heavily away; the only sounds that reached him were the loud monotonous dashing of the cascade, and the duller rush of the stream as it swept past the mill wheel. He piled up fuel on the fire till the flames rose half-way to the ceiling, and every beam and rafter stood out from the smoke as clearly as by day; and then yawning, as he thought how companionable a thing a good fire is, he longed for something to amuse him. A sudden cry rose from the further gable, accompanied by a flutter of wings, and one of the miller's ducks, a fine plump bird, came swooping down among the live embers. "Poor bird!" said Jock, "from the fox to the fire; I had almost forgotten that I wanted my supper." He dashed the duck against the floor—plucked and emboweled it—and then, suspending the carcass by a string before the fire, began to twirl it round and round to the heat. The strong odoriferous fume had begun to fill the apartment, and the dripplings to hiss and sputter among the embers, when a burst of music rose so suddenly from the green without, that Jock, who had been so engaged with the thoughts of his supper as almost to have forgotten the fairies, started half a yard from his seat. "That maun be Tam's pipes," he said; and giving a twirl to the duck he rose to a window. The moon, only a few days in her wane, was looking aslant into the dell, lighting the huge melancholy cliffs with their birches and hazels, and the white flickering descent of the cascade. The little level green on the margin of the stream lay more in the shade; but Jock could see that it was crowded with figures marvelously diminutive in stature, and that nearly one-half of them were engaged in dancing. It was enough for him, however, that the music was none of Tam's making; and, leaving the little creatures to gambol undisturbed, he returned to the fire.

He had hardly resumed his seat when a low tap was heard at the door, and shortly after a second and a third. Jock sedulously turned his duck to the heat, and sat still. He had no wish for visitors, and determined on admitting none. The door, however, though firmly bolted, fell open of itself, and there entered one of the strangest-looking creatures he had ever seen. The figure was that of a man, but it was little more than three feet in height; and though the face was as sallow and wrinkled as that of a person of eighty, the eye had the roguish sparkle and the limbs all the juvenile activity of fourteen. "What's your name, man?" said the little thing, coming up to Jock, and peering into his face till its wild elfish features were within a few inches of his. "What's your name?" "Mysel' an' Mysel' "—i.e., myself—said Jock, with a policy similar to that resorted to by Ulysses in the cave of the giant. "Ah, Mysel' an' Mysel'!" rejoined the creature; "Mysel' an' Mysel'! and what's that you have got there, Mysel' an' Mysel'?" touching the duck as it spoke with the tip of its finger, and then transferring part of the scalding gravy to the cheek of Jock. Rather an unwarrantable liberty, thought the poor fellow, for so slight an acquaintance; the creature reiterated the question, and dabbed Jock's other cheek with a larger and still more scalding application of the gravy. "What is it?" he exclaimed, losing in his anger all thought of consequences, and dashing the bird, with the full swing of his arm, against the face of his visitor, "It's that!" The little creature, blinded and miserably burnt, screamed out in pain and terror till the roof rung again; the music ceased in a moment, and Jock Hossack had barely time to cover the fire with a fresh heap of fuel, which for a few seconds reduced the apartment to total darkness, when the crowd without came swarming like wasps to every door and window of the mill. "Who did it, Sanachy—who did it?" was the query of a thousand voices at once. "Oh, 'twas Mysel' an' Mysel'," said the creature; " 'twas Mysel' an' Mysel'." "And if it was yoursel' and yoursel', who, poor Sanachy," replied his companions, "can help that?" They still, however, clustered round the mill; the flames began to rise in long pointed columns through the smoke, and Jock Hossack had just given himself up for lost, when a cock crew outside the biulding, and after a sudden breeze had moaned for a few seconds among the cliffs and the bushes, and then sunk in the lower recesses of the dell, he found himself alone. He was married shortly after to the sister of the lost jockey, and never again saw the good people, or, what he regretted nearly as little, his unfortunate brother-in-law. There were some, however, who affirmed that the latter had returned from Fairyland seven years after his mysterious disappearance, and supported the assertion by the fact that there was one Thomas M'Kechan who suffered at Perth for sheep-stealing a few months after the expiry of the seventh year.

[7]

Pipi Menou and the Flying Women

Once there was a young fellow named Pipi Menou who guarded sheep on a hill overlooking a fine little lake. He had noticed that often, when the weather was good, some large white birds alighted near this lake and as soon as they touched the ground, the feathered covering of each divided lengthwise, opened up, and out stepped a beautiful girl all naked. Then wading into the water, the maidens swam and frolicked in the sun. A little before sunset they emerged from the lake, got again into their downy envelopes and soared aloft, very, very high up, with a great sound of beating wings.

The young shepherd observed all this from the top of his hill. Indeed, he was so amazed that he was afraid to go closer. The whole thing seemed so extraordinary that one evening he spoke about it when he returned home. His grandmother, as she sat in the ingle nook turning her spindle between her fingers, had an explanation.

"My boy, these are swan maidens, daughters of a powerful magician who lives in a fine palace all shining with gold and precious stones, and it is supported high over the sea by four golden chains."

"Is there a way to go and see this fine castle, grandmother?" asked the boy.

"That is not easy, my boy; however it can be done, for when I was young it was said that a boy of about your age, Roll Dagorn, went there and returned, and he talked about what he saw."

"What does one have to do to go there, grandmother?"

"O! for that, first of all one must be fearless. Then one must hide in the bushes by the lake and keep very still. When the princesses (for they are princesses) have emerged from their feather wrappings, seize one of these skins and do not give it back to its owner no matter how much she pleads or threatens, until she promises to carry you to the castle, to protect and help you, and finally to marry you. There is no other way."

Pipi listened attentively to the words of his grandmother and did nothing but dream all the night about the swan maidens and their palace.

The next morning he left with his sheep as usual, but he had made up his mind to make the venture. He hid among the willows and alders along the lake shore, and at the usual hour the sky darkened and he saw three great white birds with enormous wings sailing over the lake. They settled on the shore, their envelopes opened, and three marvelously beautiful girls emerged and, diving into the water, swam, chased each other, and frolicked about. Pipi was intent on his business: he did not linger to watch the beautiful swimmers but seized upon the feathery covering of one of them. She was the youngest and fairest of the three. Seeing what Pipi had done, they all emerged from the lake and ran to get hold of their plumy envelopes. The two older ones got theirs but the younger, seeing hers in Pipi's hands, ran to him crying, "Give me my feathers."

"Certainly," was the answer, "if you will carry me to your father's palace."

"We can't do that," said all three sisters together. "He would beat us and eat you. Give us the feathery skin right away."

"I will not give it back until you promise to carry me to your father's palace."

The two older ones, having now donned their skins, came to the rescue of their sister. "Give it back to her," they cried, "or we will tear you to pieces."

"Nonsense! I'm not afraid of you," answered Pipi, although he was not really too sure of himself. Seeing that neither entreaties nor menaces would make Pipi give in, they said to their youngest sister, "You will have to do what he asks, for without your feathers you cannot return home, and if father sees us return without you, he will punish us severely."

The young princess wept but made the promise. Pipi then gave her her feather skin. She got into it and told him to climb upon her back—which he did. Then the three sisters rose into the air so high that the boy could see neither land nor water. But soon he caught sight of the magician's castle supported above the clouds by four golden chains.

The princesses did not dare to enter the castle with the young shepherd. They put him down in the garden, which was beneath the castle, and asked the gardener to take care of him. As they had returned a little later than usual, their father scolded them and forbade them to go to the lake for some days. Naturally they became quite bored, having to stay at home. They did nothing but dream about Pipi, who was a handsome fellow; and he dreamed about them too, especially the youngest. So both began to think of ways to come together. Each evening the mother of the princesses let down a large basket on a rope to the garden and the gardener filled it with vegetables and fruit to be eaten in the castle the next day. Then, of course, the old lady pulled it up. One evening Pipi got into the basket and covered himself with the cabbages, carrots, and beets. When the old lady gave the rope a tug, she found it very heavy and asked the gardener what he had put in the basket, but he did not answer for he had let Pipi take charge of the job of sending up the food basket that evening.

The young princess was at the window and saw that Pipi was in the basket. She rushed to assist her mother and told her, "Let me do it, mother. At your age you shouldn't strain yourself. In the future, I shall pull up the basket, so don't you bother about it any more."

The old lady was pleased with the attention of her daughter and went away. Pipi was hoisted up and hidden in the princess's room, where he passed the night. Each evening he got up and each morning he got down the same way. But the two older sisters, having discovered what was going on, were jealous and threatened to tell on their sister unless Pipi came to visit them also. So Pipi and his princess resolved to leave the castle and descend to the earth. They filled their pockets with gold and precious stones, and afterward when everyone was asleep, the youngest princess donned her feather envelope and taking Pipi upon her back, flew down to earth. Next morning the old magician and his wife started in pursuit, but it was too late and the lovers got away.

As the princess was not a Christian, she asked to be baptized. Then Pipi married her and they lived happily together and had many children. But it is said that the mermaids stole their children away.

[8]

The Nix of the Millpond

There was once upon a time a miller who lived with his wife in great contentment. They had money and land, and their prosperity increased year by year more and more. But ill luck comes like a thief in the night; as their wealth had increased so did it again decrease, year by year, and at last the miller could hardly call the mill in which he lived his own. He was in great distress, and when he lay down after his day's work, found no rest, but tossed about in his bed, full of care. One morning he rose before daybreak and went out into the open air, thinking that perhaps there his heart might become lighter. As he was stepping over the mill dam the first sunbeam was just breaking forth, and he heard a rippling sound in the pond. He turned round and perceived a beautiful woman, rising slowly out of the water. Her long hair, which she was holding off her shoulders with her soft hands, fell down on both sides, and covered her white body. He soon saw that she was the nix of the Millpond, and in his fright did not know whether he should run away or stay where he was. But the nix made her sweet voice heard, called him by his name, and asked him why he was so sad? The miller was at first struck dumb, but when he heard her speak so kindly, he took heart, and told her how he had formerly lived in wealth and happiness, but that now he was so poor that he did not know what to do. "Be easy," answered the nix; "I will make thee richer and happier than thou hast ever been before, only thou must promise to give me the young thing which has just been born in thy house." "What else can that be," thought the miller, "but a young puppy or kitten?" and he promised her what she desired.

The nix descended into the water again, and he hurried back to his mill, consoled and in good spirits. He had not yet reached it, when the maidservant came out of the house, and cried to him to rejoice, for his wife had given birth to a little boy. The miller stood as if struck by lightning; he saw very well that the cunning nix had been aware of it, and had cheated him. Hanging his head, he went up to his wife's bedside and when she said, "Why dost thou not rejoice over the fine boy?" he told her what had befallen him, and what kind of a promise he had given to the nix. "Of what use to me are riches and prosperity," he added, "if I am to lose my child; but what can I do?" Even the relations, who had come thither to wish them joy, did not know what to say. In the meantime prosperity again returned to the miller's house. All that he undertook succeeded; it was as if presses and coffers filled themselves of their own accord, and as if money multiplied nightly in the cupboards. It was not long before his wealth was greater than it had ever been before. But he could not rejoice over it untroubled; the bargain which he had made with the nix tormented his soul. Whenever he passed the millpond, he feared she might ascend and remind him of his debt. He never let the boy himself go near the water. "Beware," he said to him, "if thou dost but touch the water, a hand will rise, seize thee, and draw thee down." But as year after year went by and the nix did not show herself again, the miller began to feel at ease. The boy grew up to be a youth and was apprenticed to a huntsman. When he had learnt everything, and had become an excellent huntsman, the lord of the village took him into his service. In the village lived a beautiful and true-hearted maiden, who pleased the huntsman, and when his master perceived that, he gave him a little house, the two were married, lived peacefully and happily, and loved each other with all their hearts.

One day the huntsman was chasing a roe; and when the animal turned aside from the forest into the open country, he pursued it and at last shot it. He did not notice that he was now in the neighborhood of the dangerous millpond, and went, after he had disemboweled the stag, to the water, in order to wash his bloodstained hands. Scarcely, however, had he dipped them in than the nix ascended, smilingly wound her dripping arms around him, and drew him quickly down under the waves, which closed over him. When it was evening, and the huntsman did not return home, his wife became alarmed. She went out to seek him, and as he had often told her that he had to be on his guard against the snares of the nix, and dared not venture into the neighborhood of the millpond, she already suspected what had happened. She hastened to the water, and when she found his hunting pouch lying on the shore, she could no longer have any doubt of the misfortune. Lamenting her sorrow, and wringing her hands, she called on her beloved by name, but in vain. She hurried across to the other side of the pond, and called him anew; she reviled the nix with harsh words, but no answer followed. The surface of the water remained calm, only the crescent moon stared steadily back at her. The poor woman did not leave the pond. With hasty steps, she paced round and round it, without resting a moment, sometimes in silence, sometimes uttering a loud cry, sometimes softly sobbing. At last her strength came to an end, she sank down to the ground and fell into a heavy sleep.

Presently a dream took possession of her. She was anxiously climbing upward between great masses of rock; thorns and briers caught her feet, the rain beat in her face, and the wind tossed her long hair about. When she had reached the summit, quite a different sight presented itself to her; the sky was blue, the air soft, the ground sloped gently downward, and on a green meadow, gay with flowers of every color, stood a pretty cottage. She went up to it and opened the door; there sat an old woman with white hair, who beckoned to her kindly.

At that very moment, the poor woman awoke; day had already dawned, and she at once resolved to act in accordance with her dream. She laboriously climbed the mountain; everything was exactly as she had seen it in the night. The old woman received her kindly, and pointed out a chair on which she might sit. "Thou must have met with a misfortune," she said, "since thou hast sought out my lonely cottage." With tears, the woman related what had befallen her. "Be comforted," said the old woman, "I will help thee. Here is a golden comb for thee. Tarry till the full moon has risen, then go to the millpond, seat thyself on the shore, and comb thy long black hair with this comb. When thou hast done, lay it down on the bank, and thou wilt see what will happen." The woman returned home, but the time till the full moon came passed slowly. At last the shining disk appeared in the heavens, then she went out to the millpond, sat down, and combed her long black hair with the golden comb, and when she had finished, she laid it down at the water's edge. It was not long before there was a movement in the depths, a wave rose, rolled to the shore, and bore the comb away with it. In not more than the time necessary for the comb to sink to the bottom, the surface of the water parted, and the head of the huntsman arose. He did not speak, but looked at his wife with sorrowful glances. At the same instant, a second wave came rushing up, and covered the man's head. All had vanished, the millpond lay peaceful as before, and nothing but the face of the full moon shone on it.

Full of sorrow, the woman went back, but again the dream showed her the cottage of the old woman. Next morning she again set out and complained of her woes to the wise woman. The old woman gave her a golden flute, and said, "Tarry till the full moon comes again, then take this flute; play a beautiful air on it, and when thou hast finished, lay it on the sand; then thou wilt see what will happen." The wife did as the old woman told her. No sooner was the flute lying on the sand than there was a stirring in the depths, and a wave rushed up and bore the flute away with it. Immediately afterward the water parted, and not only the head of the man, but half of his body also arose. He stretched out his arms longingly toward her, but a second wave came up, covered him, and drew him down again. "Alas, what does it profit me," said the unhappy woman, "that I should see my beloved, only to lose him again?" Despair filled her heart anew, but the dream led her a third time to the house of the old woman. She set out, and the wise woman gave her a golden spinning wheel, consoled her, and said, "All is not yet fulfilled, tarry until the time of the full moon, then take the spinning wheel, seat thyself on the shore, and spin the spool full, and when thou hast done that, place the spinning wheel near the water, and thou wilt see what will happen." The woman obeyed all she said exactly; as soon as the full moon showed itself, she carried the golden spinning wheel to the shore, and span industriously until the flax came to an end, and the spool was quite filled with the threads. No sooner was the wheel standing on the shore than there was a more violent movement than before in the depths of the pond, and a mighty wave rushed up, and bore the wheel away with it. Immediately the head and the whole body of the man rose into the air, in a water spout. He quickly sprang to the shore, caught his wife by the hand and fled. But they had scarcely gone a very little distance, when the whole pond rose with a frightful roar, and streamed out over the open country. The fugitives already saw death before their eyes, when the woman in her terror implored the help of the old woman, and in an instant they were transformed, she into a toad, he into a frog. The flood which had overtaken them could not destroy them, but it tore them apart and carried them far away.

When the water had dispersed and they both touched dry land again, they regained their human form, but neither knew where the other was; they found themselves among strange people, who did not know their native land. High mountains and deep valleys lay between them. In order to keep themselves alive, they were both obliged to tend sheep. For many long years they drove their flocks through field and forest and were full of sorrow and longing. When spring had once more broken forth on the earth, they both went out one day with their flocks, and as chance would have it, they drew near each other. They met in a valley, but did not recognize each other; yet they rejoiced that they were no longer so lonely. Henceforth they each day drove their flocks to the same place; they did not speak much, but they felt comforted. One evening when the full moon was shining in the sky, and the sheep were already at rest, the shepherd pulled the flute out of his pocket, and played on it a beautiful but sorrowful air. When he had finished he saw the shepherdess was weeping bitterly. "Why art thou weeping?" he asked. "Alas," answered she, "thus shone the full moon when I played this air on the flute for the last time, and the head of my beloved rose out of the water." He looked at her, and it seemed as if a veil fell from his eyes, and he recognized his dear wife, and when she looked at him, and the moon shone in his face, she knew him also. They embraced and kissed each other, and no one need ask if they were happy.

[9]

The Black Rock Mermaid

On the twenty-ninth of April last one Mr. James Dixon, captain and commander of the ship *Dolphin* in her passage from Amsterdam in Holland, was beat back by a tempestuous wind, and all the men perished, except a young man named John Robinson, who was taken very ill on board the ship, and was left to Almighty Providence, and to the mercy of the seas and winds, and was also in great fear and dreadful fright on the Main Ocean, for the said John Robinson dreamt that he was on the top of a high mountain, whose top he thought reached up to the Heavens, and that there was a fine castle, about the circumference of a mile, and furnished with all sorts of diamonds and precious stones, and likewise on the top of the mountain was a well, which water was as sweet as honey and as white as milk, that whosoever drank of that water should never be dry again; with all sorts of music very delightful to hear, so one would think, as one supposed seven years in that place not so long as a day.

After having viewed the castle round, he observed to his great admiration a beautiful young lady who was guarded by seven serpents very frightful to behold.

Suppose the young lady was very beautiful, yet he wished rather to be a thousand miles off than in the sight of those serpents; and looking round about, he espied (to his great comfort) a green gate, and a street paved with blue marble, which opened at his coming to it, and so he got away from the serpents. But coming to the top of the hill, he did not know how to get down, it being very high and steep, but he found a ladder to his comfort; it being very slender, he was afraid to venture but at last was obliged to go down it, for one of the serpents having taken notice of him pursued him so very close that he was in great danger, and though he fell and broke his leg, and that the serpent fell upon him, which awakened him in great fright and almost made him mad.

By this you may think what a great trouble he was in, awaked alone on the Main Ocean, when missing all the rest of the ship's crew, and also the great danger he was in.

But to his great amazement, he espied a beautiful young lady combing her head, and tossed on the billows, clothed all in green (but by chance he got the first word with her). Then she with a smile came on board and asked how he did. The young man, being something smart and a scholar, replied, "Madam, I am the better to see you in good health, in great hopes trusting you will be a comfort and assistance to me in this my low condition"; and so caught hold of her comb and green girdle that was about her waist. To which she replied, "Sir, you ought not to rob a young woman of her riches and then expect a favor at her hands; but if you will give me my comb and girdle again, what lies in my power I will do for you."

At which time he had no power to keep them from her but immediately delivered them up again; she, then smiling, thanked him and told him, if he would meet her again next Friday she would set him on shore. He had no power to deny her, so readily gave his consent; at which time she gave him a compass and desired him to steer southwest. He thanked her and told her he wanted some news.

She said she would tell him the next opportunity when he fulfilled his promises; but that he would find his father and mother much grieved about him, and so jumping into the sea she departed out of his sight.

At her departure the tempest ceased and blew a fair gale to south-west; so he got safe on shore; but when he came to his father's house he found everything as she had told him. For she told him also concerning his being left on shipboard, and how all the seamen perished, which he found all true what she had told him, according to the promise made him.

He was still much troubled in his mind concerning his promise, but yet while he was thus musing, she appeared to him with a smiling countenance and (by his misfortune) she got the first word of him, so that he could not speak one word, but was quite dumb, yet he took notice of the words she spoke; and she began to sing. After which she departed out of the young man's sight, taking from him the compass.

She took a ring from off her finger and put it on the young man's, and said she expected to see him once again with more freedom. But he never saw her more, upon which he came to himself again, went home, and was taken ill, and died in five days, to the wonderful admiration of all people who saw the young man.

[10]

The Cat on the Dovrefell

Once on a time there was a man up in Finnmark who had caught a great white bear, which he was going to take to the King of Denmark. Now, it so fell out, that he came to the Dovrefell just about Christmas Eve, and there he turned into a cottage where a man lived, whose name was Halvor, and asked the man if he could get houseroom there, for his bear and himself.

"Heaven never help me, if what I say isn't true!" said the man;

"but we can't give any one houseroom just now, for every Christmas Eve such a pack of trolls come down upon us that we are forced to flit, and haven't so much as a house over our own heads, to say nothing of lending one to anyone else."

"Oh?" said the man; "if that's all, you can very well lend me your house; my bear can lie under the stove yonder, and I can sleep in the side room."

Well, he begged so hard, that at last he got leave to stay there; so the people of the house flitted out, and before they went, everything was got ready for the trolls; the tables were laid, and there was rice porridge, and fish boiled in lye, and sausages, and all else that was good, just as for any other grand feast.

So, when everything was ready, down came the trolls. Some were great, and some were small; some had long tails, and some had no tails at all; some, too, had long, long noses; and they ate and drank, and tasted everything. Just then one of the little trolls caught sight of the white bear, who lay under the stove; so he took a piece of sausage and stuck it on a fork, and went and poked it up against the bear's nose, screaming out:

"Pussy, will you have some sausage?"

Then the white bear rose up and growled, and hunted the whole pack of them out of doors, both great and small.

Next year Halvor was out in the wood, on the afternoon of Christmas Eve, cutting wood before the holidays, for he thought the trolls would come again; and just as he was hard at work, he heard a voice in the wood calling out:

"Halvor! Halvor!"

"Well," said Halvor, "here I am."

"Have you got your big cat with you still?"

"Yes, that I have," said Halvor; "she's lying at home under the stove, and what's more, she has now got seven kittens, far bigger and fiercer than she is herself."

"Oh, then, we'll never come to see you again," bawled out the troll away in the wood, and he kept his word; for since that time the trolls have never eaten their Christmas brose with Halvor on the Dovrefell.

V

DEVILS AND A GIANT

The term "devil" as used in folktales is a broad and elastic one. It may mean "stupid ogre," "giant," "dragon," "evil magician," "Oriental demon," "Arabic jinn," or even "Death." However, the European medieval Devil is the Prince of Hell, the Grand Master of the witches, who wanders over the face of the earth looking for persons in such desperate straits that they would make a pact with him and risk or sell their souls for a price. Often this type is clever and wily, and he is always willing to let a single soul escape him if by so doing he can win two others. Yet sometimes a cunning man outwits him by solving his riddles or getting a supernatural helper to perform impossible tasks, or by proposing tasks which the Devil himself cannot perform. Giants may be either human or animal in form, and as a rule they are not too clever. They are usually male, have a keen appetite for human flesh, and can smell human beings from afar.

"The Devil a Lawyer" is translated from a tale in Paul Lacroix's *Curiosités de l'Histoire des Croyances Populaires au Moyen Age*, 1859. "The Devil and His Grandmother" is from the Grimms' *Household Tales*, Margaret Hunt's translation, 1884. "Fearless John" is translated from Emmanuel Cosquin's *Contes Populaires de Lorraine*, 1886. "Of a Haunted Chamber in St. Mary's Abbey, York" is from *The Early English Versions of the "Gesta Romanorum,"* 1879. "Nix Nought Nothing" is from Joseph Jacobs' *English Fairy Tales*, 1892, and "The Giant That Was a Miller" is from *Fairy Gold*, 1907, and is printed by permission of E. P. Dutton and Company, Inc. and J. M. Dent & Sons (Canada) Limited.

[1]

The Devil a Lawyer

A German adventurer, who was returning from the wars—perhaps from the sack of Rome—and who carried a well-lined wallet, fell sick at a Brandenburg inn and believed himself in danger of dying. Summoning his hostess, he spoke to her in secret. "My good woman," said he, "I have a great sum of money with me. I planned to invest it in some honest enterprise when I got home, but now I fear I shall never return, for my sickness is stubborn and strong. However, I want you to keep on trying to cure me. I authorize you to keep my money—you will find it under my pillow—until I recover. If I die, the money is yours, and I hope you will not let my soul suffer from lack of Masses."

The hostess took the wallet from under the soldier's pillow and promised to return it to him when he got well. But she was certain that he was going to die, and the physician whom she had summoned assured her that the malady was without remedy. She and her husband ceased nursing the dying man and buried his money in the cellar. The next day they peeped into his room to see if he was dead. But to their great disappointment they found him on the way to recovery and quite determined not to die this time. He demanded food and drink. Excusing themselves for neglecting him, they declared that the doctor had believed him dead and had gone away with the confessor, who, unfortunately, had been summoned too late.

"My good woman," cried the soldier, "this was but a false alarm of Madame Death. I now feel disposed to celebrate my recovery at the table. Therefore kill the fat calf, pick the goose, and draw wine that I may drink to your precious healths."

The host and his wife tried to persuade their guest to stay in bed and keep to the diet prescribed by the physician but to no avail.

Under pretext of preparing supper, they descended to the cellar and came to the decision to poison the poor fellow who wouldn't die despite the decree of the Faculty. The soldier, tormented by hunger and thirst, got up, dressed himself, and came downstairs to see if supper was ready. The hostess, pretending to be very busy, paid little attention to him.

"Now then, my good woman," he said to her, "where have you locked up the money? I can take it off your hands, for I fear no longer that it will be stolen from me while I sleep. My trusty blade will protect it better than the lock of your coffer." "What are you saying?" asked the hostess, who was embarrassed because this question was put in the presence of her servants. "What money do you mean? Apparently you haven't got completely well, for your brain is filled with strange fantasies."

"O yes I have, my dear. I am talking about the wallet I gave you yesterday just before the doctor came."

"There's a bold rascal for you," cried the woman, who acted as if she were highly indignant. "That wallet existed only in your imagination, my friend."

"Bless me! Would you be so dishonest as to deny me my property? Villainous woman, give me my property immediately. Give it up or I will accuse you of robbery before the podesta."

"And you, cheat, if you persist in this false accusation, I will denounce before the judge and demand justice for this imposture."

"*Corbleu!* You are a shameless thief. Return my gold or it will go hard with you."

"Help me, husband," screamed the hostess, pushing the soldier toward the door. "He's hurting me." This brought the host and the servants running, and they beat the soldier and kicked him out the door. When he realized he was outside, he drew his sword and broke the windowpanes. Swearing that he would kill these dishonest innkeepers, he told the assembled crowd that this man and his wife had stolen his money. The hostess, thrusting her head out of an upstairs window, accused the soldier of having extorted a great sum of money from her and of having planned to assassinate her, her husband, and their servants. She begged the crowd to prevent the soldier from doing violence. So the people seized him, and he was put in chains and thrown into prison.

After listening to the witnesses, the podesta was convinced that the soldier had really plotted to commit the robbery and murder. His repeated denials of guilt only made his condemnation more certain. The penalty would surely be death. But a day or two before this penalty was to be pronounced, the poor soldier heard the prison door open. As he supposed that the jailer or the headsman was entering, he was not a little surprised to find himself face to face with a visage which had nothing human in it. It was the Devil himself. Had he not seen him depicted in statuary, church windows, and religious paintings often enough to make identification easy? As the soldier was a good Christian, he drew back, invoked his guardian angel, and began making signs of the cross.

"Stop it, my friend," cried Satan, who had been forced to cower on the floor to avoid being knocked down by those fine signs of the cross. "Upon the word of the damned, I will not rise until you give permission," he cried. "If we could have a little sensible conversation, you would find it much more to your advantage than conversing with the hangman's noose."

"Back! stand away from me, tempter," cried the soldier, who, to tell the truth, was much impressed by the intrepidity with which Satan braved the sign of the redemption of man.

"Cease making those gestures if you wish to hear the purpose of my visit. You will find that if you cross your arms on your breast you will have adequate protection against my claws." The prisoner, conquered by the Evil Spirit's obstinacy, left off crossing himself for a moment and consented to listen, if not to answer. Satan arose, chewing his claws and brushing off the flies with his tail, just like a cow.

"I come to tell you, my brother," said he in a derisive tone, "it is a certainty that you will be condemned to be hanged high and short."

"But, by the grace of God, I am perfectly innocent," cried the poor soldier.

"If that is true, then why climb the gallows steps? If you sell yourself to me, body, blood, and all, I promise to make you live to be as old as Methusalem."

"But I would rather die a thousand deaths than give myself to Hell!"

"To each according to his inclination, my fine fellow. What do you know about the other world? Next to nothing! It's my job to get another soul, no matter whose. I promise to let you keep yours if you will help me to get another's."

"But where can I find a soul? Show me one all rotten with sin and weighed down by crimes so that it will be worthy of you."

"All I want you to do is to help me: I'll get the soul myself. Just choose the lawyer in the blue bonnet to defend you. I will point him out in the courtroom."

"Will this lawyer get me off?"

"Yes, on my word."

"Will he get back the money the hostess unjustly keeps from me?"

"Yes, indeed."

"Will I be declared innocent and set free?"

"Yes, I tell you. If these things do not come about, let me be forever only a miserable stupid devil without subjects, domain, or power."

So the soldier decided to follow the advice of the Devil, who, after all, seemed to be a good fellow at bottom. Did not he show respect for religion by keeping out of range of the signs of the cross?

The moment the soldier was led into the courtroom, he looked for a lawyer wearing a blue bonnet. Not finding such a one his heart sunk, for he imagined Satan was mocking his misfortune. He protested his innocence and asked the podesta for a lawyer to defend him. The host and hostess of the inn in which he had been plundered were present and keenly enjoying the prospect of seeing him hanged. They arose and offered to swear that all they had accused him of was true.

"I doubt," said the podesta, "that anyone would dare defend this thief, murderer, and calumniator, but nevertheless I give him permission to get a lawyer."

Just then the accused caught sight of a lawyer in a blue bonnet. He pointed to him and he was brought to the bar. No one there had ever seen him before. He aroused both curiosity and fear. He was a little catlike creature who kept rolling about his eyeballs, which were inflamed and sent forth fiery sparks. He kept his hands hidden in the sleeves of his robe, and he did not take off his bonnet because of a cold which, he said, had afflicted him for six thousand years. The sardonic tone of his voice made the podesta shiver on his bench and the people in the room tremble. Only the guilty innkeepers were unaffected: they laughed at the unknown lawyer.

He began his plea without even consulting his client. He averred that the soldier was falsely accused, described in detail the circumstances in which the money had been entrusted to the hostess, revealed the plot of this woman and her husband, said that the money could be found in the cellar of the inn under an empty cask, and described the place just as if he were looking at it as he spoke.

The people there were deeply impressed and the podesta began to change his opinion. The innkeeper, pale and shaking, interrupted the advocate in the blue bonnet.

"Whoever you are, you lie," he cried in a broken voice. "The soldier is a malefactor and his lawyer a teller of falsehoods."

"Yes, indeed, this lawyer is a past master of rascality," added the hostess, whose impudence surpassed her husband's. "He is, I suppose, the soldier's accomplice, and he knows how to lie more cleverly than Satan, who is his master."

"I deny, and will go on denying all that this blue bonnet has dared to say against my dear and honored wife," said the innkeeper. And his wife cried, "May the lie twist his tongue. I say in answer to his false accusations that we are certainly guilty if they are true. But if he is not a liar, may the great Devil of Hell take us!"

The instant she uttered this imprecation, thunderous laughter burst from the diabolic lawyer's mouth. The spectators thought that lightning had touched off a powder barrel. And from the lawyer's blue bonnet sprang forth two great ram's horns and from his sleeves shot out two long sooty arms. With these he seized the innkeeper and his wife, and carrying them right up through the ceiling, he hurled them against the wall of the church belfry. Here their bloody silhouettes were imprinted as clearly as if a painter had traced them with his brush.

The podesta set the soldier free, and the money was found in the cellar just as the lawyer had said. To commemorate how God's justice had operated through the intervention of the Devil, the soldier placed a plaque in a chapel of the place.

Joint School Library Blairsville, Pa.

[2]

The Devil and His Grandmother

There was a great war, and the king had many soldiers but gave them small pay, so small that they could not live upon it, so three of them agreed among themselves to desert. One of them said to the others: "If we are caught we shall be hanged on the gallows; how shall we manage it?" Another said: "Look at that great cornfield; if we were to hide ourselves there no one could find us; the troops are not allowed to enter it, and tomorrow they are to march away." They crept into the corn; only the troops did not march away but remained lying all round about it. They stayed in the corn for two days and two nights and were so hungry that they all but died, but if they had come out their death would have been certain. Then they said: "What is the use of our deserting if we have to perish miserably here?"

But now a fiery dragon came flying through the air, and it came down to them and asked why they had concealed themselves there. They answered: "We are three soldiers who have deserted because the pay was so bad, and now we shall have to die of hunger if we stay here, or to dangle on the gallows if we go out." "If you will serve me for seven years," said the dragon, "I will convey you through the army so that no one shall seize you." "We have no choice and are compelled to accept," they replied. Then the dragon caught hold of them with his claws and carried them away through the air over the army and put them down again on the earth far from it; but the dragon was no other than the Devil. He gave them a small whip and said: "Whip with it and crack it, and then as much gold will spring up round about as you can wish for; then you can live like great lords, keep horses, and drive your carriages, but when the seven years have come to an end, you are my property." Then he put before them a book which they were all three forced to sign. "But first I will ask you a riddle," said he, "and if you guess it, you shall be free and released from my power."

Then the dragon flew away from them, and they went away with their whip, had gold in plenty, ordered themselves rich apparel, and traveled about the world. Wherever they were they lived in pleasure and magnificence, rode on horseback, drove in carriages, ate and drank, but did nothing wicked. The time slipped quickly by, and when the seven years were coming to an end, two of them were terribly anxious and alarmed; but the third took the affair easily and said: "Brothers, fear nothing. I still have my wits about me; I shall guess the riddle." They went out into the open country and sat down, and the two pulled sorrowful faces. Then an aged woman came up to them who inquired why they were so sad. "Well," said they, "what has that to do with you? After all, you cannot help us." "Who knows?" she said, "just confide your trouble to me." So they told her that they had been the Devil's servants for nearly seven years, and that he had provided them with gold as though it were hay, and that they had sold themselves to him, and were forfeited to him if at the end of the seven years they could not guess a riddle. The old woman said: "If you are to be saved, one of you must go into the forest. There he will come to a fallen rock which looks like a little house; he must enter that, and then he will obtain help." The two melancholy ones thought to themselves: "That will still not save us," and stayed where they were, but the third, the merry one, got up and walked on in the forest until he found the rock house.

In the little house a very aged woman was sitting, who was the Devil's grandmother, and asked the soldier where he came from and what he wanted there. He told her everything that had happened, and as he pleased her well, she had pity on him and said she would help him. She lifted up a great stone which lay above a cellar, and said: "Conceal yourself there. You can hear everything that is said here; only sit still and do not stir. When the dragon comes, I will question him about the riddle. He tells everything to me, so listen carefully to his answer."

At twelve o'clock at night the dragon came flying thither and asked for his dinner. The grandmother laid the table and served up food and drink, so that he was pleased, and they ate and drank together. In the course of conversation she asked him what kind of a day he had had, and how many souls he had got. "Nothing went very well today," he answered, "but I have laid hold of three soldiers—I have them safe." "Indeed! three soldiers; they're clever, they may escape you yet." The Devil said mockingly: "They are mine! I will set them a riddle which they will never be able to guess!" "What riddle is that?" she inquired. "I will tell you: in the great North Sea lies a dead dogfish; that shall be your roast meat, and the rib of a whale shall be your silver spoon, and a hollow horse's hoof shall be your wineglass." When the Devil had gone to bed, the old grandmother raised up the stone and let out the soldier. "Did you give heed to everything?" "Yes," said he, "I know enough and will save myself." Then he had to go back another way, through the window, secretly and with all speed to his companions. He told them how the Devil had been outwitted by the old grandmother, and how he had learned the answer to the riddle from him. Then they were all delighted and of good cheer and took the whip and whipped so much gold for themselves that it ran all over the ground.

When the seven years had fully gone by, the Devil came with the book, showed the signatures, and said: "I will take you with me to Hell. There you shall have a meal! If you can guess what kind of roast meat you will have to eat, you shall be free and released from your bargain, and may keep the whip as well." Then the first soldier began and said: "In the great North Sea lies a dead dogfish; that no doubt is the roast meat." The Devil was angry and began to mutter "Hm!hm!hm!" and asked the second: "But what will your spoon be?" "The rib of a whale; that is to be our silver spoon." The Devil made a wry face, again growled, "Hm!hm! hm!" and said to the third: "And do you also know what your wineglass is to be?" "An old horse's hoof is to be our wineglass." Then the Devil flew away with a loud cry and had no more power over them. But the three kept the whip, whipped as much money for themselves with it as they wanted, and lived happily to their end.

[3]

Fearless John

There once was a young fellow named John who had never once in his whole life been really frightened. His parents wanted him to marry, but he said he never would until he had been frightened. They then inquired of his uncle, a village curate, asking whether he knew any way to make their son know what fear was. The curate promised to take the matter in hand, and he invited John to spend the Christmas holidays with him.

John went and was very well entertained by his uncle. The day after his arrival, the curate asked him to go to the belfry and ring the bell for Mass. "Willingly," he answered. On opening the vestry door, he found himself face to face with six men armed with lances. "Well," he said, "what are you doing here? You certainly go on guard early in the morning." No one answered because these were manikins. Then John gave them a shove and they all fell to the floor. Then he passed through a room which he had to cross to get to the belfry. There he saw six men seated at a table at which there were seven places set. "Good day, gentlemen," said he on entering, "good appetite." As there was no response, he said, "Evidently people aren't very polite in this part of the country." Taking his place at the table, he ate all that was served up. The uncle, who was looking through the keyhole, laughed to see how cleverly his nephew handled the situation.

Then John began to climb the stairs of the belfry. Halfway up he encountered some men armed with big sabers. He told them, "You certainly do get up early here to take your posts." Seeing that they did not answer him, he tumbled them down the stairs, and they fell on top of the uncle who was following his nephew. When he got to the top, John saw men holding the bell rope. "Do you wish to ring the bell," he asked, "or would you prefer that I do it?" But these men were mute like the others. So John pitched them down to the bottom of the belfry. After ringing for Mass, he descended and found his uncle stretched out at the foot of the stairs. He lifted up the poor man, who moaned, "Well, nephew, were you frightened?" "Uncle," said John, "you were more frightened than I." "John," then said the curate, "you can't stay here any longer. Come take this stole and this baton. With the stole you can make yourself either invisible or visible. And anything you strike with this baton will be struck very hard."

John then said good-by to his uncle and took to the road, marching through rain, wind, and snow. Night caught him in the midst of a great forest. After wandering around aimlessly for a time, he caught sight of a distant light, and heading in that direction he came to a cottage which stood at some distance from the light he had seen. He knocked and was welcomed by a woman and her daughter who lived in the cottage. He asked them about the light he had seen. "That light," they answered, "comes from a castle which is visited by a devil each midnight." They added that the castle belonged to them, for they were princesses, but that they did not dare live there because they feared the devil. "Give me a pack of cards," John said, "and I will enter that castle." "Oh!" cried the princess, "please do not risk your life for me!" But John did not wish to back down: he took the pack of cards and set out.

When he entered the castle, he kindled a good fire and found a seat by the hearth. Scarcely had he settled down than a shower of arms, legs, and dead men's heads came down the chimney. He gathered them up and made a game of nine-pins out of them. Finally the devil himself descended and asked the young man, "What are you doing here?" "That's none of your business," answered John. "I have as much right to be here as you have." The devil then sat down by the hearth, facing John, and glared at him for some time without saying a word. Finding that the young man was not frightened, he asked him to play a game of cards with him. "Gladly," answered John. "If one of us lets a card drop," said the devil, "he must pick it up." "I agree," said John, and they began to play.

In a little while the devil let one of his cards fall, and he asked John to pick it up. "No," said John; "we agreed that the one who dropped the card should pick it up." The devil had no answer to this, and just when he bent down to pick up the card, John took his baton and beat him with it on the shoulders, hard and often. The devil cried out like a blind man, but the blows continued to rain down.

When the devil was well thrashed, John said to him, "If you have had enough, promise to quit this house, and put it in writing." The devil made a note to this effect and signed it in a hurry. He believed that this would get him out of his disagreeable situation, but John did not trust him and threw the note into the fire, where it burst into flames. "How is this?" cried the devil; "is that all you think of my signature?" "Your note is worthless," said John, as he began to beat the devil again harder than ever. The devil bellowed like the devil he was. He rewrote the note and this time it was good.

Then John punctured the window with his baton and told the devil he had to leave through the little hole he had made. The latter at first pretended that this was impossible. Then he asked the young man to give his feet a push. When John did this, the devil gave him a tremendous kick in the face and then fled.

John was now alone. And he was tired. Finding a bed adorned with pearls, rubies, emeralds, and diamonds, he climbed in and slept soundly.

Meanwhile the princess and a little Negress, her servant, came to the courtyard of the castle to listen. They had heard the row and feared that John was dead. When morning came she sent the little Negress to find out what had happened. She called to him and he awoke with a start. Catching sight of the Negress, he thought it was the devil who had returned. He shot her with his gun and killed her. The princess, greatly distressed by the death of her servant, rushed in and called for John. "O it is you, my princess," he said. "What makes you cry?" "Alas! you have just slain my servant!" "Forgive me," cried John, "I mistook her for the devil."

The princess was very grateful to John for delivering her castle and to reward him offered her hand in marriage. But John declared that he would never marry until he knew what fear was. "Better forget me," he advised, "for it will be a long time before I return here, perhaps never—and besides you ought to marry a man of your rank." So the only reward he would take was a silk handkerchief to remember her by. Then he left. He bought a horse and rode it to Paris, where he put up at a hotel which was full of princes. These princes did not want to admit an adventurer like John to their table, but the hostess, who liked his money as much as theirs, would not send him away.

The chief subject of conversation at the hotel was the king's daughter who on the morrow was to be delivered up to the devil to be devoured. John asked to be awakened early the next morning. As soon as he was up, he ate a good breakfast and left the hotel. The streets were full of people on the way to church where the *Libera* was to be sung for the princess, just as if she were already dead. There was a great scaffold erected in Rue Montmartre, and the princess stood upon that scaffold. John climbed up upon it and said to the princess as he passed her a piece of paper, "My princess, take this letter. When the devil approaches to seize you, present it as coming from your father, the king. I will answer for the rest."

When he had said this, he put on the stole and instantly became invisible. But he was there waiting for the devil, who did not delay but arrived shouting, "Ah! the delicious girl I am going to eat! How young and tender!" The princess trembled but handed him the letter. While he paused to look at it, John recognized him as the same devil he had chased from the castle, and began to beat him with his baton. The devil was furious and wished to attack whatever was beating him, but he saw nothing there. He let out some terrible howls. The people at the foot of the scaffold, believing that they heard the cries of the princess, were horror stricken.

John forced the devil to climb down and, tying him to a tree which stood near by, forced him to sign a paper setting the princess free. Wishing to make certain that the writ was good—for he had his reasons for suspicion—he turned over his baton to the princess and ordered her to keep on striking until he came back. Entering a blacksmith shop, he threw the paper into the fire of the forge. The paper burned instantly. When he came back, he found that the devil had got loose from all his bonds but one. John tied him more securely and made him write another note. Then while the princess continued the flogging, John went to test the second writ. This time it did not burn. On his return John said to the devil, "Now you are going to get into this oat sack." And instantly the devil squatted down in it without breathing a word.

The princess thanked John for delivering her. She presented him with a handkerchief upon which was traced her portrait and the portraits of her entire family. She offered to marry him, but John declared he would not wed until he had been frightened. "Good-by, my princess," said he, "perhaps in a year or eighteen months I will return this way." Then he threw the sack in which the devil was tied over his shoulder, carried it down to the Seine, and dumped it in. Then he left Paris.

After a year had passed, one fine morning John told himself that it was time to return to Paris. So he did, and he put up at the hotel of the princes where he noticed preparations for a grand banquet were being made. The whole city was celebrating. "What does this all mean?" he asked a young man in the dining room, and he said, "Just a year ago preparations were being made for the princess's funeral, but today she is going to marry the man who saved her." "And who then saved her?" asked John. "I did," answered the young man. "I saved her from the devil; and for proof, here is the handkerchief she gave me." (Someone had made him a handkerchief just like the one the princess had given John.) "If this is so," declared John, "it will be fine for you."

Meanwhile the king took his daughter to the church, where instead of the *Libera* they were going to sing the *Te Deum*. John, wearing his smock frock, went to the street down which the procession was passing. The princess saw him and said to the king, "Father, there is the one who delivered me." Instantly the king ordered the procession to turn around and go back to the castle, much to the astonishment of the crowd, which wondered if the king had lost his head. John, summoned before the king, described how the princess had been saved and showed him the handkerchief she had given him. The king wished to have the young man who had deceived him put to death, but John asked that his offense be forgiven and even arranged a marriage between him and the princess's lady-in-waiting. As for himself, John declared again he did not wish to wed until he had felt fear.

The king made it known that he fervently wished someone or something would frighten John. Finally the prime minister had an idea. He had all the sparrows of Paris caught and put in a pie. As the king, the royal household, and John sat at table, the pie was brought in. It was presented first to the king and then to the other diners. But each excused himself, saying that John was the one who should open it. At first John refused, but as everyone insisted he finally yielded and lifted the top crust. Like a flash a big sparrow flew right in his face. He gave a great start. "Ah!" cried the king, "you were really frightened!" John did not wish to admit it, but finally those present persuaded him that he had experienced fear. Therefore he no longer had a reason not to marry. So he consented to marry the princess and the wedding was celebrated in great style.

[4]

Of a Haunted Chamber in St. Mary's Abbey, York

Once there was an English king who held his parliament at York, and hither came all the nobles of the realm and many others. The last to arrive was a great justice, but he could find no lodgings because all the hostels were full. So he went to St. Mary's Abbey, a house of monks. However, there also all the chambers were taken, save one which was haunted by a ghost. No man dared to lie in this place, for the ghost had brought grief and harm to many a one. Nevertheless, the justice, declaring that he would spend the night here, bade his men hurry and kindle a fire in the fireplace. But the men, being afraid, would not prepare the chamber for their master until after they had found a priest and made a full confession of all their sins. Then the justice came into the chamber, drank, and got ready to retire. He placed his two-handed sword at the head of the bed and sat on the bed in his doublet. He had rested thus but a little while when an ape came out of the privy and sat himself down before the fire. He scratched first one leg and then the other. Then he leaped over the bench and did many a trick. Going to the foot of the bed where the men slept, he seized hold of the bedclothes and shook them up and down, causing a wind to blow on the occupants of the bed, who were much frightened and held on fast to their blankets. After this prank the ape again warmed himself at the hearth. Next he went to the justice's bed. The justice saw him coming and made an attempt to seize his sword, but the ape got hold of it first. Then the judge, seizing the creature in his arms, threw him into the fire. However, the ape leaped from the fire and catching hold of his antagonist threw him into it. But leaping quickly out of the flames, the justice grasped the ape and wrestled with him. Because of their great fear, not one of his men dared to come to his assistance. After the contest had gone on for a very long time, the ape got the justice on his back and started to carry him through the privy door, but the justice's head struck one of the doorposts. It was such a terrible blow that the justice cried out, "Lady, help." Instantly he saw a beautiful Lady stand before him. The ape-ghost dropped him and fled away.

"What Lady are you?" asked the justice.

"I am," she replied, "Mary, the mother of Christ; and I came because you called for me. If you had called before, I would have come to help you sooner. If I had not come, the ape-ghost would have slain you."

"O sweet Lady, gramercy. Protect me from the thing, for I am afraid he will come back and kill me."

"My son, be not afraid," said she, "for I shall fasten the door with a hasp and pin. Therefore go and take your rest. When you arise in the morning, go and confess your sins. Take the pin from the hasp and put it in your purse. As long as you keep yourself from deadly sin, so long will the pin be in your possession. But if you fall into deadly sin, the pin will disappear."

The justice arose in the morning, and taking the pin, he wrapped it in a pretty piece of cloth, as the Lady had bidden him. Then he went to confession. For many a day afterward he lived happily. However, the enemy of mankind, the false fiend, once led him into deadly sin and the pin vanished. When he realized that it was gone, he was very sorry and went to confession and did his penance. Then he found that the pin had returned to his purse. He rejoiced and ever afterward lived a happy life. When he died, he went to heaven. And so may we all, I pray God! Amen.

[5]

Nix Nought Nothing

There once lived a king and a queen as many a one has been. They were long married and had no children; but at last a baby boy came to the queen when the king was away in the far countries. The queen would not christen the boy till the king came back, and she said, "We will just call him *Nix Nought Nothing* until his father comes home." But it was long before he came home, and the boy had grown a fine, bonny laddie. At length the king was on his way back; but he had a big river to cross, and there was a whirlpool, and he could not get over the water. But a giant came up to him, and said: "I'll carry you over." But the king said: "What's your pay?"

"O give me Nix, Nought, Nothing, and I will carry you over the water on my back."

The king had never heard that his son was called Nix Nought Nothing, and so he said: "O I'll give you that and my thanks into the bargain."

When the king got home again, he was very happy to see his wife again, and his young son. She told him that she had not given the child name, but just Nix Nought Nothing, until he should come home again himself. The poor king was in a terrible case. He said: "What have I done? I promised to give the giant who carried me over the river on his back Nix Nought Nothing." The king and the queen were sad and sorry, but they said: "When the giant comes we will give him the henwife's boy; he will never know the difference." The next day the giant came to claim the king's promise, and he sent for the henwife's boy; and the giant went away with the boy on his back. He traveled till he came to a big stone, and there he sat down to rest. He said: "Hidge, Hodge, on my back, what time of day is that?"

The poor little lad said: "It is the time that my mother, the henwife, takes up the eggs for the queen's breakfast."

Then the giant was very angry and dashed the boy on the stone and killed him.

Back he went on a tower of a temper and this time they gave him the gardener's boy. He went off with him on his back till they got to the stone again when the giant sat down to rest. And he said: "Hidge, Hodge, on my back, what time of day do you make that?"

The gardener's boy said: "Sure it's the time that my mother takes up the vegetables for the queen's dinner."

Then the giant was as wild as could be, and killed him too.

Then the giant went back to the king's house in a terrible temper and said he would destroy them all if they did not give him Nix Nought Nothing this time. They had to do it; and when he came to the big stone, the giant said: "What time of day is that?" Nix Nought Nothing said, "It is the time that my father the king will be sitting down to supper." The giant said, "I've got the right one now," and took Nix Nought Nothing to his own house and brought him up till he was a man.

The giant had a bonny daughter, and she and the lad grew very fond of each other. The giant said one day to Nix Nought Nothing: "I've work for you tomorrow. There is a stable seven miles long and seven miles broad, and it has not been cleared for seven years, and you must clear it tomorrow, or I will have you for my supper."

The giant's daughter went out next morning with the lad's breakfast and found him in a terrible state, for always as he cleared out a bit, it just fell in again. The giant's daughter said she would help him, and she cried all the beasts in the field and all the fowls of the air, and in a minute they all came and carried away everything that was in the stable and made it all clean before the giant came home. He said: "Shame on the wit that helped you; but I have a worse job for you tomorrow." Then he said to Nix Nought Nothing: "There's a lake seven miles long and seven miles deep and seven miles broad and you must drain it tomorrow by nightfall or else I'll have you for supper."

Nix Nought Nothing began early next morning and tried to lave the water with his pail, but the lake was never getting any less, and he didn't know what to do. But the giant's daughter called on all the fish in the sea to come and drink the water, and very soon they drank it dry. When the giant saw the work done he was in a rage and said: "I've a worse job for you tomorrow. There is a tree seven miles high, and no branch on it till you get to the top; and there is a nest with seven eggs in it, and you must bring down all the eggs without breaking one or else I'll have you for my supper."

At first the giant's daughter did not know how to help Nix Nought Nothing, but she cut off first her fingers and then her toes, and made steps of them, and he clomb the tree and got all the eggs safe till he came just to the bottom, and there one was broken. So they determined to run away together, and after the giant's daughter had gone back to her room and got her magic flask, they set out together as fast as they could run. And they hadn't got but three fields away when they looked back and saw the giant walking along at full speed after them. "Quick, quick," called out the giant's daughter, "take my comb from my hair and throw it down." Nix Nought Nothing took her comb from her hair and threw it down, and out of every one of its prongs there sprung up a fine thick brier in the way of the giant. You may be sure it took him a long time to work his way through the brier bush, and by the time he was well through, Nix Nought Nothing and his sweetheart had run far far away from him. But he soon came along after them and was just like to catch 'em up when the giant's daughter called out to Nix Nought Nothing, "Take my hair dagger and throw it down, quick, quick." So Nix Nought Nothing threw down the hair dagger and out of it grew as quick as lightning a thick hedge of sharp razors placed crisscross. The giant had to tread very cautiously to get through all this, and meanwhile they both ran hard, and on and on and on till they were nearly out of sight. But at last the giant was through, and it wasn't long before he was like to catch them up. But just as he was stretching out his hand to catch Nix Nought Nothing, his daughter took out her magic flask and dashed it on the ground. And as it broke, out of it welled a big, big wave that grew and grew till it reached the giant's waist and then his neck. And when it got to his head, he was drowned dead, and dead, and dead indeed.

But Nix Nought Nothing fled on till where do you think they came to? Why, to near the castle of Nix Nought Nothing's father and mother. But the giant's daughter was so weary that she couldn't move a step further. So Nix Nought Nothing told her to wait there while he went and found out a lodging for the night. And he went on toward the lights of the castle, and on the way he came to the cottage of the henwife whose boy, you'll remember, had been killed by the giant. Now she knew Nix Nought Nothing in a moment, and hated him because he was the cause of her son's death. So when he asked his way to the castle, she put a spell upon him, and when he got to the castle, no sooner was he let in than he fell down dead asleep upon a bench in the hall. The king and queen tried all they could do to wake him up, but all in vain. So the king promised that if any maiden could wake him she should marry him.

Meanwhile the giant's daughter was waiting and waiting for him to come back. And she went up into a tree to watch for him. The gardener's daughter, going to draw water in the well, saw the shadow of the lady in the water and thought it was herself, and said: "If I'm so bonny, if I'm so brave, why do you send me to draw water?" So she threw down her pail and went to see if she could wed the sleeping stranger. And she went to the henwife, who taught her an unspelling charm which would keep Nix Nought Nothing awake as long as the gardener's daughter liked. So she went up to the castle and sang her charm and Nix Nought Nothing was wakened for a while and they promised to wed him to the gardener's daughter. Meanwhile the gardener went down to draw water from the well and saw the shadow of the lady in the water. So he looked up and found her, and he brought the lady from the tree and led her into the house. And he told her that a stranger was to marry his daughter, and took her up to the castle and showed her the man. And it was Nix Nought Nothing asleep in a chair. And she saw him and cried to him: "Waken, waken, and speak to me!" But he would not waken, and soon she cried:

> I cleansed the stable, I laved the lake, and I clomb the tree,
> And all for the love of thee,
> And thou wilt not waken and speak to me.

The king and the queen heard this, and came to the bonny young lady, and she said: "I cannot get Nix Nought Nothing to speak to me for all that I can do."

Then were they greatly astonished when she spoke of Nix Nought Nothing, and asked where he was, and she said, "He that sits there in the chair." Then they ran to him and kissed him and called him their own dear son. So they called for the gardener's daughter and made her sing her charm, and he awakened and told them all that the giant's daughter had done for him, and of all her kindness. Then they took her in their arms and kissed her, and said she should now be their daughter, for their son should marry her. But as for the henwife, she was put to death. And they lived happy all their days.

[6]

The Giant That Was a Miller

Once upon a time there was a giant that was a miller. He lived in Yorkshire at a place called Dalton. His mill has been rebuilt; but when I was a boy there, the great old building still stood. In front of the house was a long mound, which went by the name of "the giant's grave," and in the mill was shown a long blade of iron something like a scythe blade, but not curved, which was the Giant's knife. Now, the giant who lived at Dalton mill ground men's bones to make his bread.

One day he captured a lad called Jack, on Pilmoor, and instead of grinding him body and bones in the mill he kept him as his servant, and never let him get away. Jack served the giant many years, and never was allowed a holiday. At last he could bear it no longer. Topcliffe Fair was coming on, and very hard Jack entreated that he might be allowed to go there to see the lasses and buy some fairings. The giant surlily refused leave; but Jack resolved to take it.

The day was hot, and after dinner the giant lay down in the mill with his head on a sack and dozed. He had been eating in the mill, and had laid down a great loaf of bone bread by his side, and the knife was in his hand, but his fingers relaxed their hold of it in sleep. Jack seized the moment, drew the knife away, and holding it with both his hands drove the blade into the single eye of the giant, who woke with a howl of agony and, starting up, barred the door. Jack thought he was dead and done for, then; but he soon found a way out. The giant had a favorite dog, which lay sleeping in the corner by the fire; but sprang up when his master was blinded. Jack killed the dog with the fire tongs, skinned it while his master was getting the knife out of his eye and, throwing the hide over his back, ran on all-fours barking between the legs of the giant, and so escaped.

VI

WEREWOLVES AND SOME OTHER ANIMALS

The werewolf tradition is very old. It was known to the ancient Greeks and Romans. Jean Bodin, who in *Dæmonomania* gives grisly descriptions of werewolves devouring the corpses of their victims, also mentions Pliny's account of a certain Demarch, who after eating the entrails of a child consecrated to the Lycæan Jupiter, turned instantly into a wolf. The tradition is still very much alive and is virtually world-wide. According to it, certain men, usually wizards, can take the form of a wolf (tiger, hyena, fox, leopard, etc.), hunt as an animal during the night, and then resume their human form at daybreak. If wounded, the werewolf becomes a human in form almost immediately but retains the wound. Sometimes the transformation is the result of a sorcerer's evil spell inflicted on the victim as an act of hate. Usually werewolves are men but in Fouqué's *Magic Ring* a girl becomes one.

In this section there are also a fable and two etiological or "because" animal stories. "Werewolves" is from Henry Boguet's *Discours Exécrable des Sorciers*, 1606, and "Niceros and the Werewolf" from Petronius's *Satyricon*. "Werewolves in Leon" is translated from the Abbé Prevost's novel, *Memoirs of a Man of Quality*, 1728–30. "The Ungrateful Snake" is a fable from *Oriental Folklore Tales*, 1890. "The Sole" is No. 172 in Grimms' *Household Tales*, Margaret Hunt's translation, 1884, and "Why the Bear is Stumpy-tailed" is from G. W. Dasent's *Tales from the Norse*, 1877.

[1]

Werewolves

Herodotus tells us that the natives of a certain part of Scythia used to turn themselves into wolves and that this was also a common habit among the peoples of the north. While the Romans were trying to keep Hannibal from passing the Alps, a wolf ran boldly into their army, bit and tore any soldiers he encountered, and finally escaped without even a scratch. The people of Constantinople in 1042 were terrorized by a pack of more than one hundred and fifty wolves. And in the territory of Geneva in 1148 a gigantic wolf killed thirty persons. Now who can doubt but that these wolves were lycanthropes?

Likewise the three wolves seen on the eighteenth of July, 1603, in the district of Douvres about half an hour after a hail storm had come in a mysterious fashion and destroyed all the fruit of that countryside. These three wolves were without tails. Moreover, as they ran through herds of cows and goats, they touched no single animal except one little kid which a wolf carried off a little distance without harming it in the least. All this shows that these were not common natural wolves but rather witches who had helped to cause the hail storm and had come to look over the damage it had done. One of them was Satan; for one of the wolves was larger than the others and he was the leader. Groz-Jacques Bocquet, Thievenne Paget, la Michollette, and several other witches said that when they took the form of wolves and ran about, Satan, assuming the same shape, led them on.

The natives of this country ought to know as much about werewolves as anybody, for they have always had them. In 1521 three wizards were executed: Michel Udon of Plane, which is a little village near Poligny; Philibert Montot; and a person called Big Pierre.

These confessed that they took lupine forms and had killed and eaten many people. While in wolflike form Michel Udon was wounded by a gentleman who followed and found him in a cabin where his wife was dressing his wound. But he had already changed back into human form. There have been pictures of these three wizards in the Church of the Jacobins at Poligny for a long time. In 1573 Gilles Garnier, having, it seems, confessed that he had transformed himself into the shape of a wolf and killed and eaten many infants, was burned alive at Dôle by order of the court. It will be fitting to tell here what happened in the year 1588 in a village about two leagues from Apchon in the high mountains of Auvergne. One evening a gentleman, standing at the window of his château, saw a hunter with whom he was acquainted passing by. And he asked him to give him a share of his game on his return. Pursuing his way through some flat lands, the hunter was attacked by a big wolf, and he discharged his arquebus at it, but did not wound it at all. Therefore he had to grapple with the beast, and he seized its ears. But he became fatigued and let go: then drawing back he drew a large hunting knife and cut off one of the wolf's paws, putting this in his hunting bag after the wolf had taken flight. He then returned to the gentleman's château, in sight of which he had fought the wolf. As this gentleman had asked for part of the game, he thought it might be comical to give him the wolf's paw. But when he pulled it from his bag, it had changed into a woman's hand and there was a gold ring on one of the fingers. And the gentleman recognized the ring as belonging to his wife. This made him suspicious of her, and going into the kitchen, he found his wife warming herself, and she hid her arm under her apron. Pulling the apron away, he saw that her hand had been severed. Thereupon the gentleman seized her, and as soon as her severed right hand was shown to her, she confessed that it was none other than she, who, in the form of a wolf, had attacked the hunter. The lady was afterward burned at Ryon. This was told me by a person who may be believed, and who passed through that country fifteen days after this thing had happened.

[2]

Niceros and the Werewolf

I was still in service and we lived in a little alley which was near the spot where Gavilla's house now stands. There, because the gods willed it, I fell in love with the wife of Terence, the tavernkeeper. You all were acquainted with Melissa of Tarentia, the choicest morsel of womanhood in the world. However, on my honor, I did not love her for physical delights but for her excellent nature. She surpassed anything I could imagine: never did she refuse me anything. I let her take charge of my little household affairs and never regretted it. Her husband, one day, died in the country. Immediately I began to try to think up some scheme to join her. It is in critical circumstances that one finds his true friends.

By a happy chance my master had gone to Capua to sell some articles of apparel which were in good demand. Taking advantage of the occasion, I persuaded our guest to accompany me on my way for five miles. He was a soldier, strong as a demon. When the first cock crowed in the morning we started. The moon made everything as bright as day. After walking along for a while, we found ourselves among the tombs. Suddenly the soldier began to conjure by the stars. As for me, I sat down and hummed a tune as I merely counted them. Then, turning to observe my companion, I saw him strip off all his clothes, and put them down at the side of the road. My heart was in my mouth and I was as motionless as a corpse. But imagine my surprise when I saw him make circles around his clothes with his urine and that instant transform himself into a wolf. Do not think that I am telling lies! I would not lie about this for all the gold in the world. But where am I in the story? Oh, yes. As soon as he became a wolf, he began to howl; and he fled into the forest. At first I did not know where I was. In a moment I went to pick up his clothes but found that they had become stone. If ever a man should have died of fright, it was I. However, I had enough courage to draw my sword, and I swung it around in circles through the air to drive away the evil spirits from my path until I arrived at the house of my mistress.

As soon as I passed over the threshold, I almost died. Cold sweat poured down my limbs, everything turned black, and it took all my strength to come to myself. My dear Melissa expressed her surprise at seeing me arrive so late. "If you had come sooner," she said, "you could have been of great help. A wolf broke into our sheepfold and killed all our sheep. What butchery! But although he has escaped, he cannot vaunt himself on his expedition since one of our servants ran a lance through his neck."

When I heard this, you might guess that I opened my eyes wide. And when daylight came, I ran toward home as fast as my legs could carry me—just like a merchant robbed by bandits. When I came to the place where I had left the clothes which had become stone, there was nothing except some blood on the ground. But when I entered the house, I found the soldier stretched out on his bed. He bled like a steer, and a doctor was busy dressing the wound on his neck. I understood then that the soldier was a werewolf. And from that day on, I would have died before eating a crust of bread with him. Those who do not wish to believe me do not have to, but if I lie, let the gods crush me under the weight of their anger.

[3]

Werewolves in Leon

One of the young Spanish gentlemen who were so hospitable to us when we were traveling through the mountainous wooded country around Plasencia, pointing to a forest where I had lost myself the day before, said that a strange thing had happened to him about two months before as he was hunting near there.

"After a day in which we had got our share of game," he said, "I decided that conditions were favorable for shooting from cover. So ordering my whipper-in to take the hounds and wait for me at the edge of the forest, I climbed a tree in the hope of shooting a roebuck or wild boar. I had not been in the tree ten minutes before a great wolf, emerging suddenly from the underbrush, ran to within twenty paces of where I was, and came to a stand. Just as I was about to shoot it, it pulled off its skin and became a man. This man appeared to be quite fatigued, and he sat down at the foot of a tree.

"Need I say that I was surprised? An instant afterward I was still more so, for a second wolf, coming from another direction, appeared and ran up to the first one. On pulling off his skin, the new one too became a man. And the two of them began to talk. My astonishment began to turn into fear. If these were not devils, they were certainly sorcerers—a dangerous tribe capable of the most terrible crimes. I trembled at the idea and arranged some branches as quietly as I could so that they would hide me.

"After talking for about an hour, the two men arose, donned their wolfskins, and instantly appeared as if true wolves. They trotted off toward the place where my whipper-in, with four of my strongest hounds on leash, awaited me. Now these hounds, catching the scent of the werewolves and breaking loose, rushed after them. I could hear the shouts of my man and the baying of the hounds. Guessing that the hunt would turn and run by me, I put two "chewed" bullets in my gun and got into position to fire. The wolves came by just ten paces away. I shot and one of them fell, badly wounded. Believing him dead, I climbed down from my tree. The hounds, baying fiercely, surrounded the fallen wolf, but there was not one of them that dared to take hold of him. After consulting with the whipper-in, I decided it would be safer for all if we killed the creature, whether wolf or man. When the wolf understood that we meant to slay him, he called me by my name and begged for his life. I ordered my servant to pull off the man's wolfskin covering, and we saw that it was fastened with hooks under the belly. When the skin was removed, I recognized the man as a peasant of a neighboring village.

" 'Wretch,' I cried, 'you deserve death. Where were you going and what were you bent on doing?'

" 'You have given me my death wound,' he whimpered,' and I beg you to help me.'

" 'First explain the strange form in which you appear,' said I, 'and tell me how you, who are a man, can run like a wolf.'

" 'It is a secret I learned from my father,' said he, trembling, 'and if you will save me, I will gladly teach it and others just as wonderful to you.'

"As he was too badly wounded to walk, I hoisted him onto my man's shoulders and he was carried to my château. On the way he was too feeble to talk much. Just as we entered the courtyard and I was ordering my people to make ready a bedroom, my servant received a mysterious blow that knocked him to the ground. At first I supposed that fatigue had caused him to sink down, but it was not so. He arose and we saw then that the wounded man had vanished. What art he used to escape or what became of him I do not know. But I do know that the night was not very dark and that I would have seen him if his disappearance had been a natural phenomenon."

[4]

The Ungrateful Snake

It is related that a man, mounted upon a camel, in the course of traveling arrived at a place where others from the same caravan had lighted a fire before proceeding on their journey. The fanlike wind, breathing on the embers, had produced a flame; and the sparks flying over the jungle, the dry wood had become ignited, and the whole plain glowed like a bed of tulips.

In the midst of this was an enormous snake, which, encircled by the flames, possessed no means of escape, and was about to be broiled like a fish, or kabobed like a partridge for the table. Blood oozed from its poison-charged eyes; and, seeing the man and the camel, it thus supplicated for assistance:

> What if in kindness thou vouchsafe me thy pity;
> Loosen the knot with which my affairs are entangled.

Now the traveler was a good man, and one who feared God. When he heard the complaint of the snake, and saw its pitiable condition, he reasoned thus with himself: "This snake is, indeed, the enemy of man, but being in trouble and perplexity, it would be most commendable in me to drop the seed of compassion, the fruit of which is prosperity in this world, and exaltation in the next." Thus convinced, he fastened one of his saddlebags to the end of his spear, and extended it to the snake, which, delighted at escape, entered the bag, and was rescued from the flames. The man then opening the mouth of the bag, addressed it thus: "Depart whither thou wilt, but forget not to offer up thanksgiving for thy preservation; henceforth seek the corner of retirement, and cease to afflict mankind, for they who do so are dishonest in this world and the next—

> Fear God—distress no one;
> This indeed is true salvation."

The snake replied, "O young man, hold thy peace, for truly I will not depart until I have wounded both thee and this camel."

The man cried out, "But how is this? Have I not rendered thee a benefit? Why, then, is such to be my recompense?

> On my part there was faithfulness,
> Why then this injustice upon thine?"

The snake said, "True, thou hast shown mercy, but it was to an unworthy object; thou knowest me to be an agent of injury to mankind; consequently, when thou savedst me from destruction, thou subjectedst thyself to the same rule that applies to the punishment due for an evil act committed against a worthy object.

"Again, between the snake and man there is a long-standing enmity, and they who employ foresight hold it as a maxim of wisdom to bruise the head of an enemy; to thy security my destruction was necessary, but, in showing mercy, thou hast forfeited vigilance. It is now necessary that I should wound thee, that others may learn by thy example."

The man cried, "O snake, call but in the counsel of justice; in what creed is it written, or what practice declares, that evil should be returned for good, or that the pleasure of conferring benefits should be returned by injury and affliction?"

The snake replied, "Such is the practice amongst men. I act according to thy own decree; the same commodity of retribution I have purchased from thee I also sell.

Buy for one moment that which thou sell'st for years."

In vain did the traveler entreat, the snake ever replying, "I do but treat thee after the manner of men." This the man denied. "But," said he, "let us call witnesses: if thou prove thy assertion, I will yield to thy will." The snake, looking round, saw a cow grazing at a distance, and said, "Come, we will ask this cow the rights of the question." When they came up to the cow, the snake, opening its mouth, said, "O cow, what is the recompense for benefits received?"

The cow said, "If thou ask me after the manner of men, the return of good is always evil. For instance, I was for a long time in the service of a farmer; yearly I brought forth a calf; I supplied his house with milk and ghee; his sustenance, and the life of his children, depended upon me. When I became old, and no longer produced young, he ceased to shelter me, and thrust me forth to die in a jungle. After finding forage, and roaming at my ease, I grew fat, and my old master, seeing my plump condition, yesterday brought with him a butcher, to whom he has sold me, and today is appointed for my slaughter."

The snake said, "Thou hast heard the cow; prepare to die quickly." The man cried, "It is not lawful to decide a case on the evidence of one witness, let us then call another." The snake looked about and saw a tree, leafless and bare, flinging up its wild branches to the sky. "Let us," said it, "appeal to this tree." They proceeded together to the tree; and the snake, opening its mouth, said, "O tree, what is the recompense for good?"

The tree said, "Amongst men, for benefits are returned evil and injury. I will give you a proof of what I assert. I am a tree which, though growing on one leg in this sad waste, was once flourishing and green, performing service to everyone. When any of the human race, overcome with heat and travel, came this way, they rested beneath my shade, and slept beneath my branches; when the weight of repose abandoned their eyelids, they cast up their eyes to me, and said to each other, 'Yon twig would do well for an arrow; that branch would serve for a plough; and from the trunk of this tree what beautiful planks might be made!' If they had an ax or a saw, they selected my branches, and carried them away. Thus they to whom I gave ease and rest rewarded me only with pain and affliction.

> Whilst my care overshadows him in perplexity,
> He meditates only how best to root me up."

"Well," said the snake, "here are two witnesses; therefore, form thy resolution, for I must wound thee." The man said, "True; but the love of life is powerful, and while strength remains, it is difficult to root the love of it from the heart. Call but one more witness, and then I pledge myself to submit to his decree." Now it so wonderfully happened that a fox, who had been standing by, had heard all the argument, and now came forward. The snake on seeing it exclaimed, "Behold this fox, let us ask it." But before the man could speak the fox cried out, "Dost thou not know that the recompense for good is always evil? But what good hast thou done in behalf of this snake, to render thee worthy of punishment?" The man related his story. The fox replied, "Thou seemest an intelligent person, why then dost thou tell me an untruth?

> How can it be proper for him that is wise to speak falsely?
> How can it become an intelligent man to state an untruth?"

The snake said, "The man speaks truly, for behold the bag in which he rescued me." The fox, putting on the garb of astonishment, said, "How can I believe this thing? How could a large snake such as thou be contained in so small a space?" The snake said, "If thou doubt me, I will again enter the bag to prove it." The fox said, "Truly if I saw thee there, I could believe it, and afterward settle the dispute between thee and this man." On this the traveler opened the bag, and the snake, annoyed at the disbelief of the fox, entered it; which observing the fox cried out, "O young man, when thou hast caught thine enemy, show him no quarter.

> When an enemy is vanquished, and in thy power,
> It is the maxim of the wise to show him no mercy."

The traveler took the hint of the fox, fastened the mouth of the bag, and, dashing it against a stone, destroyed the snake, and thus saved mankind from the evil effects of its wicked propensities.

[5]

The Sole

The fishes had for a long time been discontented because no order prevailed in their kingdom. None of them turned aside for the others, but all swam to the right or the left as they fancied, or darted between those who wanted to stay together, or got into their way; and a strong one gave a weak one a blow with its tail, which drove it away, or else swallowed it up without more ado. "How delightful it would be," said they, "if we had a king who enforced law and justice among us!" and they met together to choose for their ruler the one who could cleave through the water most quickly and give help to the weak ones.

They placed themselves in rank and file by the shore, and the pike gave the signal with his tail, on which they all started. Like an arrow, the pike darted away, and with him the herring, the gudgeon, the perch, the carp, and all the rest of them. Even the sole swam with them, and hoped to reach the winning place. All at once, the cry was heard, "The herring is first! The herring is first!" "Who is first?" screamed angrily the flat envious sole, who had been left far behind. "Who is first?" "The herring! The herring," was the answer. "The naked herring?" cried the jealous creature. "The naked herring?" Since that time the sole's mouth has been at one side for a punishment.

[6]

Why the Bear Is Stumpy-tailed

One day the Bear met the Fox, who came slinking along with a string of fish he had stolen.

"Whence did you get those from?" asked the Bear.

"Oh! my Lord Bruin, I've been out fishing and caught them," said the Fox.

So the Bear had a mind to learn to fish too, and bade the Fox tell him how he was to set about it.

"Oh! it's an easy craft for you," answered the Fox, "and soon learnt. You've only got to go upon the ice, and cut a hole and stick your tail down into it; and so you must go on holding it there as long as you can. You're not to mind if your tail smarts a little; that's when the fish bite. The longer you hold it there the more fish you'll get; and then all at once out with it, with a cross pull sideways, and with a strong pull too."

Yes; the Bear did as the Fox had said, and held his tail a long, long time down in the hole, till it was fast frozen in. Then he pulled it out with a cross pull, and it snapped short off. That's why Bruin goes about with a stumpy tail this very day.

VII

VAMPIRES

When the cocks crow and the sun rises, or when the morning church bells ring, the vampire, or living corpse, must return to its grave. Although typically a Slavic superstition, belief in vampirine creatures is virtually world-wide, and very old. A vampire is a ghost that has substance; it comes from its burial place and seeks human blood or flesh. It is either a corpse which has become tenanted by a demon or the walking cadaver of a suicide, witch, or wizard, notorious sinner, or a person under a curse. If exhumed, the body will be found to be red-cheeked and in fair condition, not decomposed like normal corpses. To lay it, the head must be cut off and the body burned or buried at the crossroads, or a wooden stake driven through the heart.

"The Two Corpses," "The Warlock," "The Coffin Lid," "The Soldier and the Vampire," and "The Dead Witch" are from W. R. S. Ralston's *Russian Folk Tales*, 1873; and "The Shoemaker of Breslow" is from Henry More's *An Antidote against Atheism*, 1712.

[1]

The Two Corpses

A soldier had obtained leave to go home on furlough—to pray to the holy images and to bow down to his parents. And as he was going his way, at a time when the sun had long set and all was dark around, it chanced that he had to pass by a graveyard. Just then he heard that someone was running after him, and crying, "Stop! you can't escape!"

He looked back and there was a corpse running and gnashing its teeth. The soldier sprang on one side with all his might to get away from it, caught sight of a little chapel, and bolted straight into it.

There wasn't a soul in the chapel, but stretched out on a table there lay another corpse, with tapers burning in front of it. The soldier hid himself in a corner and remained there hardly knowing whether he was alive or dead, but waiting to see what would happen. Presently up ran the first corpse—the one that had chased him—and dashed into the chapel. Thereupon the one that was lying on the table jumped up and cried to it: "What hast thou come here for?"

"I've chased a soldier in here, so I'm going to eat him."

"Come now, brother! He's run into my house. I shall eat him myself."

"No, I shall!"

"No, I shall!"

And they set to work fighting; the dust flew like anything. They'd have gone on fighting ever so much longer, only the cocks began to crow. Then both the corpses fell lifeless to the ground, and the soldier went on his way homeward in peace, saying, "Glory be to Thee, O Lord! I am saved from the wizards!"

[2]

The Warlock

There was once a moujik, and he had three married sons. He lived a long while and was looked upon by the village as a wizard. When he was about to die, he gave orders that his sons' wives should keep watch over him after his death for three nights, taking one night apiece. His body should be placed in the outer chamber and his sons' wives should spin wool to make him a caftan. He ordered, moreover, that no cross should be placed upon him, and that none should be worn by his daughters-in-law.

Well, that same night the eldest daughter-in-law took her seat beside him with some gray wool, and began spinning. Midnight arrives. Says the father-in-law from his coffin: "Daughter-in-law, art thou there?"

She was terribly frightened, but answered, "I am." "Art thou sitting?" "I sit." "Dost thou spin?" "I spin." "Gray wool?" "Gray." "For a caftan?" "For a caftan."

He made a movement toward her. Then a second time he asked again: "Daughter-in-law, art thou there?"

"I am." "Art thou sitting?" "I sit." "Dost thou spin?" "I spin." "Gray wool?" "Gray." "For a caftan?" "For a caftan."

She shrank into a corner. He moved again, came a couple of yards nearer her.

A third time he made a movement. She offered up no prayer. He strangled her and then lay down again in his coffin.

His sons removed her body, and next evening in obedience to his paternal behest, they sent another of his daughters-in-law to keep watch. To her just the same thing happened: he strangled her as he had done the first one.

But the third was sharper than the other two. She declared she had taken off her cross but in reality she kept it on. She took her seat and spun, but said prayers to herself all the while.

Midnight arrives. Says her father-in-law from his coffin: "Daughter-in-law, art thou there?"

"I am," she replies. "Art thou sitting?" "I sit." "Dost thou spin?" "I spin." "Gray wool?" "Gray." "For a caftan?" "For a caftan."

Just the same took place a second time. The third time, just as he was going to rush at her, she laid the cross upon him. He fell down and died. She looked into the coffin; there lay ever so much money. The father-in-law wanted to take it away with him, or, at all events, that only someone who could outdo him in cunning should get it.

[3]

The Shoemaker of Breslow

A certain shoemaker in one of the chief towns of Silesia in the year 1591 (September 20) on a Friday betimes in the morning, in the further parts of his house where there was adjoining a little garden, cut his own throat with his shoemaker's knife. The family, to cover the foulness of the fact, and that no disgrace might come upon his widow, gave out that he died of apoplexy, declined all visits of friends and neighbors, in the meantime got him washed and laid linens so handsomely about him, that even they that saw him afterward, as the parson and some others, had not the least suspicion but that he did die of that disease. And so he had honest burial with a funeral sermon and other circumstances becoming one of his rank and reputation.

Six weeks had not passed but so strong a rumor broke out, that he died not of any disease but had laid violent hands upon himself, that the magistracy of the place could not but bring all those that had seen the corpse to a strict examination. They shuffled off the matter as well as they could at first with many fair apologies, in behalf of the deceased, to remove all suspicion of so heinous an act: but it being pressed more home to their conscience, at last they confessed that he died a violent death, but desired their favor and clemency to his widow and children, who were in no fault; adding also that it was uncertain but that he might be slain by some external mishap, or, if by himself, in some irresistible fit of frenzy or madness.

Hereupon the council deliberate what is to be done. Which the widow hearing, and fearing they might be determining something that would be harsh and to the discredit of her husband and herself, being also animated thereto by some busybodies, makes a great complaint against those that raised these reports of her husband, and resolved to follow the law upon them, earnestly contending that there was no reason, upon mere rumors and idle defamations of malevolent people, that her husband's body should be digged up, or dealt with as if he had been either magician or self-murderer. Which boldness and pertinacity of the woman, though after the confession of the fact, did in some measure work upon the council and put them to a stand.

But while these things were in agitation, to the astonishment of the inhabitants of the place, there appears a specter in the exact shape and habit of the deceased—and that not only in the night but at midday. Those that were asleep it terrified with horrible visions; those that were waking it would strike, pull, or press, lying heavy upon them like an incubus: so that there were perpetual complaints every morning of their last night's rest through the whole town. But the more freaks this specter played, the more diligent were the the friends of the deceased to suppress the rumors of them, or at least to hinder the effects of those rumors; and therefore made their address to the president, complaining how unjust a thing it was that so much credit should be given to idle reports and blind suspicions, and therefore besought him that he would hinder the council from digging up the corpse of the deceased, and from all ignominious usage of him: adding also, that they intended to appeal to the emperor's court, that their wisdom might rather decide the controversy than that the cause should be determined from the light conjectures of malicious men.

But while by this means the business was still protracted, there were such stirs and tumults all over the town that they are hardly to be described. For no sooner did the sun hide his head but this specter would be sure to appear, so that everybody was fain to look about him and stand upon his guard, which was a sore trouble to those whom the labors of the day made more sensible of the want of rest in the night. For this terrible apparition would sometimes stand by their bedsides, sometimes cast itself upon the midst of their beds, would lie close to them, would miserably suffocate them, and would so strike them and pinch them, that not only blue marks but plain impressions of his fingers would be upon sundry parts of their bodies in the morning. Nay, such was the violence and impetuousness of this ghost that when men forsook their beds and kept to their dining rooms, with candles lighted, and many of them in company together the better to secure themselves from fear and disturbance; yet he would then appear to them and have a bout with some of them, notwithstanding all this provision against it. In brief, he was so troublesome that the people were ready to forsake their houses and seek other dwellings, and the magistrate so awakened at the perpetual complaints of them, that at last they resolved, the president agreeing thereto, to dig up the body.

He had lain in the ground near eight months, viz. from September 22, 1591 to April 18, 1592. When he was digged up, which was in the presence of the magistracy of the town, his body was found entire, not at all putrid, no ill smell about him, saving the mustiness of the graveclothes, his joints limber and flexible, as in those that are alive, his skin only flaccid, but a more fresh grown in the room of it, the wound of his throat gaping but no gear nor corruption in it. There was also observed a magical mark in the great toe of his right foot, viz. an excrescency in the form of a rose. His body was kept out of the earth from April 18 to the 24th, at what time many, both of the same town and others, came daily to view him. These unquiet stirs did not cease for all this, which they after attempted to appease by burying the corpse under the gallows, but in vain; for they were as much as ever, if not more, he now not sparing his own family: insomuch that his widow at last went herself to the magistrate and told them that she should be no longer against it, if they thought fit to fall upon some course of more strict proceedings touching her husband.

Wherefore the 7th of May he was again digged up, and it was observable that he was grown more sensibly fleshy since his last internment. To be short, they cut off the head, arms, and legs of the corpse, and opening his back, took out his heart, which was as fresh and entire as in a new killed. These, together with his body, they put on a pile of wood, and burnt them to ashes, which they carefully sweeping together and putting into a sack (that none might get them for wicked uses) poured them into the river, after which the specter was never seen more.

[4]

The Coffin Lid

A moujik was driving along one night with a load of pots. His horse grew tired, and all of a sudden it came to a standstill alongside of a graveyard. The moujik unharnessed his horse and set it free to graze; meanwhile he laid himself down on one of the graves. But somehow he didn't go to sleep.

He remained lying there some time. Suddenly the grave began to open beneath him: he felt the movement and sprang to his feet. The grave opened, and out of it came a corpse—wrapped in a white shroud and holding a coffin lid—came out and ran to the church, laid the coffin lid at the door, and then set off for the village.

The moujik was a daring fellow. He picked up the coffin lid and remained standing beside his cart, waiting to see what would happen. After a short delay the dead man came back, and was going to snatch up his coffin lid—but it was not to be seen. Then the corpse began to track it out, traced it up to the moujik, and said: "Give me my lid: if you don't, I'll tear you to bits!"

"And my hatchet, how about that?" answered the moujik. "Why, it's I who'll be chopping you into small pieces!"

"Do give it back to me, good man!" begs the corpse.

"I'll give it when you tell me where you've been and what you've done."

"Well, I've been in the village, and there I've killed a couple of youngsters."

"Well then, now tell me how they can be brought back to life."

The corpse reluctantly made answer: "Cut off the left skirt of my shroud and take it with you. When you come into the house where the youngsters were killed, pour some live coals into a pot and put the piece of the shroud in with them, and then lock the door. The lads will be revived by the smoke immediately."

The moujik cut off the left skirt of the shroud and gave up the coffin lid. The corpse went to its grave—the grave opened. But just as the dead man was descending into it, all of a sudden the cocks began to crow, and he hadn't time to get properly covered over. One end of the coffin lid remained sticking out of the ground.

The moujik saw all this and made a note of it. The day began to dawn: he harnessed his horse and drove into the village. In one of the houses he heard cries and wailing. In he went—there lay two dead lads.

"Don't cry," says he, "I can bring them to life."

"Do bring them to life, kinsman," say their relatives. "We'll give you half of all we possess."

The moujik did everything as the corpse had instructed him, and the lads came back to life. Their relatives were delighted, but they immediately seized the moujik and bound him with cords, saying: "No, no, trickster! We'll hand you over to the authorities. Since you knew how to bring them back to life, maybe it was you that killed them!"

"What are you thinking about, true believers! Have the fear of God before your eyes!" cried the moujik.

Then he told them everything that had happened to him during the night. Well, they spread the news through the village; the whole population assembled and swarmed into the graveyard. They found out the grave from which the dead man had come out; they tore it open, and they drove an aspen stake right into the heart of the corpse, so that it might no more rise up and slay. But they rewarded the moujik richly, and sent him away home with great honor.

[5]

The Soldier and the Vampire

A certain soldier was allowed to go home on furlough. Well, he walked and walked, and after a time he began to draw near to his native village. Not far off from that village lived a miller in his mill. In old times the soldier had been very intimate with him: why shouldn't he go and see his friend? He went. The miller received him cordially, and at once brought out liquor; and the two began drinking and chattering about their ways and doings. All this took place toward nightfall, and the soldier stopped so long at the miller's that it grew quite dark. When he proposed to start for his village, his host exclaimed, "Spend the night here, trooper! It's very late now, and perhaps you might run into mischief."

"How so?"

"God is punishing us! A terrible warlock has died among us, and by night he rises from his grave, wanders through the village, and does such things as bring fear upon the very boldest! How could even you help being afraid of him?"

"Not a bit of it! A soldier is a man who belongs to the crown, and 'crown property cannot be drowned in water nor burnt in fire.' I'll be off: I'm tremendously anxious to see my people as soon as possible."

Off he set. His road lay in front of a graveyard. On one of the graves he saw a great fire blazing. "What's that?" thinks he. "Let's have a look." When he drew near, he saw that the warlock was sitting by the fire, sewing boots.

"Hail, brother!" calls out the soldier.

The warlock looked up and said, "What have you come here for?"

"Why, I wanted to see what you're doing."

The warlock threw his work aside and invited the soldier to a wedding.

"Come along, brother," says he; "let's enjoy ourselves. There's a wedding going on in the village."

"Come along!" says the soldier.

They came to where the wedding was; there they were given drink, and treated with the utmost hospitality. The warlock drank and drank, reveled and reveled, and then grew angry. He chased all the guests and relatives out of the house, threw the wedded pair into a slumber, took out two phials and an awl, pierced the hands of the bride and bridegroom with the awl, and began drawing off their blood. Having done this, he said to the soldier, "Now let's be off."

Well, they went off. On the way the soldier said, "Tell me; why do you draw off their blood in those phials?"

"Why, in order that the bride and bridegroom might die. Tomorrow morning no one will be able to wake them. I alone know how to bring them back to life."

"How's that managed?"

"The bride and bridegroom must have cuts made in their heels, and some of their own blood must then be poured back into those wounds. I've got the bridegroom's blood stowed away in my right-hand pocket, and the bride's in my left."

The soldier listened to this without letting a single word escape him. Then the warlock began boasting again.

"Whatever I wish," says he, "that I can do!"

"I suppose it's quite impossible to get the better of you?" says the soldier.

"Why impossible? If anyone were to make a pyre of aspen boughs, a hundred loads of them, and were to burn me on that pyre, then he'd be able to get the better of me. Only he'd have to look out sharp in burning me; for snakes and worms and different kinds of reptiles would creep out of my inside, and crows and magpies and jackdaws would come flying up. All these must be caught and flung on the pyre. If so much as a single maggot were to escape, then there'd be no help for it; in that maggot I should slip away!"

The soldier listened to all this and did not forget it. He and the warlock talked and talked, and at last they arrived at the grave.

"Well, brother," said the warlock, "now I'll tear you to pieces. Otherwise you'd be telling all this."

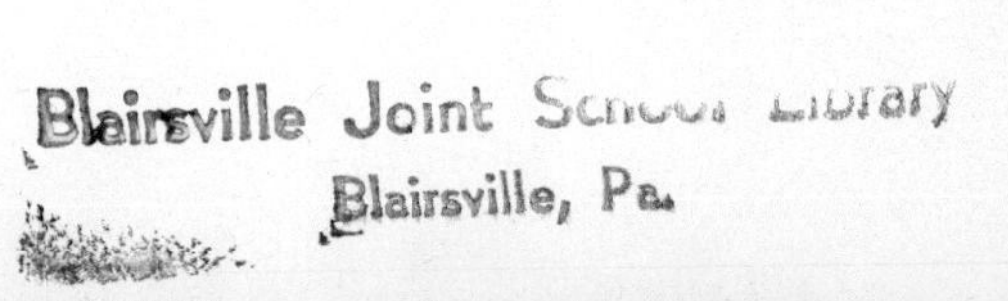
Blairsville Joint School Library
Blairsville, Pa.

"What are you talking about? Don't you deceive yourself; I serve God and the emperor."

The warlock gnashed his teeth, howled aloud, and sprang at the soldier—who drew his sword and began laying about him with sweeping blows. They struggled and struggled; the soldier was all but at the end of his strength. "Ah!" thinks he, "I'm a lost man—and all for nothing!" Suddenly the cocks began to crow. The warlock fell lifeless to the ground.

The soldier took the phials of blood out of the warlock's pockets and went on to the house of his own people. When he had got there and had exchanged greetings with his relatives, they said: "Did you see any disturbance, soldier?"

"No, I saw none."

"There now! Why we've a terrible piece of work going on in the village. A warlock has taken to haunting it."

After talking a while, they lay down to sleep. Next morning the soldier awoke and began asking, "I'm told you've got a wedding going on somewhere here?"

"There was a wedding in the house of a rich moujik," replied his relatives, "but the bride and bridegroom have died this very night—what from, nobody knows."

"Where does this moujik live?"

They showed him the house. Thither he went without speaking a word. When he got there, he found the whole family in tears.

"What are you mourning about?" says he.

"Such and such is the state of things, soldier," say they.

"I can bring your young people to life again. What will you give me if I do?"

"Take what you like, even were it half of what we've got!"

The soldier did as the warlock had instructed him and brought the young people back to life. Instead of weeping there began to be happiness and rejoicing; the soldier was hospitably treated and well rewarded. Then—left about, face! off he marched to the Starosta and told him to call the peasants together and to get ready a hundred loads of aspen wood. Well, they took the wood into the graveyard, dragged the warlock out of his grave, placed him on the pyre, and set it alight—the people all standing round in a circle with brooms, shovels, and fire irons. The pyre became wrapped in flames, the warlock began to burn. His corpse burst, and out of it crept snakes, worms, and all sorts of reptiles, and up came flying crows, magpies, and jackdaws. The peasants knocked them down and flung them into the fire, not allowing so much as a single maggot to creep away! And so the warlock was thoroughly consumed, and the soldier collected his ashes and strewed them to the winds. From that time forth there was peace in the village.

The soldier received the thanks of the whole community. He stayed at home some time, enjoying himself thoroughly. Then he went back to the czar's service with money in his pocket. When he had served his time, he retired from the army and began to live at his ease.

[6]

The Dead Witch

There was once an old woman who was a terrible witch, and she had a daughter and a granddaughter. The time came for the old crone to die, so she summoned her daughter and gave her these instructions: "Mind, daughter! when I'm dead, don't you wash my body with lukewarm water; but fill a caldron, make it boil its very hottest, and then with that boiling water regularly scald me all over."

After saying this, the witch lay ill two or three days and then died. The daughter ran round to all her neighbors, begging them to come and help her to wash the old woman, and meantime the little granddaughter was left all alone in the cottage. And this is what she saw there. All of a sudden there crept out from beneath the stove two demons—a big one and a tiny one—and they ran up to the dead witch. The old demon seized her by the feet, and tore away at her so that he stripped off all her skin at one pull. Then he said to the little demon, "Take the flesh for yourself and lug it under the stove."

Blairsville Junior High School
Blairsville, Pennsylvania

So the little demon flung his arms around the carcass and dragged it under the stove. Nothing was left of the old woman but her skin. Into it the old demon inserted himself, and then he lay down just where the witch had been lying.

Presently the daughter came back, bringing a dozen other women with her, and they all set to work laying out the corpse.

"Mammy," says the child, "they've pulled granny's skin off while you were away."

"What do you mean by telling such lies?"

"It's quite true, Mammy! There was ever such a blackie came from under the stove, and he pulled the skin off and got into it himself."

"Hold your tongue, naughty child! You're talking nonsense!" cried the old crone's daughter. Then she fetched a big caldron, filled it with cold water, put it on the stove and heated it till it boiled furiously. Then the woman lifted up the old crone, laid her in a trough, took hold of the caldron and poured the whole of the boiling water over her at once. The demon couldn't stand it. He leaped out of the trough, dashed through the doorway, and disappeared, skin and all. The women stared.

"What marvel is this," they cried. "Here was the dead woman, and now she isn't here. There's nobody left to lay out or bury. The demons have carried her off before our very eyes!"

VIII

MORE GHOSTS

There are many kinds of them: white ones, green ones, black ones, and luminous ones that shine like moonlit icicles. There are Grateful Dead Men who appear to help a deserving and kind-hearted person in his hour of need. Spectral Bridegrooms carry off their brides toward the graveyard, and their horses' hoofs beat a hellish nocturnal tattoo. Mystifying invisible poltergeists pull the bed-covers off the maids, and banshees announce a coming death with fearful shrieks. And there are just plain ghosts who walk the earth because they have unfinished business to do or a sin to atone for. Or, like the dutiful sons in the ballad of "The Wife of Usher's Well," they grant a mother's wish. In Brittany and Ireland there is a folk-tale about a priest who had to atone for not showing enough zeal in his holy work while alive. He had to say Mass every midnight until someone should be present to give the responses. It is believed in certain districts that the ghost of the last person to be buried in the graveyard must traverse unceasingly the road between this earth and Purgatory to carry water to slake the thirst of those confined in the last-named place. And in Scotland it was said that the first corpse buried in a new churchyard would be a "teind" to the Evil One. Of course, there are ghost stories to show that both beliefs are true. And the ballad of "The Unquiet Grave" lets us know that excessive grieving for the dead interferes with their repose. One of the simplest, and shortest, types describes how a specter returns to ask for something which he sorely misses or something which has been stolen from him. In the Man-from-the-Gallows type, for example, the ghost appears and demands part of his thigh (or his heart, or a piece of clothing) that had been cut from his corpse as it hung on a gibbet.

"Evan Kermenou, Man of His Word" is translated from F. M. Luzel's *Contes Populaires de Basse-Bretagne*, 1887. "The Book of Tobit" is from the *Apocrypha* and is slightly abridged. "Poltergeist" comes from J. P. Andrews' *Anecdotes Antient and Modern*, 1790. "The Ghost with the Black and Blue Mark" is from Hugh Miller's *Scenes and Legends of the North of Scotland*, 1874. "Laying a

Greek Ghost" is translated from Lucian's *Philopseudes*, second century A.D., and "Laying an English Ghost" is from William Henderson's *Folk-lore of the Northern Countries of England*, 1879. "The Spectral War Horse" is taken from the *Gesta Romanorum*, ed. 1824, and "The Banshee's Wail" comes from Sir Jonah Barrington's *Personal Sketches of His Own Times*, 18——.

[1]

Evan Kermenou, Man of His Word

All this happened long ago when the chickens
Had teeth and could bite like the dickens.

There once was a merchant named Jean Kermenou who had made a fortune in trading. He put many ships to sea laden with merchandise which he bought cheaply in his country and sold at a great profit in foreign ports. His dearest wish was that his only son Evan would be a merchant like himself. One day he told his son he wished to rest from his labors and retire from the sea.

"But I wish to see you," he said, "who are young and full of health and strength, sail the ocean as I have done, for every man in this world ought to have work to do. So I am giving you a ship, manned by my old sailors and laden with merchandise to sell abroad. You will gain money and experience from the voyage."

Now there was nothing Evan wanted to do more. And he put to sea. After a long voyage, during which there had been both foul and fair weather, he docked at a city whose name I do not know. He presented the letters his father had given him, was well received, and disposed of his cargo at a handsome profit.

As he was walking in the city one day he saw a number of people gathered together gaping at something lying in the street. It was the cadaver of a man and dogs were eating it. Evan asked a bystander what this meant, and he was told that the dead man had left many debts unpaid and therefore his body was thrown out to be eaten by the dogs, as was the custom in that country. Evan was moved by the sight of the dead man and cried, "Beat off the dogs. I will pay the poor fellow's debts and give him a decent burial."

And so it was done although it took a great sum to satisfy all of the creditors. After the debts were paid, the corpse was wrapped in a shroud and buried with due ceremony. As Evan did not have sufficient money now to purchase a new cargo, he turned his ship homeward unladen. At sea one day a ship all draped in black was sighted. When Evan and his sailors came near, they hailed the ship and asked, "Why is your ship draped in black? Has something disastrous happened?"

"Yes, there is misfortune enough," was the response.

"What is it then? Tell us, and if we can be of help we will gladly aid you."

"There is a serpent living on a near-by island which demands every seven years that we deliver up to him a princess of the royal blood."

"Is the princess with you?"

"Yes, she is with us and we are taking her to the serpent, and that is why the ship is draped in black."

At these words Evan boarded that ship and asked to see the princess. When he saw that she was very beautiful, he cried, "This princess shall never be the victim of the serpent!"

"Alas," groaned the master of the ship, "we must take her to him or he will destroy our kingdom."

"I tell you she shall not be taken to the serpent. She shall come with me. In exchange I will give you a great sum of money. With this you will be able to purchase or steal another princess to deliver to the serpent."

"Well, if you give us enough money."

"As much as you ask for."

And he gave them all of his remaining capital and led the princess on board his ship. Those in the other ship set out in quest of another princess, and Evan returned home with the beauty he had bought.

When his father learned that the ship had docked, he hastened to the seaside and asked, "Well, my son, did you have a good voyage?"

"Yes, indeed, father, it was good enough."

"Let me see what you brought back."

Evan conducted the old man to his cabin and showed him the princess. "Look, father, that's what I brought back."

"Yes, she is beautiful, but there are many beauties in our own country. Do you have some money too?"

"I did have much money, but I don't have it any more."

"What did you do with it, son?"

"I used half of it to pay the debts of a dead man and save his cadaver from being eaten by dogs, and the other half to save this princess from being devoured by a serpent."

"You must be a fool to have perpetrated such follies!"

"I tell you nothing but the truth, father."

"Never again let me see you! You or your princess. I curse you!"

And the old man went away in a rage. Evan was much put out by his father's action, for now he had neither money nor a lodging for his princess. But he went to the home of an aunt he had in the town and told her everything. She took pity upon him and offered the couple hospitality.

Soon Evan wished to marry the princess and went to his father to ask his consent.

"Is the girl rich?" asked the father.

"She will be one day, father, since she is the daughter of a king."

"A king, no less! She must be a woman of ill repute who made you believe she was a king's daughter. Do with her whatever you want to, but if you marry her you shall not inherit anything from me."

Evan was very sad: returning to his princess and aunt, he described the reception his father had given him. Nevertheless, the marriage was celebrated. The aunt paid for it and gave them a little house not far from the town to live in. About nine or ten months afterward the princess gave birth to a son, a very fine baby.

Now Evan's maternal uncle was also a merchant and had ships on the sea. He was rich and old and wished to retire. He put his nephew in charge of a good ship, laden with merchandise to be sold in Oriental ports. When the princess heard of this, she persuaded Evan to have portraits of them and their baby carved and displayed on the front of the ship. Then he bade his wife good-by, tenderly kissed his baby, and set sail. Without his knowing anything about it, the wind propelled the ship to the city in which the father and mother of his wife lived. The people ran to look at the boat and, seeing the sculptured portraits on the bowsprit, recognized one of them as a likeness of the princess, and ran to tell the king. The king, hurrying down to the water front, looked at the portrait and cried,

"Yes, it's certainly my daughter! Could she still be alive? This instant I must find out."

And he asked to talk with the captain. When he saw Evan, he easily recognized one of the figures on the ship as his likeness.

"Is my daughter on your ship, captain?"

"Excuse me, seignior," answered Evan, "there is neither daughter nor woman on my ship."

"I tell you she is here somewhere, and I must instantly see her."

"Believe me, seignior, your daughter is not on my boat."

"Where is she, then? You must certainly know her since her portrait is next to yours on the front of the boat."

"I can't tell you where your daughter is because I do not know her." Evan was afraid to reveal the truth lest his wife be taken from him. The king was very angry and said: "We will soon see. And as for you, you shall have your head cut off."

And the king, with two ministers and some soldiers, searched through the whole ship. But they found no princess. Evan was thrown into prison and his head was to be cut off in the morning. While waiting for this event the king allowed the people to plunder the ship. Then they burned it.

In prison, Evan told his story to the jailer, who seemed to take pity on him.

"And so," said the jailer, "you have saved the daughter of the king from the serpent, and she is at present your wife."

"Yes. I bought her from the captain who was taking her to a serpent on an island. According to what she said, she was the daughter of a king, but I do not know which king."

The jailer now ran to the king and told him what he had heard. The latter gave the order to bring the prisoner before him immediately. When he heard his story, he cried, "It is certainly my daughter. Where is she?"

"She remained at home in my country with our baby."

"If I am to see her before I die, I must go to her quickly."

And they gave Evan another boat to fetch the princess. Two of the prime ministers went along to make sure that Evan would return. They arrived in Evan's country without difficulty and brought back the child and its mother.

One of the two ministers was in love with the princess. During the return voyage he sought her society and looked on her husband with an unfriendly eye. This was so obvious that the princess feared that the minister was plotting some mischief against Evan, and she begged him to stay with her in the cabin and go less often to the bridge. But Evan loved to be on the bridge. Indeed, he liked to aid the sailors in their work. So his wife couldn't keep him by her. Seeing this, she put her golden necklace around his neck. One night while Evan was leaning on the rail looking at the sea, which was calm and beautiful, the minister slipped up quietly behind him, seized his ankles, and pitched him headfirst into the sea. No one saw this. In a little while the minister cried, "The captain has fallen overboard!" Sailors were sent out in boats to search for Evan, but it was too late and they did not find him. Then the traitor came to the princess and told her that a gust of wind had pitched her husband into the sea and he had drowned. The thought that her husband was dead distressed the poor woman terribly, but happily Evan Kermenou was a good swimmer, and he swam toward a reef which he perceived not far from where he had fallen, and he saved his life. Let us leave Evan there for a time and follow the princess to her country.

She put on mourning, dressed all in black, and gave no sign of joy. Suspecting the minister of some vile trick, she would not see him. At her arrival the king wept with joy. There was a great banquet and public celebrations. But alas, the poor princess could never laugh again or find pleasure in anything. The perfidious minister persisted in efforts to please her and finally was admitted to her favor. They became betrothed and named a date for the marriage ceremonies. During the period of the engagement the princess forbade the mention of her first husband's name in her presence. Three years had passed since she had lost Evan. Convinced that she would never see him, she thought she could now marry again.

Let us return, while waiting for the wedding, to Evan Kermenou on his rock in the middle of the sea. As we know, he had now been here three years. The only food he could procure was the cockles and mussels he found in the rocks and the fish which from time to time he succeeded in catching. He was completely naked and his body was so covered with hair that he looked more like an animal than a man. A little hollow under a large rock served as his habitation. But he still wore his wife's necklace. No ship ever passed by in those waters: he had lost all hope of ever getting away. One night while he was sleeping in his hollow, he was awakened by a voice which said: "Cold! . . . cold! . . . hou! hou! hou!" Then he heard something like teeth chattering as of a freezing man, and a moment afterward, the noise of an animal or man plunging into the water. All that astonished him; yet he did not try to find out what it was. The next night the same thing happened. Yet he did not speak, or leave his den, and he saw nothing.

"What could it be?" he asked himself. "Perhaps a soul in pain." And he decided if this happened again he would investigate. The third night he heard it again, and closer this time: "Cold! cold! hou! hou! hou!" . . . and the chattering of teeth. He came out of his hole and saw in the light of the moon a man completely naked, whose body was bleeding and covered with horrible wounds. His intestines protruded from a wide cut in the abdomen, his eye sockets were empty, and in his left side there was a wound so deep that his heart could be seen. Evan quivered with horror, yet he found his voice.

"What can be done for you, poor man? Speak, and if I can help you in any way, I promise to do it."

"Do you not then recognize me, Evan Kermenou?" asked the phantom. "I am the man whose body you saved from being devoured by the dogs; the man whose debts you paid and whose burial you provided for. I wish to show my gratitude by helping you. You must certainly wish to get away from this lonely reef upon which you have suffered for three years."

"O God! if only you could do this for me," cried Evan.

"Promise me to follow my directions exactly and I will get you away from here and lead you to your wife."

"Yes. I will do everything you say."

"Tomorrow is the day set for the marriage of your wife and the minister who pitched you in the sea."

"My God, could this be true?"

"Yes, for she believes you dead, not having received any news of you for three years. But promise to give me half of everything which will belong to you and your wife a year and a day from now, and I will lead you as far as the door of the palace court of your father-in-law by tomorrow morning before the marriage procession reaches the church."

"If you can do this, I promise to give you half," answered Evan.

"Well then! Climb upon my back, but don't forget the agreement, for in a year and a day you will see me again no matter where you are."

Evan climbed upon the back of the dead man, who, plunging into the sea, swam like a fish and carried him by the time the sun rose to the palace door of his father-in-law. Then the dead man left, saying: "Good-by. We meet again in a year and a day."

When the guard of the palace opened his door, he was badly frightened, for he saw standing there an animal such as he had never seen before, and he ran back into the palace aad called loudly for help. The valets who ran up thought Evan a wild man, but as he did not appear to be violent, they approached and threw him some chunks of bread, as to a dog. He had not eaten bread for three years and leaped upon the morsels and greedily devoured them. The woman servants and ladies' maids also came to see the wild man. The princess's maid was among these, and she recognized the golden necklace around Evan's neck and ran to tell her mistress.

"Mistress, if you only knew!" she cried.

"If I only knew what?" asked the princess.

"Your husband, Evan Kermenou . . ."

"Be careful. You know I have forbidden anyone to speak that name in my presence until I am married."

"But mistress, he is there in the courtyard of the palace!"

"That's impossible, for he has been dead for three years, as everyone knows."

"But I tell you, mistress, he is there. I recognized him because he still wore your golden necklace."

When she heard these words, the princess rushed into the courtyard, and even though Evan looked more like an animal than a man, she recognized him, and threw her arms about his neck and kissed him. Then she led him to her room and gave him some clothes to wear. The valets and maids were all astonished by what they saw, for none but the princess's maid knew that the man was her husband. All this happened early on the day on which the princess was to marry the minister. It seems that in those times it was the custom

—at least in the case of important weddings—to have the wedding banquet before the bride and groom went to the church. A great many people had been invited: there were guests from every part of the kingdom and even from neighboring countries. When the time came, the guests sat down at the table. The princess, beautiful and dressed magnificently, sat between her father and the groom. Songs were sung and pleasant tales told, as was the custom. Toward the end of the feast, the princess was urged by her future father-in-law to say something, and she spoke in this fashion:

"I pray you, sir, to give me your advice on the following case. I had a lovely little chest and a charming golden key. But I lost this key much to my sorrow. Then I had another key made, but then I found the old one. So today I have two keys instead of one. That troubles me a little. I was used to the old key: it was good and I loved it. I have never used the new one and don't know whether I will like it or not. Tell me, please, which key should I keep, the old or the new?"

"Keep your old key, my daughter," answered her father-in-law, "for it is good. But could you show me the two keys?"

"That's fair," answered the princess, "wait a moment and you will see them both."

Getting up from the table, she went to her room and came back holding Evan Kermenou by the hand. Pointing to the man who expected to marry her, she said, "There is the new key." Then indicating Evan, she continued, "And here is the old one which I have just found! It is a little rusty because it was lost for a long while, but I will soon make it as bright as it ever was. This man is Evan Kermenou, my first husband—and the last too, because I will never have any other."

On hearing this, everyone was amazed, and the minister turned as pale as the tablecloth before him. The princess told all present the adventures of Evan. Then the old king waxed extremely angry. He ordered the servants to heat the oven until it was red hot and then throw the evil minister in it. And so it was done.

Evan Kermenou lived at the court and was very happy. At the end of nine months the princess gave birth to another son—their first child had died. Almost completely forgotten were the dead man and the promise he had exacted from Evan. But when the time came, the year and a day having passed, a November day when he and his wife were sitting quietly before the fire—she was warming the baby and Evan was gazing at them--an unknown person unexpectedly entered the castle and said, "Good day, Evan Kermenou!"

The sight of this stranger of horrible aspect frightened the princess. Evan recognized the dead man whom he had snatched away from the dogs. "Do you remember, Evan Kermenou," the visitor went on, "when you were alone on your barren reef in the middle of the sea, you promised to give me one half of whatever you and your wife would possess when a year and a day had passed?"

"I remember," replied Evan, "and I am ready to keep my word." And he asked his wife for the keys, opened all the cupboards and coffers containing their gold, silver, diamonds and clothes, and said, "Look, I will gladly give you the half of all this, and more too."

"No, Evan Kermenou, I don't ask these goods from you and you may keep them, but there is something belonging to both of you that is more precious—your child. Half of him belongs to me."

"O God, no!" cried the mother on hearing those words, and she hid the child in her bosom.

"Give you half of my child?" cried Evan, seized by a sudden fear.

"If you are a man of your word," continued the dead man, "think on what you promised me on the reef—that you would give me in a year and a day the half of whatever you and your wife owned. And doesn't the child belong to both of you?"

"Alas, it is true. I made that promise," groaned the unhappy father, tears in his eyes. "But consider what I did for you when your body was thrown out to the dogs, and have pity on me!"

"I demand what is due me—half your son, as you promised me."

"Never will I allow my child to be cut in two," cried the mother. "I would rather you took all of him."

"No. I want only half of him as we agreed."

"Alas, I made the promise and I ought to keep my word," said Evan, sobbing and covering his eyes with his hand.

The clothes were then taken off the child and he was stretched out all naked on the table.

"Now take a knife, Evan Kermenou," said the dead man, "and give me my part."

"Ah! I wish I were still on my barren reef in the middle of the sea!" cried the wretched father. And, with his heart breaking with sorrow, he lifted the knife, and turned his head away. At that instant the dead man cried, "Stop. Do not strike your child, Evan Kermenou! You have shown me that you are a man of your word and that you have not forgotten what I did for you. Neither have I forgotten what I owe you, and it is because of your kind acts that I now go to Paradise, which I could not enter until my debts were paid and my body buried. Good-by, then, until we meet in the Paradise of God. Nothing now prevents me from entering there." And then he vanished.

A little while after this the old king died and Evan Kermenou became king in his place.

[2]

The Book of Tobit

. . . When I was come to the age of a man, I married Anna of mine own kindred, and of her I begat Tobias. And when we were carried away captives to Nineveh, all my brethern and those that were of my kindred did eat of the bread of the Gentiles. But I kept myself from eating; because I remembered God with all my heart. And the most High gave me grace and favor before Enemessar, so that I was his purveyor. And I went into Media, and left in trust with Gabael, the brother of Gabrias, at Rages, a city of Media, ten talents of silver.

Now when Enemessar was dead, Sennacherib his son reigned in his stead; whose estate was troubled, that I could not go into Media. And in the time of Enemessar I gave many alms to my brethren, and gave my bread to the hungry, and my clothes to the naked: and if I saw any of my nation dead, or cast about the walls of Nineveh, I buried him. And if the king Sennacherib had slain any, when he was come, and fled from Judea, I buried them privily; for in his wrath he killed many; but the bodies were not found, when they were sought for of the king. And when one of the Ninevites went and complained of me to the king, that I buried them, and hid myself; understanding that I was sought for to be put to death, I withdrew myself for fear. Then all my goods were forcibly taken away, neither was there anything left me, beside my wife Anna and my son Tobias. And there passed not five and fifty days, before two of his sons killed him, and they fled into the mountains of Ararath; and Sarchedonus his son reigned in his stead; who appointed over his father's accounts, and over all his affairs, Achiacharus my brother Anael's son. And Achiacharus entreating for me, I returned to Nineveh. Now Achiacharus was cupbearer, and keeper of the signet, and steward, and overseer of the accounts: and Sarchedonus appointed him next unto him: and he was my brother's son.

Now when I was come home again, and my wife Anna was restored unto me, with my son Tobias, in the feast of Pentecost, which is the holy feast of the seven weeks, there was a good dinner prepared me, in the which I sat down to eat. And when I saw abundance of meat, I said to my son, "Go and bring what poor man soever thou shalt find out of our brethren, who is mindful of the Lord; and, lo, I tarry for thee." But he came again, and said, "Father, one of our nation is strangled, and is cast out in the market place." Then before I had tasted of any meat, I started up, and took him up into a room until the going down of the sun. Then I returned, and washed myself, and ate my meat in heaviness, remembering that prophecy of Amos, as he said, "Your feasts shall be turned into mourning, and all your mirth into lamentation."

Therefore I wept: and after the going down of the sun I went and made a grave, and buried him. But my neighbors mocked me, and said, "This man is not yet afraid to be put to death for this matter: who fled away; and yet, lo, he buried the dead again." The same night also I returned from the burial, and slept by the wall of my courtyard, being polluted, and my face was uncovered: and I knew not that there were sparrows in the wall, and mine eyes being open, the sparrows muted warm dung into mine eyes, and a whiteness came in mine eyes; and I went to the physicians, but they helped me not: moreover Achiacharus did nourish me, until I went into Elymais.

And my wife Anna did take women's works to do. And when she had sent them home to the owners, they paid her wages, and gave her also besides a kid. And when it was in my house, and began to cry, I said unto her, "From whence is this kid? Is it not stolen? Render it to the owners; for it is not lawful to eat anything that is stolen." But she replied upon me, "It was given for a gift more than the wages." Howbeit I did not believe her, but bade her render it to the owners: and I was abashed at her. But she replied upon me, "Where are thine alms and thy righteous deeds? Behold, thou and all thy works are known."

Then I being grieved did weep, and in my sorrow prayed, saying, "O Lord, thou art just, and all thy works and all thy ways are mercy and truth, and thou judgest truly and justly forever. Remember me, and look on me, punish me not for my sins and ignorances, and the sins of my fathers, who have sinned before thee: for they obeyed not thy commandments: wherefore thou hast delivered us for a spoil, and unto captivity, and unto death, and for a proverb of reproach to all the nations among whom we are dispersed. And now thy judgments are many and true: deal with me according to my sins and my fathers': because we have not kept thy commandments, neither have walked in truth before thee. Now therefore deal with me as seemeth best unto thee, and command my spirit to be taken from me, that I may be dissolved, and become earth: for it is profitable for me to die rather than to live, because I have heard false reproaches, and have much sorrow: command therefore that I may now be delivered out of this distress, and go into the everlasting place: turn not thy face away from me."

It came to pass the same day that in Ecbatane, a city of Media, Sara the daughter of Raguel was also reproached by her father's maids; because that she had been married to seven husbands, whom Asmodeus the evil spirit had killed, before they had lain with her. "Dost thou not know," said they, "that thou hast strangled thine husbands? Thou hast had already seven husbands, neither wast thou named after any of them. Wherefore dost thou beat us for them? If they be dead, go thy ways after them; let us never see of thee either son or daughter." When she heard these things, she was very sorrowful, so that she thought to have strangled herself; and she said, "I am the only daughter of my father, and if I do this, it shall be a reproach unto him, and I shall bring his old age with sorrow unto the grave." Then she prayed toward the window, and said, "Blessed art thou, O Lord my God, and thine holy and glorious name is blessed and honorable forever: let all thy works praise thee forever. And now, O Lord, I set mine eyes and my face toward thee, and say, take me out of the earth, that I may hear no more the reproach. Thou knowest, Lord, that I am pure from all sin with man, and that I never polluted my name, nor the name of my father, in the land of my captivity: I am the only daughter of my father, neither hath he any child to be his heir, neither any near kinsman, nor any son of his alive, to whom I may keep myself for a wife: my seven husbands are already dead; and why should I live? But if it please not thee that I should die, command some regard to be had of me, and pity taken of me, that I hear no more reproach."

So the prayers of them both were heard before the majesty of the great God. And Raphael was sent to heal them both, that is, to scale away the whiteness of Tobit's eyes, and to give Sara the daughter of Raguel for a wife to Tobias the son of Tobit; and to bind Asmodeus the evil spirit; because she belonged to Tobias by right of inheritance. The selfsame time came Tobit home, and entered into his house, and Sara the daughter of Raguel came down from her upper chamber.

In that day Tobit remembered the money which he had committed to Gabael in Rages of Media, and said with himself, I have wished for death; wherefore do I not call for my son Tobias, that I may signify to him of the money before I die? And when he had called him, he said, "My son, when I am dead, bury me; and despise not thy mother, but honor her all the days of thy life, and do that which shall please her, and grieve her not. Remember, my son, that she saw many dangers for thee, when thou wast in her womb; and when she is dead, bury her by me in one grave. . . . And now I signify this to thee, that I committed ten talents to Gabael the son of Gabrias at Rages in Media. And fear not, my son, that we are made poor: for thou hast much wealth, if thou fear God, and depart from all sin, and do that which is pleasing in his sight."

Tobias then answered and said, "Father, I will do all things which thou hast commanded me: but how can I receive the money, seeing I know him not?" Then he gave him the handwriting, and said unto him, "Seek thee a man which may go with thee, whiles I yet live, and I will give him wages; and go and receive the money." Therefore when he went to seek a man, he found Raphael that was an angel. But he knew not; and he said unto him, "Canst thou go with me to Rages? And knowest thou those places well?" To whom the angel said, "I will go with thee, and I know the way well: for I have lodged with our brother Gabael." Then Tobias said unto him, "Tarry for me, till I tell my father." Then he said unto him. "Go, and tarry not." So he went in and said to his father, "Behold, I have found one which will go with me." Then he said, "Call him unto me, that I may know of what tribe he is, and whether he be a trusty man to go with thee."

So he called him, and he came in, and they saluted one another. Then Tobit said unto him, "Brother, shew me of what tribe and family thou art." To whom he said, "Dost thou seek for a tribe or family, or an hired man to go with thy son?" Then Tobit said unto him, "I would know, brother, thy kindred and name." Then he said, "I am Azarias, the son of Ananias the great, and of thy brethren." Then Tobit said, "Thou art welcome, brother; be not now angry with me, because I have inquired to know thy tribe and thy family; for thou art my brother, of an honest and good stock: for I know Ananias and Jonathas, sons of that great Samaias, as we went together to Jerusalem to worship, and offered the firstborn, and the tenths of the fruits; and they were not seduced with the error of our brethren: my brother, thou art of a good stock. But tell me, what wages shall I give thee? Wilt thou a drachma a day, and things necessary, as to mine own son? Yea, moreover, if ye return safe, I will add something to thy wages." So they were well pleased. Then said he to Tobias, "Prepare thyself for the journey, and God send you a good journey." And when his son had prepared all things for the journey, his father said, "Go thou with this man, and God, which dwelleth in heaven, prosper your journey, and the angel of God keep you company." So they went forth both, and the young man's dog with them.

But Anna his mother wept, and said to Tobit, "Why hast thou sent away our son? Is he not the staff of our hand, in going in and out before us? Be not greedy to add money to money: but let it be as refuse in respect of our child. For that which the Lord hath given us to live with doth suffice us." Then said Tobit to her, "Take no care, my sister; he shall return in safety, and thine eyes shall see him. For the good angel will keep him company, and his journey shall be prosperous, and he shall return safe." Then she made an end of weeping.

And as they went on their journey, they came in the evening to the river Tigris, and they lodged there. And when the young man went down to wash himself, a fish leaped out of the river, and would have devoured him. Then the angel said unto him, "Take the fish." And the young man laid hold of the fish, and drew it to land. To whom the angel said, "Open the fish, and take the heart and the liver and the gall, and put them up safely." So the young man did as the angel commanded him; and when they had roasted the fish, they did eat it; then they both went on their way, till they drew near to Ecbatane. Then the young man said to the angel, "Brother Azarias, to what use is the heart and the liver and the gall of the fish?" And he said unto him, "Touching the heart and the liver, if a devil or an evil spirit trouble any, we must make a smoke thereof before the man or the woman, and the party shall be no more vexed. As for the gall, it is good to anoint a man that hath whiteness in his eyes, and he shall be healed."

And when they were come near to Rages, the angel said to the young man, "Brother, today we shall lodge with Raguel, who is thy cousin; he also hath one only daughter, named Sara; I will speak for her, that she may be given thee for a wife. For to thee doth the right of her appertain, seeing thou only art of her kindred. And the maid is fair and wise: now therefore hear me, and I will speak to her father; and when we return from Rages we will celebrate the marriage: for I know that Raguel cannot marry her to another according to the law of Moses, but he shall be guilty of death, because the right of inheritance doth rather appertain to thee than to any other." Then the young man answered the angel, "I have heard, brother Azarias, that this maid hath been given to seven men, who all died in the marriage chamber. And now I am the only son of my father, and I am afraid, lest, if I go in unto her, I die, as the others before: for a wicked spirit loveth her, which hurteth nobody, but those which come unto her; wherefore I also fear lest I die, and bring my father's and my mother's life because of me to the grave with sorrow: for they have no other son to bury them." Then the angel said unto him, "Dost thou not remember the precepts which thy father gave thee, that thou shouldest marry a wife of thine own kindred? Wherefore hear me, O my brother; for she shall be given thee to wife; and make thou no reckoning of the evil spirit; for this same night shall she be given thee in marriage. And when thou shalt come into the marriage chamber, thou shalt take the ashes of perfume, and shalt lay upon them some of the heart and liver of the fish, and shalt make a smoke with it: and the devil shall smell it, and flee away, and never come again any more: but when thou shalt come to her, rise up both of you, and pray to God which is merciful, who will have pity on you, and save you: fear not, for she is appointed unto thee from the beginning; and thou shalt preserve her, and she shall go with thee. Moreover I suppose that she shall bear thee children." Now when Tobias had heard these things, he loved her, and his heart was effectually joined to her.

And when they were come to Ecbatane, they came to the house of Raguel, and Sara met them: and after they had saluted one another, she brought them into the house. Then said Raguel to Edna his wife, "How like is this young man to Tobit my cousin!" And Raguel asked them, "From whence are ye, brethren?" To whom they said, "We are of the sons of Nephthalim, which are captives in Nineveh." Then he said to them, "Do ye know Tobit our kinsman?" And they said, "We know him." Then said he, "Is he in good health?" And they said, "He is both alive, and in good health": and Tobias said, "He is my father." Then Raguel leaped up, and kissed him, and wept, and blessed him, and said unto him, "Thou art the son of an honest and good man." But when he had heard that Tobit was blind, he was sorrowful, and wept. And likewise Edna his wife and Sara his daughter wept. Moreover they entertained them cheerfully; and after that they had killed a ram of the flock, they set store of meat on the table.

Then said Tobias to Raphael, "Brother Azarias, speak of those things of which thou didst talk in the way, and let this business be dispatched." So he communicated the matter with Raguel: and Raguel said to Tobias, "Eat and drink, and make merry: for it is meet that thou shouldest marry my daughter: nevertheless I will declare unto thee the truth. I have given my daughter in marriage to seven men, who died that night they came in unto her: nevertheless, for the present be merry." But Tobias said, "I will eat nothing here, till we agree and swear one to another." Raguel said, "Then take her from henceforth according to the manner, for thou art her cousin, and she is thine, and the merciful God give you good success in all things." Then he called his daughter Sara, and she came to her father, and he took her by the hand, and gave her to be wife to Tobias, saying, "Behold, take her after the law of Moses, and lead her away to thy father." And he blessed them; and called Edna his wife, and took paper, and did write an instrument of covenants, and sealed it. Then they began to eat.

After Raguel called his wife Edna, and said unto her, "Sister, prepare another chamber, and bring her in thither." Which when she had done as he had bidden her, she brought her thither: and she wept, and she received the tears of her daughter, and said unto her, "Be of good comfort, my daughter; the Lord of heaven and earth give thee joy for this thy sorrow: be of good comfort, my daughter." And when they had supped, they brought Tobias in unto her. And as he went, he remembered the words of Raphael, and took the ashes of the perfumes, and put the heart and the liver of the fish thereupon, and made a smoke therewith. The which smell when the evil spirit had smelled, he fled into the utmost parts of Egypt, and the angel bound him. And after that they were both shut in together, Tobias rose out of the bed, and said, "Sister, arise, and let us pray that God will have pity on us." Then began Tobias to say, "Blessed art thou, O God of our fathers, and blessed is thy holy and glorious name forever; let the heavens bless thee, and all thy creatures. Thou madest Adam, and gavest him Eve his wife for an helper and stay: of them came mankind: thou hast said, 'It is not good that man should be alone; let us make unto him an aid like unto himself.' And now, O Lord, I take not this my sister for lust, but uprightly: therefore mercifully ordain that we may become aged together." And she said with him, "Amen." So they slept both that night.

And Raguel arose, and went and made a grave, saying, "I fear lest he also be dead." But when Raguel was come into his house, he said unto his wife Edna, "Send one of the maids, and let her see whether he be alive: if he be not, that we may bury him, and no man know it. So the maid opened the door, and went in, and found them both asleep, and came forth, and told them that he was alive. Then Raguel praised God, and said, "O God, thou art worthy to be praised with all pure and holy praise; therefore let thy saints praise thee with all thy creatures; and let all thine angels and thine elect praise thee for ever. Thou art to be praised, for thou hast made me joyful; and that is not come to me which I suspected; but thou hast dealt with us according to thy great mercy. Thou art to be praised, because thou hast had mercy of two that were the only begotten children of their fathers: grant them mercy, O Lord, and finish their life in health with joy and mercy."

Then Raguel bade his servants to fill the grave. And he kept the wedding feast fourteen days. For before the days of the marriage were finished, Raguel had said unto him by an oath, that he should not depart till the fourteen days of the marriage were expired; and then he should take the half of his goods, and go in safety to his father; and should have the rest when I and my wife be dead.

Then Tobias called Raphael, and said unto him, "Brother Azarias, take with thee a servant, and two camels, and go to Rages of Media to Gabael, and bring me the money, and bring him to the wedding. For Raguel hath sworn that I shall not depart. But my father counteth the days; and if I tarry long, he will be very sorry." So Raphael went out, and lodged with Gabael, and gave him the handwriting: who brought forth bags which were sealed up, and gave them to him. And early in the morning, they went forth both together, and came to the wedding: and Tobias blessed his wife.

Now Tobit his father counted every day: and when the days of the journey were expired, and they came not, then Tobit said, "Are they detained? Or is Gabael dead, and there is no man to give him the money?" Therefore he was very sorry. Then his wife said unto him, "My son is dead, seeing he stayeth long"; and she began to bewail him, and said, "Now I care for nothing, my son, since I have let thee go, the light of mine eyes." To whom Tobit said, "Hold thy peace, take no care, for he is safe." But she said, "Hold thy peace, and deceive me not; my son is dead." And she went out every day into the way which they went, and did eat no meat in the daytime, and ceased not whole nights to bewail her son Tobias, until the fourteen days of the wedding were expired, which Raguel had sworn that he should spend there.

Then Tobias said to Raguel, "Let me go, for my father and my mother look no more to see me." But his father-in-law said unto him, "Tarry with me, and I will send to thy father, and they shall declare unto him how things go with thee." But Tobias said, "No; but let me go to my father." Then Raguel arose, and gave him Sara his wife, and half his goods, servants, and cattle, and money: and he blessed them, and sent them away, saying, "The God of heaven give you a prosperous journey, my children." And he said to his daughter, "Honor thy father and thy mother-in-law, which are now thy parents, that I may hear good report of thee." And he kissed her. Edna also said to Tobias, "The Lord of heaven restore thee, my dear brother, and grant that I may see thy children of my daughter Sara before I die, that I may rejoice before the Lord: behold, I commit my daughter unto thee of special trust; wherefore do not entreat her evil."

After these things Tobias went his way, praising God that he had given him a prosperous journey, and blessed Raguel and Edna his wife, and went on his way till they drew near unto Nineveh. Then Raphael said to Tobias, "Thou knowest, brother, how thou didst leave thy father: let us haste before thy wife, and prepare the house. And take in thine hand the gall of the fish." So they went their way, and the dog went after them. Now Anna sat looking about toward the way for her son. And when she espied him coming, she said to his father, "Behold, thy son cometh, and the man that went with him." Then said Raphael, "I know, Tobias, that thy father will open his eyes. Therefore anoint thou his eyes with the gall, and being pricked therewith, he shall rub, and the whiteness shall fall away, and he shall see thee."

Then Anna ran forth, and fell upon the neck of her son, and said unto him, "Seeing I have seen thee, my son, from henceforth I am content to die." And they wept both. Tobit also went forth toward the door, and stumbled: but his son ran unto him, and took hold of his father: and he strake of the gall on his father's eyes, saying, "Be of good hope, my father." And when his eyes began to smart, he rubbed them; and the whiteness pulled away from the corners of his eyes: and when he saw his son, he fell upon his neck. And he wept, and said, "Blessed art thou, O God, and blessed is thy name for ever; and blessed are all thine holy angels: for thou hast scourged, and hast taken pity on me: for, behold, I see my son Tobias." And his son went in rejoicing, and told his father the great things that had happened to him in Media.

Then Tobit went out to meet his daughter-in-law at the gate of Nineveh, rejoicing, and praising God: and they which saw him go marveled, because he had received his sight. But Tobit gave thanks before them, because God had mercy on him. And when he came near to Sara his daughter-in-law, he blessed her, saying, "Thou art welcome, daughter: God be blessed, which hath brought thee unto us, and blessed be thy father and thy mother." And there was joy among all his brethren which were at Nineveh. And Achiacharus, and Nasbas his brother's son came: and Tobias' wedding was kept seven days with great joy. . . . [And the Angel said to Tobit], "When thou didst pray, and Sara thy daughter-in-law, I did bring the remembrance of your prayers before the Holy One: and when thou didst not delay to rise up, and leave thy dinner, to go cover the dead, thy good deed was not hid from me: but I was with thee. And now God hath sent me to heal thee and Sara thy daughter-in-law. I am Raphael, one of the seven holy angels, which present the prayers of the saints, and which go in and out before the glory of the Holy One."

[3]

Poltergeist

Friday, October 4 at eleven set out from Yarum for Skinningrave, the house of one Mr. Appleby, of which Mr. Jackson was giving a very odd account he had from the Rev. Mr. Midgeley of an apparition which haunted the house in a very remarkable manner. As I am very incredulous in these notions of spirits, I was determined to take a journey thither to know the truth, and, if possible, to have all conviction, either by ocular or auricular proof. Accordingly, I arrived there about eight at night, and asking for Mr. Appleby (whom I found a sensible man, with a great gentility of behavior for a tanner), I told him I had taken the liberty, after hearing such and such reports, to come and ask a few questions relating to a spirit that was said to trouble his house; and that if it would not be inconvenient, I should be obliged to him if he would accommodate me with a room all night.

He told me I was extremely welcome, and that he was obliged to any gentlemen that would give themselves the trouble to come; and did not doubt but that he should satisfy them, by the account he would give them, which he declared, as he should answer at the great tribunal, should be true, sincere, and undisguised, and should contain no incident but what had happened and been transacted in his house (at first to the grief and amazement of himself, his wife, and four servants) by this invisible and unaccountable agent. He said that it was five weeks since it had left them, and that once before they were quiet of it for three weeks, and then it returned, with double the noise and confusion they had before.

In the first place he assured me they had never seen anything, but that the noise and havoc which they had in the house was amazing; that they all were so frightened that one night about one o'clock they thought to quit the house and retire to a neighbor; that they could get no sleep by reason of their beds being stripped of the clothes and thrown upon the ground; that the women were thrown into fits by being oppressed with a weight upon their stomachs, equal to an hundredweight. Upon this they moved all their beds into one room, determined to share an equal fate; so that two men lay in one bed, two women in another, and the man and his wife in the third. No sooner were they in bed but the spirit visited them, the door being locked and barred. It first walked along the room, something like a man, but with an uncommon step. Immediately the maids cried out they were next to death, by a monstrous weight upon them; on which Mr. Appleby immediately came to their relief; that upon approaching the beds, something leaped off, walked round him, which he, being a man of courage, followed and endeavored to take hold of, but in vain. Upon this he retired to his bed, and immediately the maids called out they were losing the clothes off the bed. He told them to pull hard, which they did, but they were immediately taken with a violent force and thrown upon the men. After this it rattled a chain with a great noise round the room; and instantaneously they were alarmed with a noise over their heads of a man threshing, as it were, threshing corn with a flail, and in a minute was answered by another; and this continued for fifteen minutes in a very regular way, stroke for stroke, as if two men were threshing. Then it descended into the room where they were in bed, and acted the same.

Another night it came grunting like a hog, and after imitated the noise of a swine eating its food; sometimes it would, in the middle of the room, make a noise like the pendulum of a clock, only much faster. And he assured me that it continued in their room one morning in June till past five o'clock; and Mrs. Appleby and all of them saw the clothes taken off them and flung with violence upon the maidservants; but nothing could they discover, neither conceive how they were thus strangely conveyed.

Upon these surprising things being done, it was rumored abroad that the house was strongly haunted; and Mr. Moore, the landlord, and Justice Beckwith went to Appleby, and often talking with him and examining the servants, and telling them this was a concerted scheme among them for some purpose, they agreed to sit up all night. As they were putting the glass about, something entered the room, accompanied with a noise like squirting water out of a squirt, upon which they, with a change of countenance, asked him what that was. Appleby answered, "It was only a taste of what he every night had a sufficiency of." Mr. Moore advised him to keep a gun laden, and when he heard it in the room to discharge the piece.

The night following, the family being in bed as usual, it came, and making a sudden stand, threw something upon the ground, which seemed to them as if some sort of seed had fallen out of a paper. In the morning Mrs. Appleby, looking about the room, wondering what it could be that had been cast upon the ground, gathered up a considerable quantity of gunpowder in corns, which greatly surprised her. The next night it came in the same manner, but what it let fall made a greater noise, like shot, and in the morning they, to their real astonishment, found a great many shots. This afforded room for strange conjectures; and accordingly she told me she then did not know what to think, whether it was really an apparition or not: for that the scattering of this powder and shot the very two succeeding nights after Mr. Moore advised them to shoot

Blairsville Joint School Library
Blairsville, Pa.

greatly disconcerted them, though again, upon reflection, they had had so many proofs of something more than it was possible for any human creature to perform, that she was again led to believe it must be something not of this world, and that in the throwing down the powder and shot, it might be done in contempt, and was as much as to say, "What, you would shoot me?"

Once when it was in the midst of its career, one of the men, after composing himself for the purpose, addressed it in these words: In the name of God the Father, Son, and Holy Ghost, what art thou, and what dost thou want? If any person here can contribute to thy ease, speak, and nothing shall be omitted that can procure it. During the time he was speaking it was silent, but immediately upon his ceasing it began its usual noise. Then he spoke again the same words, but no answer followed. Mr. Appleby declared that one night when his servants were very merry, dancing and making a considerable noise, this goblin made so much greater disturbance over their heads, as one would have thought that twenty people were dancing there. Upon which he went up then with a light, but nothing could he discover.

When he told me this surprising narration, which he delivered with so much plainness and sincerity, free from embarrassment, I own I was something staggered, for he gave not the least cause to suspect his veracity. And upon my examining all his servants, they, without any hesitation, confirmed what their master had advanced: so that my expectation of hearing the reports, which I had heard, refuted was entirely frustrated, and I no little surprised to hear them so strongly vouched. I desired to lie in the room which this troublesome guest the most frequented; but they told me it occupied the whole house and no room escaped. So I retired to my apartment at eleven and read Milton till about one, then went to bed, not without wishing (yet not presumptuously) that I might have some strange conviction before morning, but met with none; and after a good night's sleep, arose at seven.

[4]

The Ghost with the Black and Blue Mark

Two young girls who had grown up together from the days of their childhood and were mutually attached had gone to a lyke-wake of a female acquaintance, a poor orphan, and found some women employed in dressing the body. There was an indifference and even lightheartedness shown on the occasion that shocked the two friends; and they solemnly agreed before parting, that should one of them outlive the other, the survivor, and no one besides, should lay out the corpse of the departed for the grave. The feeling, however, passed with the occasion out of which it arose, and the mutual promise was forgotten, until several years after when one of the girls, then the mistress of a solitary farmhouse on the hill of Nigg, was informed one morning by a chance passenger that her old companion, who had become the wife of a farmer in the neighboring parish of Fearn, had died in childbed during the previous night. She called to mind her promise, but it was only to reflect how impossible it was for her to fulfill it. She had her infant to tend and no one to entrust it to—her maid having left her scarcely an hour before for a neighboring fair to which her husband and his ploughman had also gone. She spent an anxious day, and it was with no ordinary solicitude, as she saw the evening gradually darkening and thought of her promise and her deceased companion, that she went out to a little hillock beside the house, which commanded a view of the moor over which her husband and the servants had to pass on their way from the fair, to ascertain whether any of them were yet returning. At length she could discern through the deepening twilight a female figure in white coming along the moor; and supposing it to be the maid and unwilling to appear so anxious for her return, she went into the house.

The outer apartment, as was customary at the period, was occupied as a cow house; some of the animals were in their stalls, and on their beginning to snort and stamp as if disturbed by someone passing, the woman half turned her to the door. What, however, was her astonishment to see, instead of the maid, a tall figure wrapped up from head to foot in a winding sheet! It passed round to the opposite side of the fire where there was a chair drawn in for the farmer, and seating itself, raised its thin chalky arms and uncovered its face. The features, as shown by the flame, were those of the deceased woman; and it was with an expression of anger, which added to the horror of the appearance, that the dead and glassy eyes were turned to her old companion, who, shrinking with a terror that seemed to annihilate every feeling and faculty except the anxious solicitude of the mother, strained her child to her bosom and gazed as if fascinated on the terrible apparition before her. She could see every fold of the sheet; the black hair seemed to droop carelessly over the forehead; the livid, unbreathing lips were drawn apart, as if no friendly hand had closed them after the last agony; and the reflection of the flame seemed to rise and fall within the eyes—varying by its ceaseless flicker the statuelike fixedness of the features.

As the fire began to decay, the woman recovered enough of her self-possession to stretch her hand behind her and draw from time to time out of the child's cradle a handful of straw which she flung on the embers; but she lost all reckoning of time and could only guess at the duration of the visit by finding the straw nearly expended. She was looking forward with a still deepening horror to being left in darkness with the specter, when voices were heard in the yard without. The apparition glided toward the door; the cattle began to snort and stamp, as on its entrance; and one of them struck at it with its feet in the passing; when it uttered a faint shriek and disappeared. The farmer entered the cottage a moment after, barely in time to see his wife fall over in a swoon on the floor, and to receive the child. Next morning the woman attended the lykewake to fulfill all her engagement that she could; and on examining the body discovered that, by a strange sympathy, the mark of a cow's hoof was distinctly impressed on its left side.

[5]

Laying a Greek Ghost

"What are you saying?" asked Arignotus, eying me with disapproval. "Do you maintain that the souls of the dead do not return to walk the earth although the whole world solemnly affirms that they most certainly do?"

"You are pleading my case," I answered; "if I do not believe in them, it is because I—curiously unique in this regard—have never seen any of them. If I could see a ghost, I would, like you, say that there are ghosts."

"Well, then," he said, "if you ever visit Corinth, ask where Eubatides' house is, and when it is pointed out to you, next door to the Craneum, enter it and tell Tibias, the porter, that you want to see the spot where Arignotus the Pythagorean had the trench dug to drive away the phantom and so made the house habitable ever after."

"What was this, Arignotus?" asked Eucrates.

"Because it was haunted Eubatides' house had been abandoned for a long time," he replied. "If anyone moved into it, he was struck by a ghostly hand and forced to flee, pursued by a terrible phantom. The house became a ruin, the roof fell in, and no one courageous enough to stay in it could be found. Now when I heard people talking about this, I took some books—I had a great many Egyptian volumes on these matters—and about midnight entered the house despite the efforts of my host to keep me from it, for as soon as he learned what I intended to do he pleaded with me to desist and even pulled at my clothes to hold me back from a course which he was convinced would lead to certain death. Nevertheless, borrowing a horn lantern, I entered and alone. Putting down the lantern in the largest room, I sat on the floor and calmly began to read. Not many minutes passed before the ghost appeared. Apparently he took me for an unlettered man and assumed that he would have no more trouble terrifying me than he had had with the others.

"Now this specter was as black as night. He had a squalid, dried-up look, and his stringy hair hung down about his body. Approaching closely, he attacked me from every side, hoping to overcome me. Then he began to shift his shape. First he turned into a dog; then he became a bull, and finally a lion. But while this was going on I was not idle, but speaking in the Egyptian tongue, I assailed him with the most terrible magic formulas, the most powerful spells I knew. And by the authority of these incantations I forced him to back off into the darkest corner of the room. Then he vanished. After marking the spot where he was last seen, I went to sleep and rested until morning. Now all who knew of my adventure were anxiously waiting outside. They fully expected to find me a corpse, for none of the others who had watched in this house had come out alive. So there was great surprise when I walked out unscathed.

"I then went to find Eubatides and tell him the good news. He could now live without fear in his house, purged from horrors. Taking him along with me, and followed by a crowd drawn together by this extraordinary adventure, I led him to the exact spot where I had seen the specter vanish. And I got him to have his servants take spades and mattocks and dig. And when they did, they discovered, about a fathom down, a cadaver which had been in the earth a long time and now was nothing but bones. After drawing it up we gave it burial. And never since has that house been troubled by phantoms."

[6]

Laying an English Ghost

Some years back a clergyman, on taking possession of a living on the confines of Dartmoor, found it necessary to enlarge the house, which was really little better than the peasants' cottages around it. He lengthened the one sitting room and made it into a tolerable dining room, adding a drawing room and two or three bedrooms.

These improvements satisfied his wife and children; but there was one interested party whom he had left out of consideration–the spirit of his predecessor, an old gentleman who had outlived all his family and passed many solitary years in the remote parsonage.

And ere long the consequences of this neglect appeared. Sounds were soon heard of an evening as though a figure in a dressing gown were sweeping in and out of the rooms, and treading with a soft yet heavy tread, and this particularly in the dining room, where the old vicar had spent the last years of his life, sitting over the fire, or pacing up and down in his dressing gown and slippers. The eerie sounds began at nightfall and continued at intervals till morning. Uneasiness pervaded the household. Servants gave warning and went away; no one applied for their vacant places. The daughters fell ill and were sent away for change of air; then their mother was anxious about them and went to see how they were going on; and so the vicar was left alone, at the mercy of his predecessor's ghost. At first he bore up bravely, but one Saturday night, while he was sitting up late, and wearily going over his Sunday sermons, the "pad, pad" of the measured tread struck so painfully upon his nerves that he could bear it no longer. He started up, opened the window, jumped out, and made the best of his way to the nearest farm, where lived his churchwarden, an honest Dartmoor farmer.

There the vicar found a kind welcome; and when he told his tale, in a hesitating sort of way, owning his dislike to solitude and apologizing for the weakness of nerves which made him fancy he heard the sounds so often described to him, his host broke in with a declaration of his belief that the old vicar was at the bottom of it, just because of the alterations in the house he had lived in so many years. "He never could abide changes," pursued the farmer, "but he's had his day, and you should have yours now. He must be laid, that's certain; and, if you'll go away next week to your missis and the young ladies, I'll see to it."

And see to it he did. A jury of seven parsons was convoked, and each sat for half an hour with a candle in his hand, and it burned out its time with each, showing plainly that none of them could lay the ghost. Nor was this any wonder, for were they not all old acquaintances of his, so that he knew all their tricks? The spirit could afford to defy them; it was not worth his while to blow their candles out. But the seventh parson was a stranger, and a scholar fresh from Oxford. In his hand the light went out at once. He was clearly the man to lay the ghost, and he did not shrink from his task: he laid it at once, and in a beer barrel.

But now a fresh difficulty arose. What was to be done with the beer barrel and its mysterious tenant? Where could it be placed secure from the touch of any curious hand, which might be tempted to broach the barrel and set free the ghost? Nothing occurred to the assembled company but to roll the thing into one corner, and send for the mason to enclose it with stones and mortar. This done, the room looked very odd with one corner cut off. Uniformity would be attained if the other three were filled up as well; and besides, the ghost would be safer if no one knew the very spot in which he was reposing. So the other corners were blocked up, and with success. What matters it if the room be smaller!—the parsonage has never been haunted since.

[7]

The Spectral War Horse

There is in England . . . on the borders of the episcopal see of Ely a castle called Cathubica; a little below which is a place distinguished by the appellation of Wandlesbury, because, as they say, the Vandals, having laid waste the country and cruelly slaughtered the Christians, here pitched their camp. Around a small hillock where their tents were pitched was a circular space of level ground, enclosed by ramparts, to which but one entrance presented itself. Upon this plain, as it is commonly reported on the authority of remote traditions, during the hush of night while the moon shone, if any knight called aloud, "Let my adversary appear," he was immediately met by another, who started up from the opposite quarter, ready armed and mounted for combat. The encounter invariably ended in the overthrow of one party. Concerning this tradition, I have an actual occurrence to tell, which was well known to many, and which I have heard both from the inhabitants of the place and others.

There was once in Great Britain a knight whose name was Albert, strong in arms and adorned with every virtue. It was his fortune to enter the above-mentioned castle, where he was hospitably received. At night after supper, as usual in great families during the winter, the household assembled round the hearth and occupied the hour in relating divers tales. At last they discoursed of the wonderful occurrence before alluded to; and our knight, not satisfied with the report, determined to prove the truth of what he had heard, before he implicitly trusted it.

Accompanied, therefore, by a squire of noble blood, he hastened to the spot, armed in a coat of mail. He ascended the mount, and then dismissing his attendant, entered the plain. He shouted, and an antagonist, accoutered at all points, met him in an instant. What followed? Extending their shields and directing their lances at each other, the steeds were driven to the attaint, and both the knights shaken by the career. Their lances broke, but from the slipperiness of the armor, the blow did not take effect. Albert, however, so resolutely pressed his adversary that he fell; and rising immediately beheld Albert making a prize of his horse. On which, seizing the broken lance, he cast it in the manner of a missile weapon and cruelly wounded Albert in the thigh. Our knight, overjoyed at his victory, either felt not the blow or dissembled it; and his adversary suddenly disappeared. He, therefore, led away the captured horse and consigned him to the charge of his squire.

He was prodigiously large, light of step, and of a beautiful shape. When Albert returned, the household crowded around him, struck with the greatest wonder at the event, and rejoicing at the overthrow of the hostile knight, while they lauded the bravery of the magnanimous victor. When, however, he put off his cuisses, one of them was filled with clotted blood. The family were alarmed at the appearance of the wound; and the servants were aroused and dispatched here and there. Such of them as had been asleep, admiration now induced to watch. As a testimony of conquest, the horse, held by the bridle, was exposed to public inspection. His eyes were fierce, and he arched his neck proudly; his hair was of a lustrous jet, and he bore a war saddle on his back. The cock had already begun to crow when the animal, foaming, curvetting, snorting, and furiously striking the ground with his feet, broke the bonds that held him and escaped. He was immediately pursued but disappeared in an instant. The knight retained a perpetual memento of that severe wound; for every year upon the night of that encounter, it broke out afresh. Some time after, he crossed the seas and fell valiantly, fighting against the pagans.

[8]

The Banshee's Wail

One of the greatest pleasures I enjoyed while resident at Dunran was the near abode of the late Lord Rossmore, at that time commander-in-chief in Ireland. His lordship knew my father, and from my commencement in public life had been my friend, and a sincere one. He was a Scotsman born but had come to Ireland when very young, as page to the lord-lieutenant. He had married an heiress, had purchased the estate of Mount Kennedy, built a noble mansion, laid out some of the finest gardens in Ireland, and in fact improved the demesne as far as taste, skill, and money could accomplish.

He was what may be called a remarkably fine old man, quite the gentleman, and when at Mount Kennedy quite the country gentleman. He lived in a style few people can attain to: his table, supplied by his own farms, was adapted to the viceroy himself, yet was ever spread for his neighbors. In a word, no man ever kept a more even hand in society than Lord Rossmore, and no man was ever better repaid by universal esteem. Had his connections possessed his understanding and practiced his habits, they would probably have found more friends when they wanted them.

This intimacy at Mount Kennedy gave rise to an occurrence the most extraordinary and inexplicable of my whole existence—an occurrence which for many years occupied my thoughts and wrought on my imagination. Lord Rossmore was advanced in years, but I never heard of his having had a single day's indisposition. He bore in his green old age the appearance of robust health. During the viceroyalty of Earl Hardwick, Lady Barrington (my wife) at a drawing room at Dublin Castle met Lord Rossmore. He had been making up one of his weekly parties for Mount Kennedy, to commence the next day, and had sent down orders for every preparation to be made. The lord-lieutenant was to be of the company.

"My little farmer," said he to Lady Barrington, addressing her by a pet name, "when you go home, tell Sir Jonah that no business is to prevent him from bringing you down to dine with me tomorrow. I will have no *ifs* in the matter—so tell him that come he must!" She promised positively, and on her return informed me of her engagement, to which I at once agreed.

We retired to our chamber about twelve; and toward two in the morning I was awakened by a sound of a very extraordinary nature. I listened. It occurred first at short intervals. It resembled neither a voice nor an instrument. It was softer than any voice and wilder than any music, and seemed to float on the air. I don't know wherefore, but my heart beat forcibly: the sound became still more plaintive, till it almost died away in the air, when a sudden change, as if excited by a pang, changed its tone: it seemed *descending*. I felt every nerve tremble; it was not a *natural* sound, nor could I make out the point whence it came.

At length I awakened Lady Barrington, who heard it as well as myself. She suggested that it might be an Aeolian harp—but to that instrument it bore no similitude. It was altogether a different character of sound. My wife at first appeared less affected than I, but subsequently she was more so.

We now went to a large window in our bedroom which looked directly upon a small garden underneath. The sound seemed then obviously to ascend from a grass plot immediately below our window. It continued. Lady Barrington requested that I would call up her maid, which I did, and she was evidently more affected than either of us. The sounds lasted for more than half an hour. At last a deep heavy throbbing sigh seemed to issue from the spot, and was shortly succeeded by a sharp but low cry, and by the distinct exclamation, thrice repeated, of "Rossmore—Rossmore—Rossmore!" I will not attempt to describe my own feelings; indeed I cannot. The maid fled in terror from the window, and it was with difficulty I prevailed on Lady Barrington to return to bed. About a minute after, the sound died gradually away until all was silent.

Lady Barrington, who is not so "superstitious" as I, attributed this circumstance to a hundred different causes and made me promise that I would not mention it next day at Mount Kennedy since we should be thereby rendered laughingstocks. At length, wearied with speculations, we fell into a sound slumber.

About seven the ensuing morning a strong rap at my chamber door awakened me. The recollection of the past night's adventure rushed instantly upon my mind and rendered me very unfit to be taken suddenly on any subject. It was light: I went to the door, when my faithful servant, Lawler, exclaimed on the other side, "O lord, sir!"

"What is the matter?" said I, hurriedly.

"Oh, sir!" ejaculated he, "Lord Rossmore's footman was running past the door in great haste and told me in passing that his lord, after coming from the Castle had gone to bed in perfect health, but that about *half after two* this morning, his own man hearing a noise in his master's bed (he slept in the same room), went to him and found him in the agonies of death; and before he could alarm the other servants, all was over!"

I conjecture nothing. I only relate the incident as unequivocally matter of *fact*. Lord Rossmore was absolutely dying at the moment I heard his name pronounced. Let skeptics draw their own conclusions; perhaps natural causes may be assigned, but I am totally unequal to the task.

IX

WITCHES AND WIZARDS

There is hardly an evil deed from casting a spell on the buttermilk to slow murder by means of image magic or the evil eye that has not been charged against the witch. Many protective measures were taken against her: hanging up horseshoes, making the sign of the horn, crossing oneself, clenching the fingers over the thumbs while passing by her, jumping over a branch of the rowan tree, and many more. When she was caught, her face was likely to be scratched, since it was believed her blood broke the spell she had cast. And her clothes were certain to be pulled off. Either she was forced to sit naked for hours on a stool in expectation that her familiar in shape of cat or hare would come to her, or she was stripped to be "swum" or weighed against the Bible, or be "pricked" by a witch-finder, whose practice it was to shave off various patches of hair on her torso in his search for the Devil's mark.

It has been said that there were more witches than wizards because women were easier to beguile and naturally more "tongue ripe" than men. But the role of the medieval witch could hardly have been performed by a male, and this is doubtless an important consideration. A female was called for because a witch was thought to be the Devil's mistress and play a woman's part in the licentious orgies of the Witches' Sabbath, which affairs were in part survivals of ancient fertility rites in which the female deity or her representative was a principal actor.

Although some wizards attended Sabbaths, the wizard or magician was not necessarily anti-Christian like the witch. The typical wizard was a scholar and therefore was considered worthy of some respect. At least, he was not often an outcast. He had studied his *grimoire*, or black book, and, becoming an adept in the black art, was powerful enough to command Satan and his imps to do his bidding. It will be remembered that before Dr. Faustus signed the pact, he had studied magic and was able to command the evil spirit to come to him. Friar Bacon never signed a pact with the Devil (although the inferior magicians, Bungay and Vandermast, did and were destroyed) and finally burned his magic books and became an anchorite. Both Virgilius and Bacon often employed their magic to help their fellow men. The magician of this type was sometimes invited to the palace, where he raised the spirits of the dead, conjured up magic entertainment for the court, and astonished the king and his courtiers with his marvelous feats.

"The Story of Telephron, the Student" and "The Enchanted Goatskins" are from Apuleius's *Golden Ass*, ed. 1878. "The Witch of Treva" is from Robert Hunt's *Popular Romances of the West of England*, 1865, and "The Witch Cat" is a Tuscan folktale from C. G. Leland's *Etruscan Roman Remains*, 1892. "The Bewitched Buttermilk" is from E. Lynn Linton's *Witch Stories*, 1861. "Hag-ridden" is from William Henderson's *Folk-lore of the Northern Counties of England*, 1879, and "Virgilius, the Necromancer" from W. J. Thom's *Early English Prose Romances*. "Friar Bacon" is the editor's shortened version of *The Famous Histoire of Fryer Bacon.*

[1]

The Story of Telephron, the Student

While I was yet pursuing my studies, I went from Miletus to see the Olympic games; and as I wished also to pay a visit to the chief places of this celebrated province, I traveled over all Thessaly, and arrived under unlucky auspices at Larissa. As the money I had brought with me for my journey had been nearly all got rid of in my rambles, I was put to my shifts to repair my impoverished state. While so doing, I saw a tall old man, standing on a stone in the middle of the forum, and making proclamation in a loud voice: "If anyone will undertake to guard the body of a dead man, he shall be well rewarded for his services."

On this, I said to one of the bystanders, "What am I to understand by this? Are the dead in the habit of running away in this country?"

"Hold your tongue," replied he, "for you are a boy, and a green one too, and a foreigner all over, not to know that you are in Thessaly, where it is a universal practice with witches to tear off pieces from the faces of the dead with their teeth, in order to use them as ingredients in the magic art."

"Pray, tell me," said I, "in what does this funeral wardenship consist?"

"In the first place," he replied, "you must watch incessantly the livelong night, with eyes fixed steadily on the corpse, wide open and not indulging in a wink; nor must your gaze ever be turned away to the one side or the other, no, not even may you cast a glance aside it. For these most abominable shifters of their skins, changing, in appearance, into any animal they please, creep upon you unawares, so that they can easily elude the very eyes of Justice and of the Sun. For they assume the forms of birds, dogs, mice, ay, and even of flies; and thus disguised, they exert their dire incantations, and overwhelm the guardians with sleep. Nor can any person sufficiently describe the extent of the devices which they make use of, for the sake of gratifying their libidinous appetite. And yet, after all, no larger pay than four or six pieces of gold is offered as the reward of such a dangerous service as this. But stop; there is one thing I had almost forgotten: if the person who watches does not on the following morning give up possession of the dead body in an entire state, he is compelled to make good the whole of it with strips cut from his own face, to match whatever has been torn off from that of the corpse."

On learning these facts, I summoned up all my courage, and going straightway to the crier, "Cease from making proclamation," said I; "here is a guardian ready to your hand; tell me what is to be the reward."

"A thousand pieces of money will be paid you," said he. "But look, young man, you must be very careful to preserve the dead body, which is that of the son of one of the principal persons of this city, from the abominable Harpies."

"You are talking nonsense to me," said I, "and mere trifles. You behold in me a man of iron nerve, proof against sleep, and, beyond a doubt, more sharp-sighted than Lynceus himself, or Argus; in fact, one who is eyes all over."

I had no sooner said this, than he at once led me to a certain house, the main entrance of which being closed, he introduced me through a low back door, and into a darkened bedchamber, with closed window shutters, where there was a lady dressed in black garments, and weeping. Going up to her, the crier said, "This person has agreed to your terms, and confidently undertakes to watch the body of your husband."

On this, the lady, throwing back on each side the hair that hung down over her face, which even in grief was beautiful, and turning toward me, said, "Take care, I beg of you, to perform vigilantly the duty which you have undertaken."

"Never fear," said I, "only have in readiness something to throw into the bargain as a present."

Assenting to this request, she hastily arose, and bade me follow her into another bedchamber. There, in the presence of seven witnesses who had been introduced into the room, she pointed with her hand to a dead body that was covered with a linen cloth of the purest white; and having wept for a considerable time at the sight of it, she called upon those present to bear testimony, and carefully pointed out to them every particular; while a person made notes on tablets of the parts of the body, which were severally touched for the purpose.

"Behold," said she, "the nose entire, the eyes in a sound condition, the ears safe, the lips untouched, and the chin perfect. Do you, worthy citizens, bear testimony to this." Having thus said, and the tablets duly signed and sealed, she was departing, when I said to her:

"Have the goodness, madam, to order that all things may be furnished to me which are requisite for my use."

"And what are they?" said she.

"A good large lamp," I replied, "sufficient oil for keeping it alight till daylight, some warm water, with wine vessels and a cup, and a dish furnished with the remains of the dinner."

"Begone, foolish man," said she, shaking her head, "do you expect to find in a house of sorrow remains of suppers, in which no smoke whatever has been seen for these many days? Do you think you have come hither for the purpose of eating and drinking? Rather betake yourself to sorrow and tears, as best suited to this place." Then turning to her maidservant, she said, "Myrrhina, give him the lamp and oil directly," and so saying, she went out and left the guardian shut up in the bedchamber.

Being thus left alone to comfort the corpse, I rubbed my eyes, to fortify them for their duty of watchfulness, and kept up my spirits by singing. And now behold twilight came on, night fell, then night deeper and deeper still, and at last the hour of midnight; then, of a truth, my fears, that had some time been increasing, became redoubled. All of a sudden a weasel, creeping into the apartment, stopped close before me, and fixed its eyes most intently upon me, so much so, that the little creature quite agitated my mind by its unusual confidence. At length, however, I said to it: "Out with you, nasty little beast! and go hide yourself to the mice that are just like you, before you get a knockdown blow from me. Be off with you, I say!"

The animal turned tail, and immediately ran out of the chamber: and at the very instant a profound sleep suddenly seized and engulfed me; so that not even the God of Delphi himself could have easily determined which of us two, who lay there prostrate, was the more dead. In fact, I was so insensible, and so much in need of someone else to take care of me, that I might just as well have not been there at all.

Hardly had the clarion of the crested cohort sounded a truce to the night, when I, at length aroused, and terrified in the extreme, ran up to the dead body; holding the light to it, and uncovering its face, I scrutinized every feature, and found everything in proper order. Presently, the poor widow burst into the room in tears and great distress, with the witnesses of yesterday; and, immediately throwing herself on the body, and kissing it again and again, she began to examine it all over, with the assistance of the lamp. Then turning, she called Philodespotus, the steward of her house, and ordered him, without delay, to pay the promised reward to one who had acted as so good a guardian.

This being given me without delay, "We thank you sincerely, young man," said she, "and, by Hercules! for having so well performed this service, we will henceforth enroll you among the rest of our household."

Overjoyed at this unlooked-for piece of good fortune, and enchanted at the sight of the glittering pieces of gold, which every now and then I shook up and down in my hand, "By all means, madam," said I, "consider me one of your servants; and, as often as you stand in need of my services, you may confidently command me."

Hardly had I thus spoken, when all the servants, heaping curses upon the dreadful ominousness of my words, snatched up whatever came to hand, and fell upon me. One began to strike me in the face with his fist, another to dig me in the back and ribs with his elbows, a third to kick me with his feet, a fourth to pull out my hair, a fifth to tear my clothes. Thus, mauled and mangled almost as badly as was Adonis or Orpheus, I was thrust out of doors.

I stopped to recover myself in the next street, and reflecting too late on my inauspicious and imprudent remark, I could not but acknowledge that I had fully deserved to suffer even still more blows than I had received. By and by the dead person was carried out, accompanied, for the last time, by lamentations and outcries; and, according to the custom of the country, was borne with all the pomp of a public funeral, as being one of the principal men, through the forum. To the side of the corpse there runs up an old man, bathed with tears, and tearing his venerable white hair; and then, seizing the bier with both his hands, and with a voice raised to the highest pitch, though interrupted with frequent sobs, "O Romans," exclaimed he, "by your faith, and by the public morality, espouse the cause of your murdered fellow citizen, and wreak your severe vengeance on this abominable and wicked woman, for her most atrocious crime; for she, and no one else, has cut off by poison this unfortunate young man, my sister's son, for the sake of her paramour, and made a prey of the inheritance."

After this manner, the old man loudly uttered complaints and lamentations, broken by his sobs. In the meantime, the people began to express their indignation, being impelled to a belief in the charge, on the grounds of its probability alone. They shouted for fire; for stones; they incited the boys to the destruction of the woman; but she, pretending to shed tears, and adjuring all the divinities, denied most solemnly that she had perpetrated a crime of such great enormity.

"Well then," said the old man, "let us refer the decision of the truth to divine providence. Here is Zachlas, the Egyptian, a first-rate prophet, who has already agreed with me, for a considerable sum, to recall the soul for a few moments from the realms beneath, to reanimate the body." Thus saying, he brought forward into the midst of the people a young man, clothed in linen garments, with his head close shaven, and having on his feet sandals made of palm leaves. After having for some time kissed his hands and embraced his very knees, "O priest," said he, "take pity on me, by the stars of the heavens, by the Gods of the infernal regions, by the elements of nature, by the silence of night, by the Coptic enclosures, by the overflowing of the Nile, by the mysteries of the Memphis, and by the sistrum of Pharos, I implore you. Give to this dead body a short enjoyment of the sun, and infuse a portion of light into eyes that have been buried in eternal night. We are not offering resistance to fate, nor do we deny to the earth what is her property; but we only request a short space of life, that we may have the consolation of avenging her death."

The prophet, being thus propitiated, laid a certain herb three times on the mouth of the corpse, and placed another on its breast. He then turned toward the east, and silently prayed to the rising disk of the glorious Sun, whilst an intense interest was excited among the bystanders, by the sight of such awful preparations, and the prospect of a miracle. I mingled with the crowd, and standing on an elevated stone, close behind the bier, observed everything with inquisitive eyes.

Presently the breast of the corpse began to be inflated, the artery to throb with pulsation, the body to be filled with breath; at last the corpse arose, and thus addressed the young man: "Why, I beseech thee, dost thou bring me back to the duties of a momentary existence, after having drunk of the Lethean cup, and floated upon the Stygian lake? Cease, I beseech thee, cease and leave me to my repose." These were the words heard to proceed from the body.

On this, the prophet, becoming still more excited, exclaimed, "Why dost thou not relate to this crowd each particular, and disclose the mysteries of thy death? Knowest thou not that the Furies can be summoned by my imprecations to rack thy wearied limbs?"

The body looked up from the bier, and with a deep groan thus addressed the people: "Cut off through the nefarious arts of my newly married wife, and by a poisonous draught, I have yielded my yet warm bed to her paramour."

Then that choice specimen of a wife, arming herself with audacity, began to contradict the accusation of her husband in a wrangling and sacrilegious manner. The excited mob took different sides; one party contended that this most iniquitous woman should immediately be buried alive, with the corpse of her husband; the other declared that credit ought not to be given to the lying testimony of the dead body. The subsequent disclosures, however, of the young man put an end to this dispute; for, again heaving a deep groan, "I will give you," he said, "I will give you incontrovertible evidence of the truth of my statements, and will disclose to you what is known to no other person whatever."

Then, pointing with his fingers: "When that most sagacious guardian of my body," said he, "was diligently keeping watch over me, the hags of sorceresses who eagerly hovered over my mortal spoils, and who, to gain possession thereof, had often changed themselves in vain into other forms, on finding that they could not deceive his unwearied vigilance, at length threw over him a cloud of drowsiness, and buried him in a profound sleep; after which, they did not cease to call on me by my name, till my weakened joints and chilled limbs struggled, with convulsive efforts, to obey the mandates of the magic art. Then this person, who though alive was still dead, so far as sleep goes, happening to be of the same name as myself, unconsciously arose on hearing his name called, and spontaneously walking just like an inanimate shadow, suffered the intended mutilation instead of myself; for although the doors of the bedchamber were carefully bolted, the witches entered through a chink, and cut off his nose first, and then his ears. And, that the rest of the transaction might correspond with their artful doings, they with the greatest exactness fitted on to him wax, fashioned in imitation of his ears that had been cut off, and provided him with a nose of the same substance, just like his own. And here now stands the unfortunate wretch who has obtained the reward dearly earned, not by his vigilance, but by his sore mutilation."

Exceedingly terrified on hearing this, I began to test my fortune. Clapping my hand to my nose, I took hold of it, and off it came: I touched my ears, and they fell to the ground. Meanwhile the spectators pointed their fingers at me, nodded their heads, and greeted me with loud roars of laughter, until streaming with cold perspiration I dashed through the surrounding crowd, and effected my escape. Nor, thus mutilated and an object of ridicule, could I return to my native place; but, with my hair falling on each side of my face, I concealed the wounds of my ears, and decently covered the disgrace of my nose with this linen cloth, closely applied to it by means of glue.

[2]

The Enchanted Goatskins

[Returning one night after having imbibed too freely at a banquet, Lucius encountered three shadowy shapes trying to break into Pamphile's house, where he was staying. Taking these to be robbers, he set upon them with his sword and left them for dead upon the road. But for this he was arrested, charged with murder, and made the butt of ridicule at a mock trial held in honor of Momus. Fotis, a maidservant with whom Lucius was carrying on an affair, is the narrator of the following story. Pamphile, a notable sorceress, had just fallen in love with a Boeotian youth and planned to employ magic to force him to love her.]

Yesterday, happening to catch sight of this youth in a barber's shop, as she was returning from the bath, Pamphile secretly gave me orders to bring away the cuttings of his hair, which were lying on the ground. As I was in the act of carefully and stealthily collecting them, the barber caught me; and because from other circumstances we were publicly notorious as exercising the black art, he laid hold on me, and rudely abused me: "What, you good-for-nothing jade, you can't leave off pilfering the hair of the good-looking young men every now and then? If you don't, once for all, put an end to this, I will take you without more ado before the magistrates." Then, suiting the action to the words, thrusting in his hands between my breasts, and groping about them in a rage, he drew out the hair I had previously concealed there. Grievously afflicted by this treatment, and reflecting on the temper of my mistress, who is always excessively enraged, and beats me in the most cruel manner, when she is thwarted in a matter of this nature, I had serious thoughts of running away, but when I thought of you, I instantly abandoned that design. On my way home, sad and empty-handed, I espied a man clipping some goat skins with a pair of shears. Seeing them so nicely sewn together, inflated, and standing by themselves, I took up a parcel of the hair from them which lay scattered on the ground, and being of a yellow color, resembled that of the young Boeotian; and this goat's hair I gave to my mistress, concealing the truth.

Accordingly, at nightfall, before you returned from the entertainment, Pamphile, my mistress, now in a state of frenzy, went up into a belvedere covered with shingles, which she secretly frequents, as being especially adapted to these pursuits of hers, for it is open on every side to the winds, and commands a prospect of the eastern and all the other points. There she began by arranging in her deadly workshop all the customary implements of her art, such as aromatics of all kinds, plates of metal engraved with talismanic characters, nails from shipwrecked vessels, as also, multitudes of limbs and fragments stolen from graves. Here, were noses and fingers, there, the nails by which culprits had been fixed to the cross, and to which portions of flesh adhered; and, in another place, the blood of murdered persons, bottled up, and mangled skulls of men who had been devoured by wild beasts.

Next, having pronounced an incantation over entrails still warm and palpitating, she makes a libation with various liquors, first, with water from the spring; next, with the milk of cows; and then, with mountain honey and mead. Then, after plaiting the goats' hairs together and tying them in a knot, she burns them on live coals, with abundance of perfumes. That instant, through the irresistible power of the magic art, and through the occult might of the coerced divinities, those same bodies, the hairs of which were smoking and crackling, received human breath, were endowed with understanding, heard, and walked. Whither the odor of the burning spoils attracted them, thither came they; and instead of that Boeotian youth, it was they who bumped away at the door, endeavoring to effect an entrance. Just at that moment up came you, well steeped in liquor, and deceived by the darkness of the night, you drew your sword, just like the frantic Ajax, but not like him to slay whole flocks of sheep; a far more valiant deed was yours, for you deprived of breath three inflated goatskins, so that, having laid your adversaries prostrate, without staining yourself with a drop of blood, I can now clasp you in my arms, not as a homicide, but as a wine-bagicide.

[3]

The Witch of Treva

Once upon a time, long ago, there lived at Treva, a hamlet in Zennor, an uncanny old lady, deeply skilled in necromancy. Her charms, spells, and dark incantations made her the terror of the neighborhood. However, this old lady failed to impress her husband with any belief in her supernatural powers, nor did he fail to proclaim his unbelief aloud.

One day this skeptic came home to dinner, and found, being exceedingly hungry, to his bitter disappointment, that not only was there no dinner to eat but that there was no meat in the house. His rage was great, but all he could get from his wife was, "I couldn't get meat out of the stones, could I?" It was in vain to give the reins to passion, the old woman told him, and he must know "that hard words buttered no parsnips." Well, at length he resolved to put his wife's powers to the proof, and he quietly but determinedly told her that he would be the death of her if she did not get some dinner; but if in half an hour she gave him some good cooked meat, he would believe all she had boasted of her power, and be submissive to her for ever. St. Ives, the nearest market town, was five miles off; but nothing doubting, the witch put on her bonnet and cloak, and started. Her husband watched her from their cottage door, down the hill, and at the bottom of the hill he saw his wife quietly place herself on the ground and disappear. In her place a fine hare ran on at its full speed.

He was not a little startled, but he waited, and within the half hour in walked his wife with "good flesh and taties all ready for eating." There was no longer any doubt, and the poor husband lived in fear of the witch of Treva to the day of her death.

This event took place after a few years, and it is said the room was full of evil spirits, and that the old woman's shrieks were awful to hear. Howbeit, peace in the shape of pale-faced death came to her at last, and then a black cloud rested over the house when all the heavens were clear and blue.

She was borne to the grave by six aged men, carried, as is the custom, under hand. When they were about half way between the house and the church, a hare started from the roadside and leaped over the coffin. The terrified bearers let the corpse fall to the ground and ran away. Another lot of men took up the coffin and proceeded. They had not gone far when puss was suddenly seen seated on the coffin, and again the coffin was abandoned. After long consultation, and being persuaded by the parson to carry the old woman very quickly into the churchyard, while he walked before, six others made the attempt, and as the parson never ceased to repeat the Lord's Prayer, all went on quietly. Arrived at the church stile, they rested the corpse, the parson paused to commence the ordinary burial service, and there stood the hare, which, as soon as the clergyman began, "I am the resurrection and the life," uttered a diabolical howl, changed into a black, unshapen creature, and disappeared.

[4]

The Witch Cat

When I was a child I went frequently to the house of a woman who had a *bambina*—a girl baby—and we often made a noise when playing together, but woe to us whenever we did so playing with the cat, for the child's mother said that cats are all wizards and witches. As I indeed learned only too soon how true it was.

There lived near us another woman who had also a little girl. This child was very impertinent. One day while we three were playing together and making a tumult, my friend gave this other one a cuff. So she ran howling to her mother; and the woman said to the mother of my friend, "I will be revenged for this"; and *per troppo fu vero*—it was only too true. For after a few days my little friend fell ill and no one knew what was the matter, nor could any doctor explain the malady.

Then her mother began to think that the woman who had threatened vengeance was a witch. And she was sure of it when she observed that a cat came by night into her house, and that it, instead of lying down, always remained standing! So she watched, and when at midnight the cat came again, she took it and bound it to the child's bed and beat it with all her might, saying, "Cure my child or I will kill you!"

Then the cat spoke with a human voice and said, "I can endure no more. Let me go and your child shall be well." But at that instant there was heard a horrible roar and clanking of chains as if many demons were about, and the mother, instead of letting the cat free, went and called the priest that he might give his blessing. And the mother clipped the hair from the cat, and in the morning when the church bell rang, the cat became nothing more nor less than the woman who had vowed revenge. And so she could no longer be a witch; and all the neighbors, seeing her naked, and without a hair left, knew what she was, and so she practiced witchcraft no more.

[5]

The Bewitched Buttermilk

Halstead, August 2, 1732

Sir—The narrative which I gave you in relation to witchcraft, and which you are pleased to lay your commands on me to repeat, is as follows:—There was one Master Collett, a smith by trade, of Haveningham, in the county of Suffolk, who as 'twas customary with him, assisting the maid to churn, and not being able (as the phrase is) to make the butter come, threw a hot iron into the churn, under the notion of witchcraft in the case, upon which a poor laborer, then employed in carrying of dung in the yard, cried out in a terrible manner, "They have killed me; they have killed me";

still keeping his hand upon his back, intimating where the pain was, and died upon the spot.

Mr. Collett, with the rest of the servants then present, took off the poor man's clothes, and found to their great surprise the mark of the iron that was heated and thrown into the churn deeply impressed upon his back. This account I had from Mr. Collett's own mouth, who being a man of unblemished character, I verily believe to be a matter of fact.

I am, Sir, your obliged humble Servant,

SAM MANNING

[6]

Hagridden

Witches and warlocks, it seems, are wont to kindle their fires in deep glens, on the wildest moors, or on the tops of high hills, there to dance or sit in ring, and hold converse while they devour the plunder of rifled graves with the choicest wines from their neighbors' cellars. Now, some years back, the blacksmith of Yarrowfoot had for apprentices two brothers, both steady lads, and, when bound to him, fine healthy fellows. After a few months, however, the younger of the two began to grow pale and lean, lose his appetite, and show other marks of declining health. His brother, much concerned, often questioned him as to what ailed him, but to no purpose. At last, however, the poor lad burst into an agony of tears and confessed that he was quite worn out, and should soon be brought to the grave by the ill-usage of his mistress, who was in truth a witch, though none suspected it. "Every night," he sobbed out, "she comes to my bedside, puts a magic bridle on me, and changes me into a horse. Then seated on my back, she urges me on for many a mile to the wild moors, where she, and I know not what other vile creatures, hold their hideous feasts. There she keeps me all night, and at early morning I carry her home. She takes off my bridle, and there I am, but so weary I can ill stand. And thus I pass my nights while you are soundly sleeping."

The elder brother at once declared he would take his chance of a night among the witches, so he put the younger one in his own place next the wall, and lay awake himself till the usual time of the witch-woman's arrival. She came, bridle in hand, and flinging it over the elder brother's head, up sprang a fine hunting horse. The lady leaped on his back and started for the trysting place, which on this occasion, as it chanced, was the cellar of a neighboring laird.

While she and the rest of the vile crew were regaling themselves with claret and sack, the hunter, who was left in a spare stall of the stable, rubbed and rubbed his head against the wall till he loosened the bridle, and finally got it off, on which he recovered his human form. Holding the bridle firmly in his hand he concealed himself at the back of the stall till his mistress came within reach, when in an instant he flung the magic bridle over her head, and behold, a fine gray mare! He mounted her and dashed off, riding through hedge and ditch, till, looking down, he perceived she had lost a shoe from one of her forefeet. He took her to the first smithy that was open, had the shoe replaced, and a new one put on the other forefoot, and then rode her up and down a ploughed field till she was nearly worn out. At last he took her home, and pulled the bridle off just in time for her to creep into bed before her husband awoke, and got up for his day's work.

The honest blacksmith arose, little thinking what had been going on all night; but his wife complained of being very ill, almost dying, and begged him to send for a doctor. He accordingly aroused his apprentices; the elder one went out, and soon returned with one whom he had chanced to meet already abroad. The doctor wished to feel his patient's pulse, but she resolutely hid her hands and refused to show them. The village Aesculapius was perplexed; but the husband, impatient at her obstinacy, pulled off the bedclothes, and found, to his horror, that horseshoes were tightly nailed to both hands! On further examination, her sides appeared galled with kicks, the same that the apprentice had given her during his ride up and down the ploughed field.

The brothers now came forward and related all that had passed.

On the following day the witch was tried by the magistrates of Selkirk, and condemned to be burned to death on a stone at the Bullsheugh, a sentence that was promptly carried into effect. It is added that the younger apprentice was at last restored to health by eating butter made from the milk of cows fed in kirkyards, a sovereign remedy for consumption brought on through being witch-ridden.

[7]

Virgilius, the Necromancer

As Virgilius was born, then the town of Rome quaked and trembled. And in his youth he was wise and subtle, and was put to school. . . .

And Virgilius was at school at Tolenten, where he studied diligently, for he was of great understanding. Upon a time the scholars had license to go to play and sport them in the fields after the usance of the old time: and there was Virgilius thereby also, walking among the hills all about. It fortuned he spied a great hole in the side of a great hill, wherein he went so deep that he could not see no more light. And then he went a little further therein, and then he saw some light again, and then went he forth straight. And within a little while after, he heard a voice that called, "Virgilius, Virgilius"; and he looked about and he could not see nobody. Then Virgilius spoke and asked, "Who calleth me?" Then heard he the voice again, but he saw nobody; then said he, "Virgilius, see ye not that little board lying beside you there marked with that word?" Then answered Virgilius, "I see that board well enough."

The voice said, "Do away that board, and let me out thereat."

Then answered Virgilius to the voice that was under the little board, and said, "Who art thou that talkest me so?"

Then answered the devil: "I am a devil conjured out of the body of a certain man, and banished here till the day of judgment, without that I be delivered by the hands of men. Thus, Virgilius, I pray thee deliver me out of this pain, and I shall show unto thee many books of necromancy, and how thou shalt come by it lightly and know the practice therein, that no man in the science of necromancy shall pass thee. And, moreover, I shall show and inform you so that thou shalt have all thy desire, whereby methinks it is a great gift for so little a doing, for ye may also thus all your poor friends help, and cause your enemies to become powerless."

Through that great promise was Virgilius tempted; he bade the fiend show the books to him that he might have and occupy them at his will. And so the fiend showed him, and then Virgilius pulled open a board, and there was a little hole, and thereat wrung the devil out like an eel, and came and stood before Virgilius like a big man. Thereof Virgilius was astoned and marveled greatly thereof that so great a man might come out at so little a hole.

Then said Virgilius, "Could ye well pass into the hole that ye came out of?"

"Yes, I could well," said the devil.

"I hold the best pledge that I have, ye shall not do it."

"Well," said the devil, "thereto I consent."

And then the devil wrung himself into the little hole again, and as he was therein Virgilius covered the hole again with the board close, and so was the devil beguiled and might not there come out again, but there abideth shut still therein.

Then called the devil dreadfully to Virgilius, and said, "What have ye done?"

Virgilius answered, "Abide there still to your day appointed." And from thenceforth abideth he there.

And so Virgilius became very cunning in the practice of the black science. . . .

[Virgilius next wins in a contest against his dishonest relatives and the emperor by means of magic walls of air, light which paralyzes, and an illusory river. He gets revenge on the lady who left him hanging in a basket under her window by forcing her to stand on a scaffold in her shift and permitting every Roman to light his torch on her body. Next he made the statue *Salvatio Romae* and a copper horse and man which destroyed all the night runners and thieves infesting the streets of Rome.

Then after making the unpopular image which took away women's lustful desires, he had a liaison with the sultan's daughter, built Naples on an egg foundation, and defended this his favorite city against the emperor.]

Then made Virgilius at Rome a metal serpent with his cunning, that whosoever put his hand in the throat of the serpent was to swear his cause right and true; and if his cause were false he should not pluck his hand out again. And if it were true they should pluck it out again without any harm doing. So it fortuned that there was a knight of Lombardy that mistrusted his wife with one of his men that was most set by in the conceit of his wife: but she excused herself right nobly and wisely. And she consented to go with him to Rome to that serpent, and there to take her oath that she was not guilty of that, that he put upon her. And thereto consented the knight.

And as they were both in the cart, and also her man with her, she said to the man; that when he came to Rome, that he should clothe him with a fool's coat, and disguise him in such manner that they should not know him, and so did he. And when the day was come that he should come to the serpent, he was there present.

And Virgilius knew the falseness of the woman by his cunning of necromancy. Then said Virgilius to the woman: "Withdraw your oath and swear not."

But she would not do after him, but put her hand into the serpent's mouth. And when her hand was in, she swore before her husband that she had no more to do with him than with that fool, that stood her by; and because she said truth she pulled out her hand again out of the throat of the serpent not hurt. And then departed the knight home and trusted her well ever after.

And Virgilius, having thereat great spite and anger that the woman had so escaped, destroyed the serpent: for thus scaped the lady away from that great danger. And then spoke Virgilius and said: that the women are clever at devising sly artifices, but in goodness they be but innocents.

Thus as Virgilius in his life had done many marvelous and subtile things, and also had promised to the emperor many other diverse things and marvelous: for he promised to make the trees and spices to bear fruit three times in a year: and every tree should have ripe fruit and also blossoms at one time thereon growing: also he should make the ships for to sail against the stream as with the stream at all times: and he would have made the penny to be as lightly got as spent. And these things aforesaid promised Virgilius to the emperor for to do, and many other diverse things that were too long for to rehearse here, if that it fortuned him not to die in the meanwhile.

And after this made Virgilius a goodly castle that had but one going in thereto, and no man might not enter in thereto, but at the one gate, or else not. And also about the same castle flowed there a water and it was impossible for any man there to have any entering. And this castle stood without the city of Rome and this entering of this gate was made with twenty-four iron flails, and on every side was there twelve men on each side, still a piece smiting with the flails never ceasing, the one after the other; and no man might come in, without the flails stood still, but he was slain. And these flails was made with such a gin that Virgilius stopped them when he listed to enter in thereat, but no man else could find the way. And in this castle put Virgilius part of his treasure therein privily; and when this was done he imagined in his mind by what means he might make himself young again, because he thought to live longer many years, to do many wonders and marvelous things.

And upon a time went Virgilius to the emperor, and asked him, of license by the space of three weeks. But the emperor in no wise would grant unto him, for he would have Virgilius at all times by him.

Then heard he that Virgilius went to his house and took with him one of his men that he above all men trusted, and knew well that he would best keep his counsel; and they departed to his castle that was without the town, and when they were afore the castle there saw the man men stand with iron flails in their hands sore smiting.

Then said Virgilius to his man: "Enter you first into the castle."

Then answered the man and said, "If I should enter the flails would slay me."

Then showed Virgilius to the man of each side the entering in and all the devices that thereto belonged; and when he had showed him all the ways, he made cease the flails and went into the castle.

And when they were both in, Virgilius turned the devices again, and so went the iron flails as they did afore.

Then said Virgilius, "My dear beloved friend, and he that I above all men trust, and know most of my secret"; and then led he the man into the cellar where he had made a fair lamp at all seasons burning. And then said Virgilius to the man: "See you the barrel that standeth here?" And he said, "Ye there must put me. First ye must slay me, and hew small to pieces, and cut my head in four pieces, and salt the head under in the bottom, and then the pieces thereafter, and my heart in the middle, and then set the barrel under the lamp, that night and day therein may drop and leak: and ye shall nine days long once in the day fill the lamp, and fail not. And when this is all done, then shall I be renewed and made young again, and live long time and many winters more, if that it fortune me not to be taken off above and die."

And when the man heard his master Virgilius speak thus, he was sore abashed, and said: "That will I never while I live, for in no manner will I slay you."

And then said Virgilius: "Ye at this time must do it, for it shall be no grief unto you."

And at the last Virgilius entreated his man so much, that he consented to him: and then took the servant Virgilius and slew him, and when he was thus slain, he hewed him in pieces and salted him in the barrel, and cut his head in four pieces as his master bade him, and then put the heart in the middle and salted them well: and when all this was done, he hung the lamp right over the barrel, that it might at all times drop in thereto. And when he had done all this, he went out of the castle and turned the devices, and then went the copper men smighting with their flails so strongly upon the iron anvils as they did before, that there durst no man enter: and he came every day to the castle and filled the lamp, as Virgilius had bidden him.

And as the emperor missed Virgilius by the space of seven days, he marveled greatly where he should be; but Virgilius was killed and laid in the cellar by his servant that he loved so well.

And then the emperor thought in his mind to ask Virgilius's servant where Virgilius his master was: and so he did, for he knew well that Virgilius loved him above all men in the world. Then answered the servant to the emperor, and said, "Worshipful lord, an it please your grace I wot not where he is, for it is seven days past that I saw him last; and then went he forth I cannot tell whither, for he would not let me go with him."

Then was the emperor angry with that answer, and said: "Thou lyest, false thief that thou art; but without thou show me shortly where he is, I shall put thee to death."

With those words was the man abashed, and said: "Worshipful lord, seven days ago I went with him without the town to the castle, and there he went in, and there I left him, for he would not let me in with him."

Then said the emperor, "Go with me to the same castle," and so he did; and when they came before the castle and would have entered, they might not, because the flails smote so fast. Then said the emperor: "Make cease these flails, that we may come in."

Then answered the man: "I know not the way."

Then said the emperor, "Then shalt thou die"; and then through the fear of death he turned the device and made the flails stand still, and then the emperor entered into the castle with all his folk, and sought all about in every corner after Virgilius; and at the last they sought so long that they came into the cellar where they saw the lamp hang over the barrel, where Virgilius lay indeed. Then asked the emperor the man: "Who had made himself so hardy as to put his master Virgilius to death?" And the man answered no word to the emperor. And then the emperor, with great anger, drew out his sword, and slew he there Virgilius's man.

And when all this was done, then saw the emperor and all folk a naked child, three times running about the barrel, saying the words: "Cursed be the time that ye came ever here"; and with those words vanished the child away, and was never seen again: and thus abode Virgilius in the barrel, dead.

Then was the emperor very heavy for the death of Virgilius, and also all Virgilius's kindred, and also all the scholars that dwelled about the town of Naples, and in special all the town of Naples, for by cause that Virgilius was the founder thereof, and made it of great worship. Then thought the emperor to have the goods and riches of Virgilius, but there were none so hardy that durst come in to fetch it, for fear of the copper men, that smote so fast with their iron flails: and so abode Virgilius's treasure in the cellar. And Virgilius did many other marvelous things that in this book is not written. And thus God give us grace that we may be in the book of everlasting bliss. Amen.

[8]

Friar Bacon

Roger Bacon's father, a rich farmer of the west of England, was not pleased when his son showed extraordinary interest in his studies. The old man locked up his son's books and gave him a cart whip in place of them, but the boy ran away to Oxford and soon became a famous scholar. The king sent for him, wishing to see him perform some of his magic. Friar Bacon, to delight the sense of hearing, waved his wand and immediately the king, queen, and nobles assembled heard ravishing music. Then to please their sight he caused five dancers to appear, and they danced beautifully. Next he conjured up a table richly covered with all sorts of delicacies: all present ate and praised the tasty dishes. Then the wand brought rich exotic perfumes and furs soft to the touch. This demonstration of magic skill pleased and satisfied the king, and he wished to reward Bacon, but the friar would accept nothing but the king's love and a ring. Just then the gentleman who had ridden to summon Bacon and had not believed the latter when he declared he would get to court two hours ahead of him arrived. The friar had promised to show this gentleman the last wench he had kissed, and when he looked, there stood a greasy kitchenmaid with a basting ladle in her hand. The company laughed to see the gentleman's embarrassment, and Bacon caused her to vanish in thin air.

There was a gentleman of Oxfordshire who through his riotous expenses had wasted a fair inheritance and was now indigent. The Devil, taking advantage of this man's desperate state, tempted him and offered to furnish him with enough money to pay off his debts and more besides provided that as soon as he had paid all debts he should be at the lender's disposal and give himself up on demand. To this the gentleman agreed and the Devil brought the money. Not long after the debts had been paid the Devil came to the man in his study and told him that now the time had come when he must give himself up, as he had agreed. It seems that this gentleman did not yet know who his creditor was, but he was not long in the dark, for when he tried to put him off with some lame excuses, the Devil became very angry and with a fearful noise changed himself into an ugly shape. "Tomorrow morning I will prove that you have lied," he cried, vanishing with a great noise and leaving the gentleman half dead with fear.

After reflecting on his miserable situation, the gentleman resolved to kill himself and would have fallen on his sword had he not met with Friar Bacon. And he told everything to Bacon. And Bacon thought of a way to save the poor man. "Tomorrow meet the Devil without fear," said the friar, "but make him agree to abide by the decision of the first man who comes along, concerning whether you belong to the Devil or no. I will attend to the rest."

In the morning the man went to the wood and found the Devil waiting for him. "I can prove that you have paid all your debts and therefore belong to me," said the Devil.

"You are a deceiver," said the man, "and gave me money to cheat me of my soul. Why otherwise would you be the sole judge in this matter? Let me have some other person to judge between us."

"I agree," said the Devil. "Take anyone you wish."

"Then let it be the next man who comes along."

No sooner were these words spoken but Friar Bacon came by. And they told him the case.

"Tell me," said Bacon to the man, "did you ever pay back to the Devil any of the money he lent you?"

"No. I haven't paid him back anything."

"Then never do, and you are a free man," said the friar. Turning to the Devil, he said, "Deceiver of mankind, it was your agreement never to bother him as long as he was indebted to anyone. Now how can you ask anything of him when he is still indebted to you for all the money you lent him? So I charge you to be gone."

At this the Devil vanished with a great noise, and Friar Bacon comforted the gentleman.

Now the friar's next adventure had to do with making a brazen head, for he thought if he could make such a head speak (and hear it when it spoke) he might wall all England about with brass and so protect the country from invaders. To assist him he got one Friar Bungay, a great scholar and magician. So they made the brazen head but did not know how to make its parts move so that it could speak. They decided to raise a spirit to teach them what they could not get from their books. Going to a near-by wood, they went through the proper ceremonies and spoke the words of conjuration. Immediately the Devil appeared and asked what they wanted. They told him, but at first he would not help them. Then they threatened him and he told them that if they would subject the head to the continual fume of the six hottest simples, it would have motion and speak at some time within the next month. If they did not hear it speak, all their labor would be lost. Having learned this, they let the Devil depart.

The two friars followed the Devil's directions, but after three weeks of waiting for the head to speak, they were so weary that they had to get some rest and sleep. So they gave the watch over to their servant Miles. Miles, however, although he had the best intentions in the world, was too simple. When the head said, "TIME IS," and then stopped, he did not wake his masters, fearing they would be angry with him if he did. When it later said, "TIME WAS," he still hesitated. Then the head spoke, saying, "TIME IS PAST," and fell down. A terrible noise and flashes of fire frightened Miles almost to death and woke the two friars. And when they saw what had happened, they knew that they had lost all their labor. They scolded Miles and struck him dumb for a whole month, but that did not do any good.

The next venture, however, was successful. After a discourse on the wonderful powers of science and magic, with mention of landships, airships, and underwater boats, Friar Bacon got the king's permission to use mathematical glasses in the siege of a French town. The friar set fire to the town and forced the French to surrender. The French ambassador, being well pleased by the kindly treatment given him by the English and wishing to entertain them, sent for a German conjurer named Vandermast. The king immediately sent for Friars Bacon and Bungay. There was a great banquet, and when it was over Vandermast asked the king if he desired to see the spirit of anyone who had died. And the king told him he wished to see Pompey the Great, who could abide no equal. So Vandermast by his art raised Pompey, armed just as he was when slain in the battle of Pharsalia. Everyone present marveled at this spectacle. But Friar Bacon then raised the ghost of Julius Caesar, who could abide no superior and had slain Pompey. At the sight of him all were amazed, and Vandermast declared that there was some magician present whom he wished to see. Then Bacon came forward and said, "I raised Caesar, Vandermast, to please those present here and to conquer your Pompey, which he will now do again." Then Caesar began to fight Pompey, and all were pleased except Vandermast. At last Caesar overcame Pompey and both spirits vanished.

"My lord ambassador," said the king, "it seems to me that my Englishman has put down your German. Cannot he do better than this?"

"I will put down your Englishman," cried Vandermast. "Therefore, Bacon, prepare your best art."

"It will not take much to beat you at this game," replied Bacon. "Try your art with my inferior, Friar Bungay, and if you beat him, I will deal with you."

After some turning and looking in his book, Friar Bungay then brought up the Hesperian Tree with its golden apples. And a dragon guarded the apples. "Now Vandermast," he cried, "find someone who dares to gather the fruit."

Then Vandermast raised the ghost of Hercules, and he had his club on his shoulder. "Here is one," said Vandermast, "who will gather these apples. Now again he will do what he did when alive—gather the fruit and make the dragon crouch."

As Hercules was going to pluck the fruit, Friar Bacon held up his wand. At this Hercules stopped and seemed fearful. When Vandermast threatened him, Hercules cried, "I cannot pluck the fruit and I dare not, for great Bacon stands here. His charms are far more powerful than yours, and I must obey him." Then Vandermast cursed Hercules, but Bacon laughed and said, "O Vandermast, do not become angry. As Hercules will do nothing at your command, I will have him do you some service at mine." And Bacon ordered

Hercules to carry Vandermast home to Germany. The Devil obeyed and, taking Vandermast on his back, disappeared with him.

"Stop, friar," cried the ambassador. "I would not lose Vandermast for half my domain." "Do not be alarmed," replied Bacon; "I have only sent him home to see his wife, and before long he may return."

The King of England then thanked Bacon and forced him to accept some gifts.

Some time after this Friar Bacon sat in his study and looked over all the dangers that were to happen to him that month. And he saw that Vandermast, who was bent on revenge, had hired a Walloon soldier to come and kill him. To avoid this danger Bacon always held a ball of brass in his hand, and beneath he placed a brazen basin so that if he perchance fell asleep while reading, the ball would fall on the basin and the noise would wake him. Now this really happened and Bacon awoke and found the Walloon standing there with his sword drawn. Bacon talked with him and he admitted that Vandermast had sent him on this murderous mission. Then discovering that this villain did not believe in Hell, Bacon raised the ghost of Julian the Apostate, who came up with his body burning and so full of wounds that he frightened the soldier almost out of his wits. And Bacon made Julian tell his sad history and describe the torments of Hell.

While this was going on the soldier stood there shaking and perspiring. Then falling to his knees, he asked Bacon to instruct him in a better course of life than that he had led. Bacon did this, and giving him money, sent him to the war in the Holy Land, where he was slain.

On another occasion three thieves forced their way into Friar Bacon's house and demanded money. Seeing that they were resolute, Bacon gave each a hundred pounds and requested them to tarry a moment and hear some of Miles's music. So Miles played lustily on his tabor and pipe. Immediately the robbers fell to dancing against their will and they could not stop. Miles led them out of the house and into the fields as they danced in a wild ludicrous manner. And they followed the music through water and mire. Finally being utterly exhausted, and coated with mud, they fell to the ground and went to sleep. Then Miles ceased playing, and taking the money away from them, sang them a song of farewell, one stanza of which runs:

> You roaring boys, and sturdy thieves,
> You pimps and apple squires:
> Lament the case of these poor knaves,
> And warm them by your fires.

Not long after this Friar Bacon played Cupid. Friar Bungay, being covetous, plotted with a certain knight to marry him to the fair maid Millisant, who loved another. Her beloved, not finding her at home one day, ran to Bacon for help. And the good friar took pity on him and showed him a magic glass which made visible anything within a fifty-mile range.

The lover, gazing in the glass, saw Millisant standing with a knight in a chapel and Bungay was about to marry them. Bacon, comforting the lover, took him along in an enchanted chair, and they sailed through the air. Arriving at the chapel, Bacon struck Bungay dumb and he could not finish the marriage ceremony. Then the good friar, raising a magic mist in the chapel, took Millisant away from the knight, who could see nothing, and led her to her lover. And they both wept for joy. Later Bacon married them and entertained them at the wedding supper with a magic masque. At first was heard sweet still music: then came a wind music. Next three apes and three monkeys, all carrying torches, entered and danced in such an odd manner that all the beholders split their sides laughing. Then the grotesque creatures departed. And the grateful bridegroom knew that it was Friar Bacon's art that gave them this grace to their wedding.

Vandermast, supposing Friar Bacon dead, came to England and met Friar Bungay in Kent. And the German magician took Bungay's horse out of the stable and left a spirit which looked like it in its place. In the morning Friar Bungay mounted this spirit and rode forth, but on crossing a stream his steed suddenly dissolved into thin air and he fell into the water. He returned dripping wet to the inn. Vandermast, meeting him at the door, asked, "Why, is this the time of year when one goes swimming here?"

"If I had been as well horsed as you were when Friar Bacon sent you to Germany," said Bungay, "I would have escaped this bath." At this Vandermast bit his lips and said no more, but went inside.

Now Vandermast loved a fair maid who dwelt in this inn, and he had sought many times to win her for gold, love, or promises. Bungay, who knew of this affair, plotted to get even with Vandermast. So he created a spirit which looked just like the maid, and Vandermast persuaded this spirit maid to come to his chamber that night. He was jubilant but his joy turned to sorrow and his wanton hopes into a bad night's lodging, for Bungay had by his art spread such a sheet on his bed that no sooner did Vandermast and his paramour lie on it than it carried them through the air and let them fall into a deep pond. The German swam to the bank and shook himself like a water spaniel. But he was lost and spent the night walking about to keep warm. When in the morning he returned to the inn, Friar Bungay asked him, "Did you like your bath?"

"So much," replied Vandermast, "that I wish you had one just like it."

Thus did they continually vex each other, both in words and ill actions. Vandermast then challenged Bungay to a contest at the diabolical art of magic to ascertain which of them was the most cunning and had the most power over the Devil. So they went to a field and each drew a circle. By his magic Vandermast raised up a fiery dragon which ran about the rim of Bungay's circle and with the flames which issued from his mouth scorched the friar. Then the latter raised up the sea monster which Perseus had killed long ago, and this creature squirted out floods of water and almost drowned Vandermast. Bungay got rid of the fiery dragon by conjuring up the spirit of Saint George, and his rival raised Perseus to slay the sea monster.

Each now summoned his Devil and asked for assistance in a supreme test of strength, and each Devil demanded three drops of blood from each magician as his price. Having given the Devils this blood, both fell again to their conjurations. Bungay raised Achilles with his Greeks, and they marched around Vandermast and threatened him. As a defense against these soldiers, Vandermast raised Hector and his Trojans. Then there was a great tempest with thunder and lightning, and both conjurers wished heartily that they were elsewhere. But wishes were in vain, for the time had come when the Devil demanded his pay for the knowledge he had lent them. He would delay no longer but took them at the height of their wickedness and bereft them of their lives. When the terrible tempest ended, the townsmen found the bodies of Vandermast and Bungay breathless and strangely burnt with fire. The first had Christian burial because he was a foreigner and the second because he was a friar. And so two famous conjurers came to the end of their lives.

One day two young men came to Bacon and asked the use of his magic glass. Looking into it they saw their fathers trying to kill each other. And this sight made the young men enemies. Drawing their daggers, they slew each other. This tragedy moved Bacon so deeply that he broke his rare and wonderful glass. "O wretched me," he cried, "wretched in my knowledge, for my art has been the ruin of these two gentlemen." And he blamed himself for studying those things that were so contrary to his order and his soul's health. He then made a great fire and burned his books of magic and turned anchorite. And he lived in a narrow cell cut in a church wall till his death.

X

SAINTS AND SINNERS

Some saints play a very important role in folklore. Accounts of their lives are called saints' legends, and the life stories of their opposites, the sinners, can be called anti-legends.

"The Legend of Saint George" is the editor's version (slightly shortened) of the account in the *Golden Legend* of Jacobus de Voragine. "Piers Shonks, the Dragon Killer of Hertfordshire" is from W. B. Gerish's *A Hertfordshire St. George*, 1905. "Saint Romuald" is from J. P. Andrews' *Anecdotes, Antient and Modern*, 1790. "Doctor Faustus" is from John Ashton's *Chap-books of the Eighteenth Century*, 1882, and "The Wandering Jew" is the editor's prose rendering of a poem in Paul Lacroix's *Curiosités de l'Histoire des Croyances Populaires au Moyen Age*, 1857. "The *Flying Dutchman*, or Vanderdecken's Message Home" is from *Legends of Terror*, 1826, and was originally printed in *Blackwood's Magazine*. "The Beggar's Curse" can be found in W. Branch Johnson's *Folktales of Brittany*, 1927, and is printed by permission of Methuen and Company, Ltd.

[1]

The Legend of Saint George

George he shaved the dragon's beard
And Askelon was his razor.

George was a native of Cappadocia and served in the Roman army with the rank of tribune. One day he came to Silena, a town in the province of Libya. Near this place there was a vast lake which was the haunt of a ferocious dragon. This monster had put to flight a band of armed men: he prowled about the city walls and with his breath slew every living thing which came near him. To keep him away from the town, the citizens gave him two sheep each day. If they failed to do this, he assailed the town walls, infected the air with his poisonous breath and killed many people. But as time went on, to provide two sheep each day became increasingly difficult. Finally it was decreed that a human being, chosen by lot, was to be substituted for one of the sheep. Before long boys and girls, and even infants had to be used. No one was spared.

Now one day the lot fell upon the daughter of the king. If his daughter could be spared, the king offered to give all his gold and silver—even the half of his kingdom—but the people would hear none of it. They reminded him that it was his edict that was destroying their children and insisted that no exception be made for the princess. They even threatened to burn him and his palace. Realizing that his daughter was doomed, he began to weep her sad fate. However, the people granted a delay of eight days, but when these had passed they came to the palace and cried, "Why are you destroying your people to save your daughter? The breath of this monster will slay us all."

So the king prepared to give up his dear daughter. Covering her with royal garments, he kissed her and said, "Alas, dear daughter, I had hoped to see myself reborn in your children, to invite royalty to your wedding, to adorn you with resplendent robes and delight you with the sound of flutes, tambourines, and other musical instruments. But instead a dragon is going to devour you! Oh! why did not I die before this misfortune came upon us?" And tears fell from his eyes as he gave her his blessing and pressed her tenderly in his arms. Then she walked out resolutely toward the lake.

George, who was passing that way, saw that she was weeping and asked her what troubled her. "Good young man," she said, "quickly get back on your horse and flee away or you will perish with me."

"Do not be afraid," said George, "and tell me what you await here and why all these people are looking at us?"

"I perceive," said she, "that your heart is great and noble, but hurry away."

"I will not leave," said he, "until you explain your situation." When she had told him everything, he comforted her and promised to help her.

"O brave knight," she begged, "do not run the risk of dying with me. Only one victim is required and you will perish too if you try to save me."

At that moment the monstrous dragon emerged from the water. The trembling maiden cried, "Flee quickly, O knight!" For answer George mounted his horse, made the sign of the cross, approached the monster, and fearlessly charged. He struck with his lance with such force that he pierced the serpent through and through and laid it low. Then, turning to the king's daughter, he asked her to throw her girdle around the monster's neck and fear nought. She did this and the monster followed her like a gentle dog. When this strange trio appeared in town, the people took to the hills, shouting that everyone was going to be destroyed. But George assured them that there was no danger. "The Lord," he said, "has sent me to deliver you from the dragon. Believe in the Lord, be baptized, and I will slay the monster." Then the king and all his subjects were baptized. George drew forth Askelon, his sword, and severed the monster's head. And four yoke of oxen dragged the carcass away. The grateful king now built a goodly church, and from the altar flowed a stream of water which cured any sick person who drank it. . . .

Now at that time Diocletian and Maximian ruled, and they ordered the proconsul Dacian to persecute the Christians. Indeed, he persecuted them so cruelly that within a month twelve thousand of them had won the crown of martyrdom. As might be expected, among those who were tortured there were a few who backslid and sacrificed to the idols. When George saw how the people were being persecuted, he was deeply grieved. Giving all his possessions to the poor and exchanging his knight's costume for the simple clothing of a Christian, he rushed into the public square and shouted, "All the pagan gods are but demons and our God alone is the creator of heavens and earth."

And the authorities questioned him, thinking him impudent and foolhardy. "My name is George," he said, "and I come from a noble family in Cappadocia. By the grace of God, I followed the wars in Palestine, and now I have given up everything to be better able to serve the God of heaven."

When he saw that his words would have no effect upon George, the proconsul ordered his men to attach the saint to a cross which was shaped like the letter U. And his flesh was torn by iron hooks and burned by flaming torches. And the wounds from out of which his vitals started were rubbed with salt. But when night came our Lord appeared to Saint George in a dream and this sweet vision comforted him so much that he ceased fearing other torments.

When Dacian understood that torture would not break Saint George's will, the tyrant went to the house of a sorcerer and told him that Christians scorned both the sorcerer's magic and his gods. "You may cut off my head," cried the sorcerer, "if I cannot conquer this man." Then after preparing his magical spells and calling upon his gods for help, he put poison in a cup of wine and gave it to Saint George, who, having made the sign of the cross, swallowed the potion without suffering any ill consequences whatsoever. And the same thing happened again even though the sorcerer doubled the amount of poison. When he saw this, he fell at the feet of the saint, begged his pardon, and asked to be made a Christian. But the judge ordered the wizard's head cut off and had Saint George bound to a wheel which was fitted on all sides with two-edged swords. At the first turn, however, the wheel fell apart and Saint George was not harmed. Then the proconsul was furious and commanded that his prisoner be thrown into a kettle of molten lead. But Saint George, after crossing himself, found the lead like lukewarm water.

Now Dacian decided to change his tactics and seduce George with honeyed words.

"George, my dear son," said he, "see how our gods have favored you, for they have sustained you during your ordeals. You blaspheme against them, yet they will pardon you if you will but believe in them. My dear child, do what I ask of you. Give up your false religion, sacrifice to our gods, and great honors will be bestowed on you by both them and me." George smiled and said, "Why didn't you speak to me like this before torturing me? I am inclined to do what you wish me to." Then Dacian was happy and published it widely that George was going to renounce Christianity and sacrifice to the pagan gods.

And the whole city shared the joy of the proconsul and came to the temple where George had been brought. He kneeled and prayed to the Lord, beseeching him to destroy everything in the temple, as much for his own glory as to convert the heathen. Instantly lightning came down and burned the temple, the idols, and the priests. And the earth opened wide and swallowed all that was left. . . .

When news of this catastrophe came to Dacian, he had George brought before him. "Most perverse of men," cried the tyrant, "what crimes have you not committed?" And Saint George twitted him, saying, "If you do not believe what you have been told, come with me and you shall see me sacrifice to your gods again."

"Your scheme is too obvious," said Dacian. "You wish now to destroy me just as you destroyed my temple and my gods."

"Tell me, pitiful creature," said George, "how you can save your gods from destruction when they cannot save themselves." This remark vexed Dacian extremely and he said to his wife, Alexandria, "This man has humiliated me so much, that I could die."

"Cruel and sanguinary tyrant," answered she, "how many times have I begged you not to persecute the Christians? Do you not know that their God fights for them? Know that now I wish to become a Christian."

"Alas," cried the astonished tyrant, "have you too let them seduce you?"

Then he had her hung up by the hair and cruelly whipped with steel rods. While she was being beaten, she turned to Saint George and said, "O light of truth! Tell me where my soul will go, for I have not been baptized."

"Dear woman, fear nothing," answered Saint George. "The blood that streams from your wounds will be sufficient substitute for baptism. You are worthy of the crown you will receive." And Alexandria died saying her prayers. . . . The day after this Saint George was dragged through the city streets and and then decapitated. In his last prayer he begged the Lord to grant that whoever should implore help and call on Saint George might have his request fulfilled; and this was accorded him. And when Dacian returned to his palace, lightning came down from heaven and pulverized both him and his wicked ministers.

[2]

Piers Shonks, the Dragon Killer of Hertfordshire

The Pelham district was troubled by an enormous dragon that committed great havoc with the flocks and herds of the neighborhood. Piers Shonks, a valiant man and a renowned hunter, determined to destroy the reptile; therefore fully armed with his hounds, so swift of foot that they were said to be winged, he sallied forth in search of the monster. The dogs soon gave tongue, and by their attacks and noise so distracted the attention of the dragon that it gave Piers an opportunity to thrust his spear into a vulnerable part and speedily dispatch it. The instant the death struggles ceased, the Evil One appeared, vowing vengeance on our hero for having destroyed his emissary, and threatening to have Shonks after his death, body and soul, whether buried in the church or out. Shonks modestly replied that his soul was his Maker's, and, as to his body, that should never be the Evil One's, for his burial would not be in the church or outside. Many years after the great event of his life, feeling his end drawing nigh, he called for bow and arrow and shot a shaft in the direction of the church. The arrow passed through the window on the south side of the chancel and struck the wall of the nave on the north side. In this wall, therefore, Piers directed his body to be buried, and expressed the wish that a representation of his achievement should be carved upon his tomb.

[3]

Saint Romuald

Romuald, born at Ravenna, of noble parentage, embraced toward the middle of the tenth century the state of a hermit under the direction of a solitary whose severity at least equaled his piety. Romuald bore for a long time without a murmur the repeated thumps which he received from his holy teacher, but observing that they were continually directed to his *left* side, "Honor my *right* ear, my dear master," said he meekly, "with some of your attention, for I have nearly lost the use of my *left* ear through your partiality to that side." Romuald, when he became master of his own conduct, showed that he could on occasion copy the rigor of his preceptor, for hearing that his own father, who had embraced the monastic life, entertained thoughts of re-entering the world again, he hurried to the monastery and by the rhetoric of a very hearty drubbing, brought his unsteady parent over to a more settled way of thinking.

St. Romuald underwent a singular species of peril from his own reputed sanctity and from the fanatical respect borne to him by his neighbors. He had long resided in Catalonia; but, when he declared his intention of quitting that country, the inhabitants, rendered almost desperate by the dread of losing this holiest of anchorets, consulted together and determined to cut the good saint's throat, that they might at least be sure of that share of miracles which the bones of so eminently pious a man might work among them. The result of this conference chancing to reach the ears of Romuald, he made a private and speedy retreat from Spain, choosing not by any means to be made into relics before his time.

[4]

Doctor Faustus

Dr. John Faustus was born in Germany: his father was a poor laboring man, not able to give him any manner of education; but he had a brother in the country, a rich man, who having no child of his own, took a fancy to his nephew and resolved to make him a scholar. Accordingly he put him to a grammar school, where he took learning extraordinary well; and afterward to the university to study divinity. But Faustus, not liking that employment, betook himself to the study of necromancy and conjuration, in which arts he made such a proficiency that in a short time none could equal him. However, he studied divinity so far, that he took his doctor's degree in that faculty; after which he threw the Scripture from him and followed his own inclinations.

Faustus, whose restless mind studied day and night, dressed his imagination with the wings of an eagle and endeavored to fly all over the world, and see and know the secrets of heaven and earth. In short, he obtained power to command the Devil to appear before him whenever he pleased.

One day as Dr. Faustus was walking in a wood near Wirtemberg in Germany, having a friend with him who was desirous to see his art and requested him to let him see if he could then and there bring Mephistopheles before them. The doctor immediately called, and the Devil at the first summons made such a hideous noise in the wood as if heaven and earth were coming together. And after this made a roaring as if the wood had been full of wild beasts. Then the doctor made a circle for the Devil, which he danced round with a noise like that of ten thousand wagons running upon paved stones. After this it thundered and lightened as if the world had been at an end.

Faustus and his friend, amazed at the noise and frightened at the Devil's long stay, would have departed; but the Devil cheered them with such music as they never heard before. This so encouraged

Faustus that he began to command Mephistopheles, in the name of the Prince of Darkness, to appear in his own likeness; on which in an instant hung over his head a mighty dragon. Faustus called him again, as he was used, after which there was a cry in the wood as if Hell had been opened and all the tormented souls had been there. Faustus in the meantime asked the Devil many questions and commanded him to show a great many tricks.

Then Faustus commanded the Spirit to meet him at his own house by ten o'clock the next day. At the hour appointed he came into his chamber demanding what he would have? Faustus told him it was his will and pleasure to conjure him to be obedient to him in all points of these articles, viz.

First, that the Spirit should serve him in all things he asked, from that time till death.

Secondly, whosoever he would have, the Spirit should bring him.

Thirdly. Whatsoever he desired for to know he should tell him.

The Spirit told him he had no such power of himself, until he had acquainted his prince that ruled over him. For, said he, we have rulers over us who send us out and call us home when they will; and we can act no farther than the power we receive from Lucifer, who you know for his pride was thrust out of heaven. But I can tell you no more, unless you bind yourself to us. I will have my request, replied Faustus, and yet not be damned with you. Then said the Spirit, you must not, nor shall not have your desire, and yet thou art mine and all the world cannot save thee from my power. Then get you hence, said Faustus, and I conjure thee that thou come to me at night again.

Then the Spirit vanished, and Doctor Faustus began to consider by what means he could obtain his desires without binding himself to the Devil. While Faustus was in these cogitations, night drew on, and then the Spirit appeared, acquainting him that now he had orders from his prince to be obedient to him and to do for him what he desired, and bid him show what he would have. Faustus replied, his desire was to become a spirit, and that Mephistopheles should always be at his command; that whenever he pleased he should appear invisible to all men. The Spirit answered, his request should be granted if he would sign the articles pronounced to him, viz. That

Faustus should give himself over body and soul to Lucifer, deny his Belief, and become an enemy to all good men; and that the writings should be made with his own blood. Faustus agreeing to all this, the Spirit promised he should have his heart's desire, and the power to turn into any shape, and have a thousand spirits at command.

The Spirit, appearing in the morning to Faustus, told him, that now he was come to see the writing executed and give him power. Whereupon Faustus took out a knife, pricked a vein in his left arm, and drew blood, with which he wrote as follows:

I, John Faustus, Doctor in Divinity, do openly acknowledge that in all my studying of the course of nature and the elements, I could never attain to my desire; I, finding men unable to assist me, have made my addresses to the Prince of Darkness, and his messenger Mephistopheles, giving them both soul and body, on condition that they fully execute my desires; the which they have promised me. I do also further grant by these presents, that if I be duly served, when and in what place I command, and have everything that I ask for during the space of twenty-four years, then I agree that at the expiration of the said term, you shall do with Me and Mine, Body and Soul, as you please. Hereby protesting, that I deny God and Christ and all the host of heaven. And as for the further consideration of this my writing, I have subscribed it with my own hand, sealed it with my own seal, and writ it with my own blood.

John Faustus

No sooner had Faustus set his name to the writing but his spirit Mephistopheles appeared all wrapt in fire, and out of his mouth issued fire; and in an instant came a pack of hounds in full cry. Afterward came a bull dancing before him, then a lion and a bear fighting. All these and many spectacles more did the spirit present to the doctor's view, concluding with all manner of music, and some hundreds of spirits dancing before him. This being ended, Faustus looking about saw seven sacks of silver, which he went to dispose of, but could not handle himself, it was so hot.

This diversion so pleased Faustus that he gave Mephistopheles the writing he had made, and kept a copy of it in his own hands. The Spirit and Faustus being agreed, they dwelt together, and the Devil was never absent from his councils.

Faustus having sold his soul to the Devil, it was soon reported among the neighbors, and no one would keep him company but his Spirit, who was frequently with him, playing of strange tricks to please him.

Not far from Faustus's house lived the Duke of Bavaria, the Bishop of Salzburg, and the Duke of Saxony, whose houses and cellars Mephistopheles used to visit and bring from thence the best provision their houses afforded. One day the Duke of Bavaria had invited most of the gentry of that country to dinner. In an instant came Mephistopheles and took all with him, leaving them full of admiration.

If at any time Faustus had a mind for wild or tame fowl, the Spirit would call whole flocks in at the window. He also taught Faustus to do the like so that no locks nor bolts could hinder them. The Devil also taught Faustus to fly in the air, and act many things that are incredible, and too large for this book to contain.

After Faustus had had a long conference with the Spirit concerning the fall of Lucifer, the state and condition of the fallen angels, he in a dream saw Hell and the devils.

Having seen this sight, he marveled much at it, and having Mephistopheles at his side, he asked him what sort of people they were who lay in the first dark pit? Mephistopheles told him they were those who pretended to be physicians and had poisoned many thousands in trying practices; and now, said the Spirit, they have the very same administered unto them which they prescribed to others, though not with the same effect; for here, said he, they are denied the happiness to die. Over their heads were long shelves full of vials and galipots of poison.

Having passed by them, he came to a long entry exceeding dark, where was a great crowd; I asked what they were? and the Spirit told me they were pickpockets, who, because they loved to be in a crowd in the other world, were also crowded here together. Among these were some padders on the highway, and others of that function.

Walking farther I saw many thousand vintners and some millions of tailors; insomuch there was scarce room enough for them in the place destined for their reception.

A little farther the Spirit opened a cellar door from which issued a smoke almost enough to choke me, with a dismal noise; I asked what they were, and the Spirit told me, they were witches, such as had been pretended saints in the other world, but now having lost their veil, they squabble, fight, and tear one another.

A few steps farther I espied a great number almost hid with smoke; and I asked who they were? The Spirit told me they were millers and bakers; but, good lack! what a noise was there among them! the miller cried to the baker and the baker to the miller for help, but all in vain, for there was none that could help them.

Passing on farther I saw thousands of shopkeepers, some of whom I knew, who were tormented for defrauding and cheating their customers.

Having taken this prospect of Hell, my Spirit Mephistopheles took me up in his arms and carried me home to my own house, where I awaked, amazed at what I had seen in my dream.

Being come to myself I asked Mephistopheles in what place Hell was? He answered, know thou that before the Fall, Hell was ordained: as for the substance or extent of Hell, we devils do not know it; but it is the wrath of God that makes it so furious.

Thirteen students meeting seven more near Faustus's house fell to words and at length to blows; the thirteen were took hard for the seven. The doctor, looking out at a window, saw the fray, and seeing how much the seven were overmatched by the thirteen, he conjured them all blind, so that they could not see each other; and in this manner they continued to fight, and so smote each other as made the public laugh heartily. At length he parted them, leading them all to their own homes, where they immediately recovered their sight, to the great astonishment of all.

There was a gallant young gentleman that was in love with a fair lady, who was of a proper personage, living at Wirtemberg near the doctor's house. This gentleman had long sought this lady in marriage, but could not obtain his desire; and having placed his affections so much upon her, he was ready to pine away, and had certainly died with grief had he not made his affairs known to the doctor, to whom he opened the whole matter. No sooner had the gentleman told his case to the doctor, but he bid him not fear, for his desire should be fulfilled, and he should have her he so much admired, and that the gentlewoman should love none but him, which was done accordingly; for Faustus so changed the mind of the damsel by his practices, that she could think of nothing else but him, whom she before hated; and Faustus's device was thus: He gave him an enchanted ring, which he ordered him to slip on her finger, which he did: and no sooner was it on but her affections began to change and her heart burned with love toward him. She instead of frowns could do nothing else but smile on him, and could not be at rest till she had asked him if he thought he could love her, and make her a good husband. He gladly answered "yes," and he should think he was the happiest man alive; so they were married the next day, and proved a very happy couple.

Faustus walking in the market place saw seven jolly women sitting all on a row, selling butter and eggs; of each of them he bought something and departed; but no sooner was he gone but all their butter and eggs were gone out of their baskets, they knew not how. At last they were told that Faustus had conjured all their goods away; whereupon they ran in haste to the doctor's house and demanded satisfaction for their wares. He resolved to make sport for the townspeople; made them put off all their clothes and dance naked to their baskets; whereupon everyone saw her goods safe and found herself in a humor to put her clothes on again.

Faustus, as he was going one day to Wirtemberg, overtook a country fellow driving a herd of swine, which were very headstrong, some running one way and some another way, so that the driver could not tell how to get them along. Faustus, taking notice of it, made every one of them dance upon their hind legs, with a fiddle in one of their fore feet and a bow in the other, and so dance and fiddle all the way to Wirtemberg, the countryman dancing all the way before them, which made the people wonder. After Faustus had satisfied himself with this sport, he conjured the fiddles away; and the countryman, offering his pigs for sale, soon sold them and got the money; but before he was gone out of the house, Faustus conjured the pigs out of the market and sent them to the countryman's house. The man who had bought them, seeing the swine gone, stopped the man that sold them and forced him to give back the money; on which he returned home very sorrowful, not knowing what to do; but to his great surprise found all the pigs in their sties.

Faustus, having spun out his twenty-four years within a month or two, began to consider what he could do to cheat the Devil, to whom he had made over both body and soul, but he could find no ways to frustrate his miserable end; which now was drawing near. Whereupon in a miserable tone he cried out, O lamentable wretch that I am! I have given myself to the Devil for a few years' pleasure to gratify my carnal and devilish appetites, and now I must pay full dear. Now I must have torment without end. Woe is me, for there is none to help me; I dare not, I cannot look for mercy from God, for I have abandoned him; I have denied him to be my God, and given up myself to the Devil to be his forever; and now the time is almost expired, and I must be tormented forever and ever.

Faustus's full time being come, the Spirit appeared to him, and showed him the writings, and told him that the next day the Devil would fetch him away. This made the doctor's heart to ache; but to divert himself he sent for some doctors, masters, and bachelors of arts, and other students to dine with him, for whom he provided a great store of varieties, with music and the like; but all would not keep up his spirits, for his hour drew near. Whereupon his countenance changing, the doctors asked the reason for his confusion? To which Faustus answered, O! my friends, you have known me these many years, and that I practiced all manner of wickedness. I have been a great conjurer, which art I obtained from the Devil; selling myself to him soul and body, for the term of twenty-four years; which time expiring tonight is the cause of my sorrow. I have called you, my friends, to see my miserable end; and I pray let my fate be a warning to you all not to attempt to search farther into the secrets of nature than is permitted to be known to man, lest your searches lead you to the Devil, to whom I must this night go, whether I will or no.

About twelve o'clock at night the house shook so terribly that they all feared it would have tumbled down on their heads, and suddenly the doors and windows were broke to pieces, and a great hissing was heard as though the house had been full of snakes; Faustus in the meantime calling out for help but all in vain. There was a vast roaring in the hall, as if all the devils in Hell had been there; and then they vanished, leaving the hall besprinkled with blood, which was most terrible to behold.

[5]

The Wandering Jew

Nothing on earth is more extraordinary than the fate of the poor Wandering Jew. How awful his sad lot! One day not long ago some kindly citizens of Brussels in Brabant saw him passing through the city, and they accosted him. Never before had they seen such a long beard! And his clothes were all out of shape and hung loosely on his frame. Their cut led one to suppose that he had bought them long ago in a far-off city. He was foreign in appearance and like a laborer wore an apron. And they addressed him: "Good day, master! Would you be so kind as to give us the pleasure of your company for a short while? Please do not refuse us. Could you walk a little slower for a moment or two?"

"Oh, sirs," he answered, "I swear on my honor I have had much misfortune in my life. Never do I stop—neither here nor elsewhere. Whether it be fair weather or foul, I keep on the march."

"O venerable father, please enter this tavern and have a cool stein of beer. We will entertain you as well as we can."

"Sirs, I accept and will drink two rounds with you, but I cannot sit down. I must always remain standing. In truth, your kindness is somewhat disconcerting."

"Sire, we would like to know how old you are. Judging from your countenance, you must be very old indeed. You are at least a hundred, are you not?"

"Yes, old age is my torment. I am more than seventeen hundred and thirty years old. When Christ was born, I was a little more than twelve."

"Are not you the man about whom there is so much talk and whom the scriptures call Isaac, the Wandering Jew?"

"My name is Isaac Laquedem, and Jerusalem, that famous city, was my birthplace. Yes, my children, I am the Wandering Jew. O just Heaven, how painful is my perpetual traveling. Fifty times have I encircled this globe. Every one else dies when his time comes, but I must live on and on eternally. I cross the seas, the streams, the forests, the valleys, the plains, the hills, and the mountains. It makes little difference to me where I go: one road is as good as another. Both in Europe and Asia I have seen armed conflicts and terrible battles that cost many lives. And never did I get a scratch! In both America and Africa I have seen thousands die, but death will have no dealings with me. Without either land or gold—I have just a few pennies in my purse—I am without means of support. And no matter what the time or where the place, it is always the same."

"O sire," cried the men of Brussels, "we were wont to take your story for an idle tale and your awful ordeal for vain imagination, but now we know it for the truth. You must have sinned greatly. Otherwise the just and kind Lord would not have punished you so cruelly. Tell us your crime."

"Cruel insolence was the cause of my misfortune. Oh, when my sin will have been blotted out, how happy I shall be. I was harsh and overbearing to my Savior. As he was carrying the cross along the road to Calvary, he addressed me gently and begged permission to rest himself for a moment. But I—what a brutal fool—called him malefactor and forbade him to pause before my dwelling. 'You disgrace me,' I cried; 'do not tarry here.' And Jesus, who is all goodness, sighed and said, 'You shall never rest until more than a thousand years have passed. You shall wander without ceasing until the Last Judgment brings your travail to an end.' Gentlemen, that very instant I was forced to bid my home farewell. Filled with sorrow and pain I began my eternal journeying. Since that day I have been wandering, wandering both day and night. And now, kind sirs, it is time to depart. When I pause I become restless: when I start off again, I feel some relief. For your hospitality thanks, and God be with you all."

[6]

The Flying Dutchman, *or* *Vanderdecken's Message Home*

Our ship, after touching at the Cape, went out again, and soon losing sight of the Table Mountain, began to be assailed by the impetuous attacks of the sea, which is well known to be more formidable there than in most parts of the known ocean. The day had grown dull and hazy, and the breeze, which had formerly blown fresh, now sometimes subsided almost entirely, and then recovering its strength for a short time, and changing its direction, blew with temporary violence, and died away again, as if exercising a melancholy caprice. A heavy swell began to come from the southeast. Our sails flapped against the masts, and the ship rolled from side to side, as heavily as if she had been waterlogged. There was so little wind that she would not steer.

About 2 P.M. we had a squall, accompanied by thunder and rain. The seamen, growing restless, looked anxiously ahead. They said we would have a dirty night of it, and that it would not be worth while to turn in to their hammocks. As the second mate was describing a gale he had encountered off Cape Race, Newfoundland, we were suddenly taken all aback, and the blast came upon us furiously. We continued to scud under a double-reefed mainsail and forestopsail till dusk; but, as the sea ran high, the captain thought it safest to bring her to. The watch on deck consisted of four men, one of whom was appointed to keep a lookout ahead, for the weather was so hazy that we could not see two cables' length from the bow. This man, whose name was Tom Willis, went frequently to the bow, as if to observe something; and when the others called to him, inquiring what he was looking at, he would give no definite answer. They therefore went also to the bow, and appeared startled, and at first said nothing; but presently one of them cried, "William, go call the watch."

The seamen, having been asleep in their hammocks, murmured at this unreasonable summons, and called to know how it looked upon deck. To which Tom Willis replied, "Come up and see. What we are minding is not on deck, but ahead."

On hearing this, they ran up without putting on their jackets, and when they came to the bow, there was whispering.

One of them asked, "Where is she? I do not see her." To which another replied, "The last flash of lightning shewed there was not a reef in one of her sails; but we, who know her history, know that all her canvas will never carry her into port."

By this time the talking of the seamen had brought some of the passengers on deck. They could see nothing, however, for the ship was surrounded by thick darkness, and by the noise of the dashing waters, and the seamen evaded the questions that were put to them.

At this juncture the chaplain came on deck. He was a man of grave and modest demeanor, and was much liked among the seamen, who called him Gentle George. He had overheard one of the men asking another, if he had seen the *Flying Dutchman* before, and if he knew the story about her. To which the other replied, "I have heard of her beating about in these seas. What is the reason she never reaches port?"

The first speaker replied, "They give different reasons for it, but my story is this: she was an Amsterdam vessel and sailed from that port seventy years ago. Her master's name was Vanderdecken. He was a staunch seaman, and would have his own way, in spite of the devil. For all that, never a sailor under him had reason to complain; though how it is on board with them now, nobody knows; the story is this, that in doubling the Cape, they were a long day trying to weather the Table Bay, which we saw this morning. However, the wind headed them, and went against them more and more, and Vanderdecken walked the deck, swearing at the wind. Just after sunset a vessel spoke him, asking if he did not mean to go into the bay that night. Vanderdecken replied, "May I be eternally damned if I do, though I should beat about to the day of judgment!" And to be sure, Vanderdecken never did go into that bay; for it is believed that he continues to beat about in these seas still, and will do so long enough. This vessel is never seen but with foul weather along with her."

To which another replied, "We must keep clear of her. They say that her captain mans his jolly boat when a vessel comes in sight, and tries hard to get alongside, to put letters on board, but no good comes to them who have communication with them."

Tom Willis said, "There is such a sea between us at present, as should keep us safe from such visits."

To which the other answered: "We cannot trust to that if Vanderdecken sends out his men."

Some of this conversation having been overheard by the passengers, there was a commotion among them. In the meantime the noise of the waves against the vessel could scarcely be distinguished from the sounds of the distant thunder. The wind had extinguished the light in the binnacle, where the compass was, and no one could tell which way the ship's head lay. The passengers were afraid to ask questions lest they should augment the secret sensation of fear which chilled every heart, or learn any more than they already knew. For while they attributed their agitation of mind to the state of the weather, it was sufficiently perceptible that their alarms also arose from a cause which they did not acknowledge.

The lamp at the binnacle being relighted, they perceived that the ship lay closer to the wind than she had hitherto done, and the spirits of the passengers were somewhat revived.

Nevertheless, neither the tempestuous state of the atmosphere, nor the thunder had ceased; and soon a vivid flash of lightning shewed the waves tumbling around us, and, in the distance, the *Flying Dutchman* scudding furiously before the wind, under a press of canvas. The sight was but momentary but it was sufficient to remove all doubt from the minds of the passengers. One of the men cried aloud, "There she goes, topgallants and all!"

The chaplain had brought up his prayer book in order that he might draw from thence something to fortify and tranquillize the minds of the rest. Therefore, taking his seat near the binnacle, so that the light shone upon the white leaves of the book, he, in a solemn tone, read out the service for those distressed at sea. The sailors stood around with folded arms and looked as if they thought it would be of little use. But this served to occupy the attention of those on deck for a while.

In the meantime, the flashes of lightning becoming less vivid shewed nothing else, far or near, but the billows weltering round the vessel. The sailors seemed to think that they had not yet seen the worst, but confined their remarks and prognostications to their own circle.

At this time the captain, who had hitherto remained in his berth, came on deck, and with a gay and unconcerned air, inquired what was the cause of the general dread. He said he thought they had already seen the worst of the weather, and wondered that his men had raised such a hubbub about a capful of wind. Mention being made of the *Flying Dutchman,* the captain laughed. He said, "he would like very much to see any vessel carrying topgallant sails in such a night, for it would be a sight worth looking at." The chaplain, taking him by one of the buttons of his coat, drew him aside and appeared to enter into serious conversation with him.

While they were talking together, the captain was heard to say, "Let us look to our own ship and not mind such things"; and accordingly, he sent a man aloft to see if all was right about the fore topsail yard, which was chafing the mast with a loud noise.

It was Tom Willis who went up; and when he came down, he said that all was tight, and that he hoped it would soon get clearer; and that they would see no more of what they were most afraid of.

The captain and first mate were heard laughing loudly together, while the chaplain observed that it would be better to repress such unseasonable gaiety. The second mate, a native of Scotland, whose name was Duncan Saunderson, having attended one of the university classes at Aberdeen, thought himself too wise to believe all that the sailors said, and took part with the captain. He jestingly told Tom Willis to borrow his grandma's spectacles the next time he was sent to keep a lookout ahead. Tom walked sulkily away, muttering that he would nevertheless trust to his own eyes till morning, and accordingly took his station at the bow and appeared to watch as attentively as before.

The sound of talking soon ceased, for many returned to their berths, and we heard nothing but the clanking of the ropes upon the masts, and the bursting of the billows ahead, as the vessel successively took the seas.

But after a considerable interval of darkness, gleams of lightning began to reappear. Tom Willis suddenly called out, "Vanderdecken again! Vanderdecken again! I see them letting down a boat."

All who were on deck ran down to the bow. The next flash of lightning shone far and wide over the raging sea and shewed us not only the *Flying Dutchman* at a distance, but also a boat coming from her with four men. The boat was within two cables' length of our ship's side.

The man who first saw her ran to the captain, and asked whether they should hail her or not. The captain, walking about in great agitation, made no reply. The first mate cried, "Who's going to heave a rope to that boat?" The men looked at each other without offering to do anything. The boat had come very near the chains when Tom Willis called out, "What do you want? Or what devil has blown you here in such weather?" A piercing voice from the boat replied in English, "We want to see your captain." The captain took no notice of this, and Vanderdecken's boat having come alongside, one of the men came upon deck, and appeared like a fatigued and weatherbeaten seaman, holding some letters in his hand.

Our sailors all drew back. The chaplain, however, looked steadfastly upon him, went forward a few steps, and asked, "What is the purpose of this visit?"

The stranger replied, "We have long been kept here by foul weather, and Vanderdecken wishes to send these letters to his friends in Europe."

Our captain now came forward, and said as firmly as he could, "I wish Vanderdecken would put his letters on board of any other vessel rather than mine."

The stranger replied, "We have tried many a ship, but most of them refuse our letters."

Upon which Tom Willis muttered, "It will be best for us if we do the same, for they say there is sometimes a sinking weight in your paper."

The stranger took no notice of this but asked where we were from. On being told that we were from Portsmouth, he said, as if with strong feeling, "Would that you had rather been from Amsterdam. Oh that we saw it again! We must see our friends again." When he uttered these words, the men who were in the boat below wrung their hands and cried in a piercing tone, in Dutch, "Oh that we saw it again! We have been long here beating about, but we must see our friends again."

The chaplain asked the stranger, "How long have you been at sea?"

He replied, "We have lost our count, for our almanac was blown overboard. Our ship, you see, is there still; so why should you ask how long we have been at sea; for Vanderdecken only wishes to write home and comfort his friends."

To which the chaplain replied, "Your letters, I fear, would be of no use in Amsterdam, even if they were delivered, for the persons to whom they are addressed are probably no longer to be found there, except under very ancient green turf in the churchyard."

The unwelcome stranger then wrung his hands and appeared to weep; and replied, "It is impossible. We cannot believe you. We have been long driving about here, but country nor relations cannot be so easily forgotten. There is not a raindrop in the air but feels itself kindred to all the rest, and they fall back into the sea to meet with each other again. How then can kindred blood be made to forget where it came from? Even our bodies are part of the ground of Holland; and Vanderdecken says, if he once were come to Amsterdam, he would rather be changed into a stone post, well fixed into the ground, than leave it again; if that were to die elsewhere. But in the meantime, we only ask you to take these letters."

The chaplain, looking at him with astonishment, said, "This is the insanity of natural affection which rebels against all measures of time and distance."

The stranger continued, "Here is a letter from our second mate to his dear and only remaining friend, his uncle, the merchant who lives in the second house on Stuncken Yacht Quay."

He held forth the letter, but no one would approach to take it. Tom Willis raised his voice and said, "One of our men here says that he was in Amsterdam last winter, and he knows for certain that the street called Stuncken Yacht Quay was pulled down sixty years ago, and now there is only a large church in that place."

The man from the *Flying Dutchman* said, "It is impossible; we cannot believe you. Here is another letter from myself in which I have sent a bank note to my dear sister to buy some gallant lace to make her a high headdress."

Tom Willis, hearing this, said, "It is most likely that her head now lies under a tombstone, which will outlast all the changes of the fashion. But on what house is your bank note?"

The stranger replied, "On the house of Vanderbrucker and Company."

The man of whom Tom Willis had spoken said, "I guess there will now be some discount upon it, for that banking house has gone to destruction forty years ago; and Vanderbrucker was afterward missing. But to remember these things is like raking up the bottom of an old canal."

The stranger called out passionately, "It is impossible! We cannot believe it! It is cruel to say such things to people in our condition. There is a letter from our captain himself to his much beloved and faithful wife, whom he left at a pleasant summer dwelling on the border of the Haarlemar Mer. She promised to have the house beautifully painted and gilded before he came back, and to get a new set of looking glasses for the principal chamber, that she might see as many images of Vanderdecken as if she had six husbands at once."

The man replied, "There has been time enough for her to have had six husbands since then; but were she still alive there is no fear that Vanderdecken would ever get home to disturb her."

On hearing this the stranger again shed tears, and said, if they would not take the letters, he would leave them; and looking around he offered the parcel to the captain, chaplain, and to the rest of the crew successively, but each drew back as it was offered and put his hands behind his back. He then laid the letters upon the deck and placed upon them a piece of iron, which was lying near, to prevent them from being blown away. Having done this, he swung himself over the gangway and went into the boat.

We heard the others speak to him, but the rise of a sudden squall prevented us from distinguishing his reply. The boat was seen to quit the ship's side, and, in a few moments, there were no more traces of her than if she had never been there. The sailors rubbed their eyes, as if doubting what they had witnessed, but the parcel still lay upon the deck and proved the reality of all that had passed.

Duncan Saunderson, the Scotch mate, asked the captain if he should take them up and put them in the letter bag. Receiving no reply, he would have lifted them if it had not been for Tom Willis, who pulled him back, saying that nobody should touch them.

In the meantime the captain went down to the cabin, and the chaplain having followed him, found him at his bottle-case, pouring out a large dram of brandy. The captain, although somewhat disconcerted, immediately offered the glass to him, saying, "Here, Charters, is what is good in a cold night." The chaplain declined drinking anything, and the captain having swallowed the bumper, they both returned to the deck where they found the seamen giving their opinions concerning what should be done with the letters. Tom Willis proposed to pick them up on a harpoon and throw them overboard.

Another speaker said, "I have always heard it asserted that it is neither safe to accept them voluntarily nor, when they are left, to throw them out of the ship."

"Let no one touch them," said the carpenter. "The way to do with the letters from the *Flying Dutchman* is to case them upon deck, by nailing boards over them, so that if he sends back for them, they are still there to give him."

The carpenter went to fetch his tools. During his absence the ship gave so violent a pitch that the piece of iron slid off the letters and they were whirled overboard by the wind, like birds of evil omen whirring through the air. There was a cry of joy amongst the sailors, and they ascribed the favorable change which took place in the weather, to our having got quit of Vanderdecken. We soon got under way again. The night watch being set, the rest of the crew retired to their berths.

[7]

The Beggar's Curse

There was once a peasant of the Forêt du Laz, near Châteauneuf-du-Faou, who visited, as he was bound to do, the Pardon of Rumengol, near Quimerch. He was not noted for the evenness of his temper, this peasant; and as he drew near the scene of the Pardon he became increasingly irritated by the beggars who lined the roadside.

"*Payez le droit des pauvres*," they cried.

One he met who came near to nauseating him. Sores, boils, and ulcers did the beggar exhibit to awaken his charity; and very repulsive was the reek of the beggar's unwashed body as it followed him along the dusty highway. "*Payez le droit des pauvres*," whined the beggar. At last the quick-tempered peasant, raising his stick, struck the beggar heavily, rolling him in the ditch.

"May you wander to Rumengol for seven years," yelled the beggar in fury. "And on your return to your fireside may fresh trouble await you."

The Pardon over, the peasant set out on his tramp home. But imagine his surprise when, on turning a sharp bend in the road, he found himself entering Rumengol once more. With an expression of disgust at his carelessness in taking the wrong path, he retraced his steps; yet after scarcely half a league found himself again on the outskirts of the village.

He slept that night under a hedge, determining to pursue his homeward journey next day. But every path he took led him back to Rumengol. Terrified, dejected, exhausted, he continued mechanically to walk, week in, week out, month in, month out. His wooden *sabots* wore thin, the substance of them peeling from his feet like paper; he walked barefoot; the skin reddened, blistered. And still, in agony, he walked. His clothes, in sun and rain, hung upon his figure like sacks; they too fell gradually to pieces until only his shirt was left. And still, in heat and cold, in sunshine and in storm, he walked. Food became scarce; he grew first hungry, then famished, then ravenous; became lean and haggard and wild-eyed, a creature despairing of very existence. And still, in starvation, he walked. For seven long years he fled from Rumengol only to find himself, a dozen times a day, on the point of re-entering it.

At the end of his strength, he sank one night into a ditch to sleep: with the morning came a thought which was like sweet cider to the drought of his mind.

"Today I am going home."

Infused by a new spirit he rose, and after washing his face in a brook set about his journey. Scarecrow though he was, he sang blithely; but his voice failed him and his lips became parched with joy as he at length beheld once more the little cottage in the Forêt du Laz he had left seven years previously. A group of people clustered round its door; and from within came a tiny wailing voice as of a new-born child.

"Away with you, tatterdemalion," exclaimed one of the watchers at the door.

"What then goes forward inside?" asked the peasant, amazed at this unexpected reception.

"Mind your own business," retorted the watcher.

"For pity's sake, tell me," persisted the distraught peasant.

"Since you seem so anxious then, know that the good wife has just given birth to a child—a bonny boy."

"But her husband?" cried the peasant in an agony of soul.

"Is at her bedside," answered the watcher.

The peasant could contain himself no longer. "Fools," he cried, "I am her husband. Let me go to her."

And he made for the door.

"Fool yourself," retorted the watcher, restraining him. "Her first husband has been dead these seven years, killed by a wolf as he returned from the Pardon of Rumengol. He who is with her now is her second."

In vain did the peasant tell them his pitiable story. They laughed at him. Finally they drove him from the door.

"Is there any man more miserable than I?" wailed the peasant. With a great sorrow upon him, he walked blindly into the forest; and was never seen nor heard of again. Beware, therefore, how you spurn God's children of the poor.

XI

THE POWER OF THE NAME AND OF MAGIC WORDS

Name-or-symbol magic is based on the theory that a close and vital relationship exists between the representation of a thing and the thing represented. A person or spirit, therefore, can be powerfully influenced through his or its name. For instance, a bad man can be reformed by boiling in a kettle the slip of paper upon which his name has been written. Or hairs taken from the cross-shaped marking on an ass's withers can cure tonsilitis. The powerful sacred names occurring in incantations are there to strengthen the magic formula. But to call nixes, magic horses, berserkers, and the like by the right name robs them of their magic power. The moment the heroine of the Danish ballad "Ribold and Guldborg" calls out her lover's name, he is fatally wounded, i.e., she "names" him dead. To let your enemy know your name is to give him power over you.

"Tom Tit Tot" is from Joseph Jacobs' *English Fairy Tales*, 1892, and "Ra and Isis" is the editor's version of this old Egyptian myth. "The Golem" is a translation of Jacob Grimm's account printed in *Kleinere Schriften*, 1868. "The Golem of Prague" is the editor's version, chiefly based on parts of the *Miracles of Naharal.* Margaret Hunt's translation of Grimms' *Household Tales*, 1884, is the source of "Simeli Mountain."

[1]

Tom Tit Tot

Once upon a time there were a woman, and she baked five pies. And when they come out of the oven, they was that overbaked the crust were too hard to eat. So she says to her darter, "Maw'r [lass]," says she, "put you them there pies on the shelf, an' leave 'em there a little, an' they'll come again." She meant, you know, the crust would get soft.

But the gal, she says to herself: "Well, if they'll come agin, I'll ate 'em now." And she set to work and ate 'em all, first and last.

Well, come suppertime, the woman she said: "Goo you, and git one o' them there pies. I dare say they've come agin now."

The gal she went an' she looked, and there warn't nothin' but the dishes. So back she come and says she: "Noo, they ain't come agin."

"Not none on 'em?" says the mother.

"Not none on 'em," says she.

"Well, come agin, or not come agin," says the woman, "I'll ha' one for supper."

"But you can't, if they ain't come," says the gal.

"But I can," says she. "Goo you and bring the best of 'em."

"Best or worst," says the gal, "I've ate 'em all, and you can't ha' one till that's come agin."

Well, the woman she were wholly bate [beaten], and she took her spinnin' to the door to spin, and as she span she sang,

> My darter ha' ate five, five pies today.
> My darter ha' ate five, five pies today.

The king he were a-comin' down the street, an' he heard her sing, but what she sang he couldn't hear, so he stopped and said, "What were that you was a-singing of, maw'r?"

The woman she were ashamed to let him hear what her darter had been a-doin', so she sang, 'stids o' that,

> My darter ha' spun five, five skeins today.
> My darter ha' spun five, five skeins today.

"S'ars o' mine!" said the king, "I never heerd tell of anyone as could do that."

Then he said: "Look you here, I want a wife, and I'll marry your darter. But look you here," says he, " 'leven months out o' the year she shall have all the vittles she likes to eat, and all the gowns she likes to get, and all the company she likes to have; but the last month o' the year she'll ha' to spin five skeins every day, an' if she doon't, I shall kill her."

"All right," says the woman; for she thought what a grand marriage that was. And as for them five skeins, when it came to the time, there'd be plenty o' ways of getting out of it, and likeliest, he'd ha' forgot about it.

Well, so they was married. An' for 'leven months the gal had all the vittles she liked to ate, and all the gowns she liked to get, and all the company she liked to have.

But when the time was gettin' over, she began to think about them there skeins an' to wonder if he had 'em in mind. But not one word did he say about 'em, an' she wholly thought he'd forgot 'em.

But the last day o' the last month he takes her to a room she'd never sets eyes on afore. There worn't nothing in it but a spinnin'-wheel and a stool. An' says he: "Now, my dear, here yow'll be shut in tomorrow with some vittles and some flax, and if you hain't spun five skeins by the night, your head will goo off."

An' awa' he went about his business.

Well, she were that frightened, she'd allus been such a useless mawther, that she didn't so much as know how to spin, an' what were she to do tomorrow, with no one to come nigh her to help her. She sat down on a stool in the kitchen, and lawk! how she did cry!

However, all on a sudden she heard a sort of a knockin' low down on the door. She upped and oped it, an' what should she see but a small little black thing with a long tail. That looked up at her right curious, an' that said, "What are you a-cryin' for?"

"Wha's that to you?" says she.

"Never you mind," that said, "but tell me what you're a-cryin' for."

"That won't do me no good if I do," says she.

"You don't know that," that said, an' twirled that's tail round.

"Well," says she, "that won't do no harm, if that don't do no good," and she upped and told about the pies and the skeins, and everything.

"This is what I'll do," says the little black thing, "I'll come to your window every morning and take the flax and bring it spun at night."

"What's your pay?" says she.

That looked out o' the corner o' that's eyes, and that said: "I'll give you three guesses every night to guess my name, an' if you hain't guessed it afore the month's up, you shall be mine."

Well, she thought she'd be sure to guess that's name afore the month was up. "All right," says she, "I agree."

"All right," that says, an' lawk! how that twirled that's tail.

Well, the next day, the king he took her into the room, an' there was the flax an' the day's vittles.

"Now there's the flax," says he, "an' if that ain't spun up this night, off goes your head." An' then he went out an' locked the door.

He'd hardly gone when there was a knockin' on the window.

She upped and she oped it, and there sure enough was the little old thing a-settin' on the ledge.

"Where's the flax?" says he.

"Here it be," says she. And she gonned [gave] it to him.

Well, in the evening a knockin' came again to the window. She upped and she oped it, and there were the little old thing with five skeins of flax on his arm.

"Here ye be," says he, and he gonned it to her.

"Now, what's my name?" says he.

"What, is that Bill?" says she.

"Noo, that ain't," says he, an' he twirled his tail.

"Is that Ned?" says she.

"Noo, that ain't," says he, an' he twirled his tail.

"Well, is that Mark?" says she.

"Noo, that ain't," says he, an' he twirled his tail harder an' away he flew.

Well, when her husband he come in, there was the five skeins ready for him. "I see I sha'nt have for to kill you tonight, my dear," says he; "you'll have your vittles and your flax in the mornin'," says he, an' away he goes.

Well, every day the flax an' the vittles they was brought, an' every day that there little black impet used for to come mornings and evenings. An' all the day the mawther she set a-trying for to think of names to say to it when it come at night. But she never hit on the right one. An' as it got toward the end o' the month, the impet that began for to look so maliceful, an' that twirled that's tail faster an' faster each time she gave a guess.

At last it came to the last day but one. The impet, that came at night along o' the five skeins, and that said, "What, ain't you got my name yet?"

"Is that Nicodemus?" says she.

"Noo, t'ain't," that says.

"Is that Sammle?" says she.

"Noo, t'ain't," that says.

"A-well, is that Methusalem?" says she.

"Noo, t'ain't that neither," that says.

Then that looks at her with that's eyes like a coal o' fire, an' that says: "Woman, there's only tomorrow night, an' then you'll be mine!" An' away it flew.

Well, she felt that horrid. Howsomeover, she heard the king a-comin' along the passage. In he came, an' when he see the five skeins, he says, says he, "Well, my dear," says he, "I don't see but what you'll have your skeins ready tomorrow night as well, an' as I reckon I sha'n't have to kill you, I'll have supper in here tonight." So they brought supper an' another stool for him, and down the two they sat.

Well, he hadn't eat but a mouthful or so, when he stops an' begins to laugh.

"What is it?" says she.

"A-why," says he, "I was out a-huntin' today, an' I got away to a place in the wood I'd never seen afore. An' there was an old chalk pit. An' I heard a sort of a hummin', kind o'. So I got off my hobby [horse], an' I went right quiet to the pit, an' I looked down. Well, what should there be but the funniest little black thing you ever set eyes on. An' what was that a-doing on, but that had a little spinnin'-wheel, an' that were a-spinnin' wonderful fast, an' a-twirlin' that's tail. An' as that span, that sang:

Nimmy Nimmy Not
My name's TOM TIT TOT."

Well, when the mawther heard this, she fared as if she could ha' jumped out of her skin for joy, but she didn't say a word.

Next day that there little thing looked so maliceful when he came for the flax. And when night came, she heard that a-knockin' on the window panes. She oped the window, an' that come right in on the ledge. That were grinnin' from ear to ear an' Oo! that's tail were twirlin' round so fast.

"What's my name?" that says, as that gonned her the skeins.

"Is that Solomon?" she says, pretendin' to be afeared.

"Noo, t'ain't," that says, and that come further into the room.

"Well, is that Zebedee?" says she again.

"Noo, t'ain't," says the impet. An' then that laughed an' twirled that's tail till you couldn't hardly see it.

"Take time, woman," that says; "next guess, and you're mine." An' that stretched out that's black hands at her.

Well, she backed a step or two, an' she looked at it, and then she laughed out, and says she, a-pointin' of her finger at it,

Nimmy Nimmy Not
Yar name's TOM TIT TOT.

Well, when that heard her, that shrieked awful and away that flew into the dark, and she never saw it no more.

[2]

Ra and Isis

Hearken to this legend if you wish to know why Ra, the god of many names and the omnipotent creator of the universe, was afraid of the reptiles of Keb, and how Isis got from him his secret name. Now Isis lived in the form of a sorceress and cast her spells upon men. However, tiring of this, she decided to exercise her magic powers on the gods. Indeed, it was her ambition to become the mistress of both earth and heaven. To achieve this she knew that she would have to find out the secret name of Ra. But it would not be easy to accomplish this, for Ra guarded his real name with great diligence and care. He knew that if it became known, his power would be transferred to the god who had found out what it was.

Now Isis decided the first step was to get a strand of hair, a fingernail cutting, or something else that had been a part of Ra. As he was becoming old and feeble, he sometimes drooled a little. So Isis got some of the saliva which had fallen from his mouth and mixing it with dust, she shaped it into the form of a poisonous snake. After uttering her spells over this mud serpent, she placed it in the path along which Ra passed every day as he went to and fro through Egypt. She wished the serpent to bite Ra.

And when Ra came this way, the serpent sunk his fangs into him and injected poison into his body. The effect was instantaneous and terrifying—the god's jaws chattered, his lips trembled, and for a time he lost the power of speech. The pain was extreme. In spite of all the words of power he knew and the secret name which had been hidden in his body when he was born, he had been bitten by this vile serpent and moreover was unable to stop the pain or the fire of the venom which swept through his body. He commanded all of the gods who knew about magical spells to come and help him. With these gods came Isis, the woman of magic, the great healer and the revivifier of the dead.

"What has happened, O divine father?" she asked.

"Alas, a serpent has poisoned me, and I am hotter than fire and colder than spring water. My legs tremble and my sight is failing."

"Divine father," urged the guileful goddess, "tell me your name, for the person who utters his own name shall live."

"I am called Khepera in the morning, Ra at noon and Temu in the evening." The god hoped these three great names would satisfy Isis, and that she would utter a word of power and bring his suffering to an end. But Isis was not fooled. She knew Ra had not spoken his hidden name. Again she begged him to tell her what this was, but the god was not yet willing to reveal it. So he waited for a time. Yet it was not long before the pain became unendurable.

"Isis shall search in me, and my name shall pass from my body," he cried, and at that moment he disappeared from the sight of the gods. His throne in his boat had no occupant. Isis was not certain he would keep his word, and agreed with Horus that Ra should be made to take an oath to part with his two eyes, that is the sun and moon. However, Ra allowed his heart to be taken from his body, and the great secret name which was hidden in his heart became the possession of Isis. And she became a greater god than he.

Then she spoke this spell: "Poison, flow out of Ra. Eye of Horus, come out of Ra and shine outside his mouth. It is Isis who works this magic and causes the poison to fall on the ground. The name of the great god is taken from him. Ra shall live and the poison shall die." And since she had composed this spell after she had learned Ra's secret name, the magic was irresistible, and straightway the pain departed from Ra.

[3]

The Golem

After observing certain fast days and repeating certain prayers, the Polish Jews mold glue or clay into the form of a man, and when they have spoken over it the mighty Ineffable Name, the Shem-Hamforesh, he comes alive. However he cannot talk. Yet he understands rather well whatever is said to him.

They call such a creature a golem and in general use him as a servant to do all kinds of housework. Some say that the golem must not be allowed to go out of the house. On his forehead there is written *aemaeth* (truth, God). No matter how small he is at first, each day he grows larger and stronger. When he has become so much greater and more powerful than the others in the house that they fear him and wish to get rid of him, they rub out the first letter of the word on his forehead, leaving only *maeth* (he is dead), and he instantly collapses and his body becomes mere clay again.

It is said that once through carelessness someone let a golen grow so tall that his forehead was out of reach. The person, becoming very much alarmed, thought of an expedient. Pointing to his boots, he commanded the golem to pull them off. When the giant bent down to do this, the person erased the first letter of the word on the golem's forehead. Unfortunately the huge creature collapsed so quickly that the entire weight of the lifeless clay fell on the person and crushed him flat.

[4]

The Golem of Prague

When in 1580 Rabbi Judah Loew learned that the bad priest Thaddeus was trying to bring forward a ritual murder charge against the Jews of Prague, he directed a dream-question to Heaven, asking for counsel. And the answer was to make a golem of clay which should be a champion and protector of the Jews. So Rabbi Loew sent for his son-in-law, Isaac ben Simson, who was a Kohen, and for his pupil, Jacob ben Chayim Sasson, who was a Levite. And they conferred together on how they could make a golem. The rabbi told them how important it was that they should carefully sanctify and purify themselves. If they did not, the attempt would surely fail because they would have then used the Holy Name in vain.

After midnight on the second day of the month of Adar, these three therefore visited the ritual baths, recited the appropriate psalms, and read aloud from the *Sefer Yezirah* (Book of Creation). Then proceeding to the outskirts of Prague, they found a bed of clay and at once began to mold a clay figure by torchlight and amidst the chanting of Psalms. They made the figure just like a man. The golem was three ells long and lay with his face upward. The three men stood at his feet so that they could gaze fully into his visage. Then the Kohen walked seven times around the clay body, from right to left, and repeated charms. The clay body became red like fire. And the Levite walked seven times around the figure from left to right and said other magic words. Now the red disappeared and water flowed through the clay body; hair sprouted on his head and nails appeared on the fingers and toes. Then Rabbi Loew, after walking once around the figure, placed in his mouth a piece of parchment on which was written the Ineffable Name (the Shem-Hamforesh). And as soon as all recited, "And he breathed into his nostrils the breath of life; and man became a living soul" from the Book of Genesis, the golem opened his eyes and gazed about him in wonder. And he looked just like an ordinary person, but he could not speak. And Rabbi Loew called him Joseph, dressed him as a sexton, and brought him home to live in his house.

Rabbi Loew's wife Pearl soon learned that Joseph was not an ordinary golem to be used about the house as a common servant. Once when she and her servants were busily engaged with the preparations for a great wedding feast, she sent the golem to buy the fish and the apples. She said to him, "Go to the Moldau and ask the fisherman for the live fish we have bespoken. Then go to the fruit market and buy a pail of nice apples." And she gave him notes to these tradespeople instructing them to give the articles to the golem. The fisherman gave him a twenty-pound live carp, but instead of waiting for it to be placed in a bag, the golem thrust it headfirst into his blouse and on the way home the fish gave the golem such a terrific slap in the face with its tail that he was knocked to the ground. When he got up he ran to the Moldau and threw the fish into the water. He did this to punish the bad fish, as he later explained by means of signs and grimaces to the *Rebitzen*. And when the fruit woman laughed at the golem when he said he could carry her whole stock of apples on his shoulders, he got mad and lifting her stand, all the baskets full of fruit, and the woman too, upon his shoulders, he rushed through the city amusing and astonishing the people. And when the *Rebitzen* sent him to draw water, he also got into trouble by drawing so much water that he caused a flood.

From this time on Rabbi Loew hardly ever used the golem except to protect his people against unjust accusations. Whenever the rabbi sent Joseph on dangerous missions, he provided him with an amulet which made him invisible. Dressed as a Christian porter, he often loitered at night in the streets of the ghetto, and whenever he observed something suspicious he investigated it. For instance, if he found someone carrying a dead child, he would drag him by force to the authorities. It is said that in those days evil men, to achieve their purposes, sometimes secretly placed a child's body on the premises of a Jew and then accused him of ritual murder.

The golem played a part in a case in which this was the charge, the case of the Jewish girl Dinah Maridi, who in 1583 left her home because of the influence of the bad priest Thaddeus. This man used her to make false accusations against her former co-religionists. Before a cardinal she averred that two servants of a certain rabbi—she meant Rabbi Loew's sexton, Abraham Chayim, and the golem—had come to her father, who, by the way, was a surgeon, and offered him a vial of Christian blood for the Passover. Questioned about the source of the blood, Dinah hinted that it probably came from the body of a Christian girl who had recently disappeared suddenly from the ghetto. This girl had been in the service of a prominent Jew of Prague and had also worked on Saturdays as a charwoman; that is, she had been a *shabbos-goya.*

When the report of this unfortunate affair came to the ears of Rabbi Loew, he was deeply troubled. As the authorities had been informed, he expected the golem and the sexton to be thrown into prison before night. Then it occurred to him that as Dinah Maridi did not know the golem very well, he could substitute for him a mute who looked somewhat like him. So when the policemen came to arrest the golem, they took away instead a mute dressed in his clothes.

The trial of the mute and sexton Chayim was to be held in one month. Rabbi Loew knew that the whole case depended upon finding the *shabbos-goya.* He made many secret inquiries about her but in vain. It was certain that she was living with her relatives in one of the four villages near Prague, but the messengers he sent to them came back without having found out anything. In his desperation the rabbi decided now to use the golem. He told him about the *shabbos-goya* and the entire story of Dinah Maridi's accusations. Then he commanded the golem to find the *shabbos-goya* and bring her back with him. And to persuade her to return, the rabbi made up a letter and signed it with the name of her former mistress, pleading for her to come back, begging forgiveness for having falsely accused her of a theft, and enclosing twenty-five gulden for traveling expenses. The golem was to hand this to her.

At the trial, feelings were becoming tense. After the mute and Chayim had been questioned, Dinah, the chief witness, was called. She glanced boldly around the room, fixed Rabbi Loew with a scornful glare, and began to repeat the ghastly lies she had told to the cardinal. Then the defense counsel asked her, "Would you know the rabbi's servants who, you said, came to visit your father, if you saw them?" She pointed to the accused men and laughing said, "Those two are the men—I would know them in the dark!" For a moment there was deep silence in the courtroom. Suddenly this was broken by a terrific noise which came from the street. The golem was driving a wagon like mad up the street, and sitting in the seat was the *shabbos-goya!* With his golem instinct Joseph had discovered her whereabouts. Soon after he had given the girl the letter and the money, she decided to come with Joseph to Prague. And they had arrived just in time!

When the evil Thaddeus and his dupe, Dinah Maridi, saw the golem enter the court with the missing girl, they knew that the tables had been turned against them. They stood stock still, motionless as mummies. The accused men were freed. Dinah was sentenced to six years imprisonment and Thaddeus, frustrated and discredited, slunk away to his cloister.

Joseph Golem was also a great help to Rabbi Loew in the affair of the Kozlovsky brothers, workers in the leather factory of Aron Gins. The youngest brother robbed Aron Gins and on that same night caught cold and died. The two older brothers had him secretly buried in a Christian cemetery and paid for it with a watch the dead brother had stolen from Aron Gins. Then to get revenge on the latter, whom they hated, they disinterred their brother, buried him outside of the wall of the Jewish cemetery of Prague, and threw his clothes into Aron Gins' house. And when the body was discovered, they accused Aron Gins of killing their brother to prepare for the Passover.

Now to unravel this sinister business Rabbi Loew knew he had to find an empty grave in the Christian cemetery. He decided that supernatural agencies must be used. "The soul of a human being hovers over his grave for a whole year," he reflected, "for it is still related to its body during that time." So he got permission from the authorities to permit Joseph Golem to examine the graves made within the preceding four months. As the golem walked from grave to grave, he suddenly came to a stop and indicated by gesturing that the grave at his feet was empty. Rabbi Loew and the prefect came at once. When the grave was opened it contained an empty coffin. So the golem instinct triumphed again and the empty grave led to the exposure of the ugly plot of the Kozlovsky brothers and exonerated the innocent Aron Gins.

Once the golem ran amuck, but it was not exactly his fault. Every Friday afternoon it was Rabbi Loew's habit to explain to Joseph exactly what he wanted him to do the next day, for in the Sabbath he spoke to him only when something extremely urgent came up. On one Friday afternoon Rabbi Loew forgot to give Joseph his program, and the poor fellow had nothing to do.

As twilight settled down and the people were preparing for the Sabbath, the golem suddenly went berserk, running up and down the streets in the Jewish section of the city and endangering the lives, limbs, and properties of everyone. The lack of chores to do made him wild, and he did not know what to do with himself. When the people saw what he was doing, they ran from him and screamed, "Joseph Golem has gone mad!" The people were badly frightened and panic threatened. However, the report of what was happening reached Rabbi Loew, who was praying at the Altneu Synagogue, and the good man was shocked by the thought of the damage Joseph might do. Yet would not the act of quieting him be a profanation of the Sabbath? In his excitement he had forgotten that the law permits and even commands the profanation of the Sabbath when it is a question of saving peoples' lives. Rabbi Loew rushed out, and although he was not within sight or hearing of Joseph, he called out, "Joseph, stop where you are!" And the rabbi learned later from the people who were near Joseph, that at that very instant he froze in his tracks and immediately overcame the fury of his passions. When the rabbi found him, he sent him to bed, and he obeyed as willingly as a good child. And the rabbi told his friends that the golem might have destroyed all of Prague had he not calmed him down. And never again did the rabbi forget to give Joseph his Friday afternoon orders.

Joseph helped the rabbi on many another occasion. Perhaps the most remarkable of these was the affair of the brother-sister wedding which the rabbi was about to celebrate when certain signs warned him to desist. To prove that the bride and groom were really brother and sister, he had the golem raise a midwife from the dead and cause her to tell how she changed two boy babies in their cradles and so made an incestuous union a possibility. But finally after Kaiser Rudolph II issued the decree making it illegal to accuse a Jew of ritual murder, Rabbi Loew decided that Joseph was needed no longer and therefore should be turned back into clay. So the rabbi summoned his disciple and his son-in-law, the two men who had helped him make the golem.

On Lag-B'Omer in 1593 Rabbi Loew ordered the golem to sleep in the garret of the Altneu Synagogue. And the rabbi asked his companions whether a dead body, such as the golem's was about to be, would constitute an object of impurity like any other dead body. If the answer was in the affirmative, the rabbi's son-in-law, who was a priest, could not participate in the act of destroying the golem, since a corpse would make him unclean. But the rabbi decided that this case did not come under the regular law and that his son-in-law could help in the business. And the sexton lighted the way with two burning candles as the three men ascended into the garret of the synagogue and began the work of destroying the golem.

They did everything they had done in creating the golem but in reverse order. At the creation they had stood at the feet of the golem; now they stood at his head. Likewise they read the words from the Book of Creation backward. And when they had finished, the golem was motionless and cold and nothing but a man-shaped mass of clay. Rabbi Loew now took the candles from the sexton and ordered him to strip the golem to his undershirt. Then they covered him with old prayer robes and the remains of Hebrew books, which according to the custom, were stored in the synagogue garret. The next day the sexton secretly burned the golem's clothes and the news spread through the ghetto that Joseph Golem had disappeared during the night. And Rabbi Loew forbade anyone to climb to the garret of the Altneu Synagogue. It was the last resting place of Joseph Golem.

However, there is a legend which describes the golem as being buried on Gallows Hill outside the city. It tells how the sexton, Abraham Chayim, with his brother-in-law, the sexton of the Pinkas Synagogue, on the night following the golem's demise, climbed up to the garret of the Altneu Synagogue and took hold of the clay golem and carried it to the Pinkas Synagogue and hid it behind the reading desk. Then Chayim got his son-in-law, who spent much time reading cabalistic books, to look for the life-giving formula in the Book of Creation, and when he thought he had found this, he and the two sextons carried the golem in the dead of night into the son-in-law's house in Zigeuner Gasse and tried to make him come alive.

But their efforts were futile. And when they repeated their attempts, an epidemic broke out in Prague and over a thousand persons died. Two of the son-in-law's five children perished, although there was no sickness in any house on that street. The mother of these children had disapproved of bringing the golem into her house. She attributed the death of the two children to the presence of the dead golem in their home. After the children had been placed in their coffins, the body of one of them was taken out and put in with the other. The remains of the golem were then laid in the empty coffin, and after nightfall carried up to the Gallows Hill and buried on that side of the hill which is turned toward the city of Prague.

[5]

Simeli Mountain

There were once two brothers, the one rich, the other poor. The rich one, however, gave nothing to the poor one, and the latter gained a scanty living by trading in corn, and often did so badly that he had no bread for his wife and children. Once when he was wheeling a barrow through the forest he saw, on one side of him, a great, bare, naked-looking mountain, and as he had never seen it before, he stood still and stared at it with amazement.

While he was thus standing he saw twelve great, wild men coming toward him, and as he believed they were robbers he pushed his barrow into the thicket, climbed up a tree, and waited to see what would happen. The twelve men, however, went to the mountain and cried, "Semsi mountain, Semsi mountain, open," and immediately the barren mountain opened down the middle, and the twelve went into it, and as soon as they were within, it shut. After a short time, however, it opened again, and the men came forth carrying heavy sacks on their shoulders, and when they were all once more in the daylight they said, "Semsi mountain, Semsi mountain, shut thyself"; then the mountain closed together, and there was no longer any entrance to be seen to it, and the twelve went away.

When they were quite out of sight the poor man got down from the tree, and was curious to know what really was secretly hidden in the mountain. So he went up to it and said, "Semsi mountain, Semsi mountain, open," and the mountain opened to him also. Then he went inside, and the whole mountain was a cavern full of silver and gold, and behind lay great piles of pearls and sparkling jewels, heaped up like corn. The poor man hardly knew what to do, and whether he might take any of these treasures for himself or not; but at last he filled his pockets with gold, but he left the pearls and precious stones where they were. When he came out again he also said, "Semsi mountain, Semsi mountain, shut thyself"; and the mountain closed itself, and he went home with his barrow.

And now he had no more cause for anxiety, but could buy bread for his wife and children with his gold, and wine into the bargain. He lived joyously and uprightly, gave help to the poor, and did good to everyone. When, however, the money came to an end he went to his brother, borrowed a measure that held a bushel, and brought himself some more, but did not touch any of the most valuable things. When for the third time he wanted to fetch something, he again borrowed the measure of his brother. The rich man had, however, long been envious of his brother's possessions, and of the handsome way of living which he had set on foot, and could not understand from whence the riches came, and what his brother wanted with the measure. Then he thought of a cunning trick, and covered the bottom of the measure with pitch, and when he got the measure back a piece of money was sticking in it. He at once went to his brother and asked him, "What hast thou been measuring in the bushel measure?" "Corn and barley," said the other. Then he showed him the piece of money, and threatened that if he did not tell the truth he would accuse him before a court of justice. The poor man then told him everything, just as it had happened. The rich man, however, ordered his carriage to be made ready, and drove away, resolved to use the opportunity better than his brother had done, and to bring back with him quite different treasures.

When he came to the mountain he cried, "Semsi mountain, Semsi mountain, open." The mountain opened, and he went inside it. There lay the treasures all before him, and for a long time he did not know which to clutch at first. At length he loaded himself with as many precious stones as he could carry. He wished to carry his burden outside, but, as his heart and soul were entirely full of the treasures, he had forgotten the name of the mountain, and cried, "Simeli mountain, Simeli mountain, open." That, however, was not the right name, and the mountain never stirred, but remained shut. Then he was alarmed, but the longer he thought about it the more his thoughts confused themselves, and his treasures were no more of any use to him. In the evening the mountain opened, and the twelve robbers came in, and when they saw him they laughed, and cried out, "Bird, have we caught thee at last! Didst thou think we had never noticed that thou hadst been in here twice? We could not catch thee then; this third time thou shalt not get out again!" Then he cried, "It was not I, it was my brother," but let him beg for his life and say what he would, they cut his head off.

XII

THE EVIL EYE AND THINGS CHARGED WITH MAGIC

Folktales abound in magic things of all kinds: amulets to protect, talismans like Aaron's rod and the fairy wand to work wonders with, the stole or cap which makes its wearer invisible, the cudgel that automatically strikes powerful blows, the napkin which when properly addressed produces a delicious banquet, music that compels one to dance, wells or springs that cure, give eternal youth or change the sex of the bather, the Hindu cow whose dung changes to glittering gold, and the shirt or stone which tests chastity. Usually these aid the hero or heroine, but there are magic things that are dangerous even for them and are to be guarded against. Such are the evil eye and the lethal image inscribed with one's name and containing one's hair, nail parings, or spittle. Witches made such images and also were likely to be *jettatores*. And the Hand of Glory made the household sleep while the thieves helped themselves.

"Afraid of the Evil Eye" is from *An Itinerary* by Fynes Moryson, ed. 1617, and "Old Madge's Spell" is from Robert Hunt's *Popular Romances of the West of England*, 1871 (where it is called "Fire Ordeal for the Cure of Disease"), and is somewhat shortened. The source of "The Wax Image," "The Serpent's Stone," and "The Chaste Mates" is the *Gesta Romanorum*, ed. 1824. "The Hand of Glory at the Old Spital Inn" is from William Henderson's *Folk-lore of the Northern Counties of England*, 1879. "The Insulted Spring" is from Hugh Miller's *Scenes and Legends of the North of Scotland*, 1874, and "The Blue Light" from Margaret Hunt's translation of the Grimms' *Household Tales*, 1884. The source of "The Friar and Boy" is John Ashton's *Chap-books of the Eighteenth Century*, 1882, and "Little Annie, the Goose Girl" is from G. W. Dasent's *Popular Tales from the Norse*, 1877.

[1]

Afraid of the Evil Eye

We might have had coaches, but since a boat passes daily to and fro between these cities [Padua and Venice], most men use this passage as most convenient. For the boat is covered with arched hatches, and there is very pleasant company, so a man beware to give no offense: for otherwise the Lombards carry shirts of mail, and being armed as if they were in a camp, are apt to revenge upon shameful advantages. But commonly there is pleasant discourse, and the proverb says that the boat shall be drowned when it carries neither monk, nor student, nor courtesan (they love them too well to call them whores), the passengers being for the most part of these kinds. I remember a young maid in the boat crossed herself whensoever an old woman looked upon her, fearing she should be a witch; whereat the passengers often smiled, seeing the girl not only cross herself for fear but thrust her crucifix toward the old woman's eyes.

[2]

Old Madge's Spell

A miner, who was also a small farmer, living in Zennor, once consulted me on the condition of his daughter, a little girl about five or six years of age. This child was evidently suffering from some scrofulous taint. She was of a delicate complexion, with, usually, a hectic flush on her cheeks, the skin being particularly fine and so transparent that the course of the veins was marked by deep blue lines. This little girl had long suffered from indolent tumors, forming on the glands in various parts of the body; and, as her father said, they had taken her to all the doctors in the country round and the child got worse and worse.

I prescribed for this child, and for two or three weeks she was brought into Penzance on the market day that I might observe the influence of the remedial agent which I was employing. Right or wrong, however, the little girl was evidently benefited by the medicine I recommended.

Suddenly my patient was removed from my care, and many months passed away without my seeing either the child or the father. Eventually I met the parent in the market place, and after some commonplace remarks he informed me, on my inquiring for his daughter, that she was cured. I expressed satisfaction at hearing this, and inquired why he had not brought the child to me again. After some hesitation he said he had discovered what ailed the child—"*she was overlooked.*" Requiring some explanation of this, I got possession of his story, which was to the following purpose:

At a short distance from their farm there resided an old woman who was feared by her neighbors owing to her savage and uncontrollable temper, and who hated all around her in consequence of the system of ill-usage to which during a long life she had been subjected.

Margery Penwarne . . . had long been used by the mothers of the parish as a means for frightening the children. Their tears were stopped more readily by a threat, "I'le give 'e to An' Madge," than by any other means; and the good conduct was insured if An' Madge was to be sent for "to tak 'e away." From this state she passed into another stage. Margery, from being a terror to the young, became the fear of the old. No one would dare refuse her a drop of milk, a few potatoes, or any of those trifles which she almost demanded from her neighbors, everyone trembling lest she should exert her evil eye, or vent her curses upon them.

This was the being who had "overlooked" the miner's daughter. He told me that the cause of this was that he caught Margery stealing some straw, and that he "kicked her out of the yard."

The gossips of the parish had for some time insisted upon the fact that the child had been ill-wished, and that she never would be better until "the spell was taken off her." The father, who was in all respects a sensible man, would not for a long period hear of this, but the reiteration of the assertion at length compelled him to give way, and he consulted some "knowing man" in the parish of St. Just.

It was then formally announced that the girl could never recover unless three burning sticks were taken from the hearth of the "overlooker," and the child was made to walk three times over them when they were laid across on the ground, and then quench the fire with water.

The father had no doubt respecting the "overlooker," his quarrel with Madge determined this in his mind; but there were many difficulties in carrying out the prescribed means for effecting the cure. Without exposing themselves to the violence of the old woman it was impossible, and there was some fear that in forcibly entering her dwelling they might be brought "under the law," with which Margery had often threatened the people.

It was found, however, that nothing could be done for the child if they neglected this, and the father and two or three friends resolved to brave alike the old woman and the law.

One evening, the smoke, mixed with sparks, arising from the hole in the roof of Margery's cottage, informed them that the evil crone was preparing her supper, and as she evidently was burning dry furze, now was the time to procure the three blazing sticks. Accordingly three men and the little girl hurried to the hovel. The door was closed, but since it was not secured on the inside, the father opened it. As they had planned, his two companions rushed in and without a word seized the old woman, who fell from her block to the floor, to which, with unnecessary violence, they pinned her, she screaming with "the shriek of a goshawk." In the meantime the parent dragged three blazing pieces of furze from the hearth, hastened to the door, laid them one across the other, and then, without losing a moment, forced the trembling child across the fire three times, and compelled her to perform the other necessary portion of the ordeal by which the spell was to be broken.

Margery, weak, aged, and violent, was soon exhausted, and she probably fainted. I was, however, informed by the man, that as the fire was quenched in the sticks, the flames which appeared to kindle in her eyes gradually died away, that all the color forsook her lips, and that at last she murmured, "My heart! my heart! bring me the girl, and I'll purge her of the spell"; upon which they left her as though dead upon the rough earth floor on which she had fallen.

[3]

The Wax Image

In the reign of Titus there lived a certain noble and devout knight who had a beautiful wife, but she dishonored herself and persisted in her dishonor. The knight, therefore, was very sorrowful and resolved to visit the Holy Land. In this determination he said to his wife, "My beloved, I go to the Holy Land and leave you to the guidance of your own discretion." No sooner had he embarked than the lady sent for a certain skillful necromancer whom she loved; and he dwelt with her. It happened that as they lay in bed, the lady observed, "If you would do one thing for me, I might become your wife." "What is it," replied he, "that will please you, and which I can perform for you?"

"My husband is gone to the Holy Land, and loves me little; now, if by your art you could destroy him, all that I possess is yours." "I acquiesce," said the clerk, "but on condition that you marry me." To this the lady bound herself, and the necromancer fashioned an image under the similitude and name of the knight, and fixed it before him on the wall.

In the meantime, while the knight was passing through the main street of Rome, a wise master met him in the way, and observing him narrowly, said, "My friend, I have a secret to communicate."

"Well, master, what would you please to say?"

"This day you are one of death's children unless you follow my advice. Your wife is a harlot and contrives your death." The knight, hearing what was said of his spouse, put confidence in the speaker and said, "Good master, save my life and I will amply recompense you." "Willingly," answered the other, "if you will do as I shall tell you." The knight promised, and the master took him to a bath, undressed him, and desired him to bathe. Then putting into his hand a polished mirror, said, "Look attentively upon this and you will see wonders." He did so, and the meanwhile the master read to him from a book. "What see you?" he asked. "I see," said the knight, "a certain clerk in my house with an image of wax which resembles me, and which he has fastened in the wall." "Look again," continued the master; "what do you perceive now?"

"He takes a bow and places in it a sharp arrow; and now he aims at the effigy."

"As you love your life, the moment you discern the arrow flying to its mark, place yourself in the bath and remain there until I tell you to come out."

As soon, therefore, as the arrow quitted the string, he plunged his body into the water. This done, the master said, "Raise your head and look into the mirror. What do you perceive now?" "The effigy is not struck, and the arrow is sticking by its side. The clerk appears much concerned." "Look in the mirror once more," said the master, "and observe what he does." "He now goes nearer to the image and refixes the arrow in the string in order to strike it."

"As you value your life, do as before."

Again the knight plunged his body into the water as soon as he saw by the mirror that the clerk was bending the bow; and then, at the command of the master, resuming his inspection of the mirror, said, "The clerk makes great lamentation and says to my wife, 'If the third time I do not strike the effigy, I shall lose my life.' Now he approaches so near that I think he cannot miss it."

"Take care," said the master, "as soon as you see him bend the bow, immerse your body as I before told you." The knight watched attentively, and as soon as he saw the clerk draw back the bow to shoot, plunged below the water. "Rise quickly, and look into the mirror." When he had done so, he began to laugh. "My friend," said the master, "why do you laugh?" "I observe," answered he, "very distinctly, that the clerk has missed the effigy and that the arrow, rebounding, has entered his bowels and destroyed him. My wife makes a hole under my bed, and there he is buried."

"Rise then, dress yourself, and pray to God."

The knight returned sincere thanks for his life, and, having performed his pilgrimage, journeyed toward his own home. His wife met and received him with much apparent pleasure. He dissembled for a few days, and then sending for her parents, said to them, "My dear friends, hear why I have desired your presence. This woman, your daughter and my wife, has committed adultery; and, what is worse, designed to murder me." The lady denied the accusation with an oath. The knight then began to relate the whole story of the clerk's actions and end. "And," he continued, "if you do not credit this, come and see where the clerk is buried." He then led them into the bedchamber and dragged the body from its hiding place. The judge was called, and sentenced her to be burnt and her ashes to be scattered in the air. The knight soon afterward espoused a beautiful virgin, by whom he had many children; and with whom he finished his days in peace.

[4]

The Hand of Glory at the Old Spital Inn

One evening, between the years 1790 and 1800, a traveler, dressed in woman's clothes, arrived at the Old Spital Inn, the place where the mail coach changed horses, in High Spital, on Bowes Moor. The traveler begged to stay all night, but had to go away so early in the morning that if a mouthful of food were set ready for breakfast there was no need the family should be disturbed by her departure. The people of the house, however, arranged that a servant maid should sit up till the stranger was out of the premises, and then went to bed themselves.

The girl lay down for a nap on the long settle by the fire, but before she shut her eyes she took a good look at the traveler, who was sitting on the opposite side of the hearth, and espied a pair of man's trousers peeping out from under the gown. All inclination for sleep was now gone; however, with great self-command, she feigned it, closed her eyes, and even began to snore. On this the traveler got up, pulled out of his pocket a dead man's hand, fitted a candle to it, lighted the candle, and passed hand and candle several times before the servant girl's face, saying as he did so, "Let those who are asleep be asleep, and let those who are awake be awake." This done, he placed the light on the table, opened the outer door, went down two or three of the steps which led from the house to the road, and began to whistle for his companions. The girl (who had hitherto had presence of mind enough to remain perfectly quiet) now jumped up, rushed behind the ruffian, and pushed him down the steps. Then she shut the door, locked it, and ran upstairs to try and wake the family, but without success: calling, shouting, and shaking were alike in vain. The poor girl was in despair, for she heard the traveler and his comrades outside the house. So she ran down again, seized a bowl of blue [skimmed] milk, and threw it over the hand and the candle; after which she went upstairs again, and awoke the sleepers without any difficulty. The landlord's son went to the window and asked the men outside what they wanted. They answered that if the dead man's hand were but given them, they would go away quietly, and do no harm to anyone. This he refused, and fired among them, and the shot must have taken effect, for in the morning stains of blood were traced to a considerable distance.

[5]

The Insulted Spring

In the upper part of the parish of Cromarty there is a singularly curious spring, termed Sludach, which suddenly dries up every year early in summer and breaks out again at the close of autumn. It gushes from the bank with an undiminished volume until within a few hours before it ceases to flow for the season, and bursts forth on its return in a full stream. And it acquired this peculiar character, says tradition, some time in the seventeenth century.

On a very warm day of summer two farmers employed in the adjacent fields were approaching the spring in opposite directions to quench their thirst. One of them was tacksman of the farm on which the spring rises, the other tenanted a neighboring farm. They had lived for some time previous on no very friendly terms. The tacksman, a coarse, rude man, reached the spring first, and taking a hasty draught, he gathered up a handful of mud and, just as his neighbor came up, flung it into the water. "Now," said he, turning away as he spoke, "you may drink your fill." Scarcely had he uttered the words, however, when the offended stream began to boil like a caldron, and after bubbling a while among the grass and rushes, sunk into the ground. Next day at noon the heap of gray sand which had been incessantly rising and falling within it, in a little conical jet, for years before, had become as dry as the dust of the fields; and the strip of white flowering cresses which skirted either side of the runnel that had issued from it lay withering in the sun. What rendered the matter still more extraordinary, it was found that a powerful spring had burst out on the opposite side of the firth, which at this place is nearly five miles in breadth, a few hours after the Cromarty one had disappeared.

The story spread. The tacksman, rude and coarse as he was, was made unhappy by the forebodings of his neighbors, who seemed to regard him as one resting under a curse; and going to an elderly person in an adjoining parish, much celebrated for his knowledge of the supernatural, he craved his advice. "Repair," said the seer, "to the old hollow of the fountain, and as nearly as you can guess, at the hour in which you insulted the water, and after clearing it out with a clean linen towel lay yourself down beside it and abide the result." He did so, and waited on the bank above the hollow from noon until near sunset, when the water came rushing up with a noise like the roar of the sea, scattering the sand for several yards around. And then, subsiding to its common level, it flowed on as formerly between the double row of cresses. The spring on the opposite side of the firth withdrew its waters about the time of the rite of cleansing, and they have not since reappeared; while those of

Sludach, from that day to this, are presented, as if in scorn, during the moister seasons when no one regards them as valuable, and withheld in the seasons of drought, when they would be prized. We recognize in this singular tradition a kind of soul or Naiad of the spring, susceptible of offense and conscious of the attentions paid to it.

[6]

The Blue Light

There was once on a time a soldier who for many years had served the king faithfully, but when the war came to an end could serve no longer because of the many wounds which he had received. The king said to him, "Thou mayst return to thy home, I need thee no longer, and thou wilt not receive any more money, for he only receives wages who renders me service for them." Then the soldier did not know how to earn a living, went away greatly troubled, and walked the whole day, until in the evening he entered a forest. When darkness came on, he saw a light, which he went up to, and came to a house wherein lived a witch. "Do give me one night's lodging, and a little to eat and drink," said he to her, "or I shall starve." "Oho!" she answered, "who gives anything to a runaway soldier? Yet will I be compassionate, and take you in, if you will do what I wish." "What do you wish?" said the soldier. "That you should dig all round my garden for me, tomorrow." The soldier consented, and next day labored with all his strength, but could not finish it by the evening. "I see well enough," said the witch, "that you can do no more today, but I will keep you yet another night, in payment for which you must tomorrow chop me a load of wood, and make it small." The soldier spent the whole day in doing it, and in the evening the witch proposed that he should stay one night more. "Tomorrow, you shall only do me a very trifling piece of work. Behind my house, there is an old dry well, into which my light has fallen; it burns blue, and never goes out, and you shall bring it up again for me." Next day the old woman took him to the well, and let him down in a basket. He found the blue light, and made her a signal to draw him up again. She did draw him up, but when he came near the edge, she stretched down her hand and wanted to take the blue light away from him. "No," said he, perceiving her evil intention, "I will not give thee the light until I am standing with both feet upon the ground." The witch fell into a passion, let him down again into the well, and went away.

The poor soldier fell without injury on the moist ground, and the blue light went on burning, but of what use was that to him? He saw very well that he could not escape death. He sat for a while very sorrowfully, then suddenly he felt in his pocket and found his tobacco pipe, which was still half full. "This shall be my last pleasure," thought he, pulled it out, lit it at the blue light, and began to smoke. When the smoke had circled about the cavern, suddenly a little black dwarf stood before him, and said, "Lord, what are thy commands?" "What commands have I to give thee?" replied the soldier, quite astonished. "I must do everything thou biddest me," said the little man. "Good," said the soldier; "then in the first place help me out of this well." The little man took him by the hand, and led him through an underground passage, but he did not forget to take the blue light with him. On the way the dwarf showed him the treasures which the witch had collected and hidden there, and the soldier took as much gold as he could carry. When he was above, he said to the little man, "Now go and bind the old witch, and carry her before the judge." In a short time she, with frightful cries, came riding by on a wild tomcat, as swift as the wind, nor was it long after that before the little man reappeared. "It is all done," said he, "and the witch is already hanging on the gallows. What further commands has my lord?" inquired the dwarf. "At this moment, none," answered the soldier; "thou canst return home, only be at hand immediately, if I summon thee." "Nothing more is needed than that thou shouldst light thy pipe at the blue light, and I will appear before thee at once." Thereupon he vanished from his sight.

The soldier returned to the town from which he had come. He went to the best inn, ordered himself handsome clothes, and then bade the landlord furnish him a room as handsomely as possible.

When it was ready and the soldier had taken possession of it, he summoned the little black manikin and said, "I have served the king faithfully, but he has dismissed me, and left me to hunger, and now I want to take my revenge." "What am I to do?" asked the little man. "Late at night, when the king's daughter is in bed, bring her here in her sleep; she shall do servant's work for me." The manikin said, "That is an easy thing for me to do, but a very dangerous thing for you, for if it is discovered, you will fare ill." When twelve o'clock had struck, the door sprang open, and the manikin carried in the princess. "Aha! art thou there?" cried the soldier. "Get to thy work at once! Fetch the broom and sweep the chamber." When she had done this, he ordered her to come to his chair, and then he stretched out his feet and said, "Pull off my boots for me," and then he threw them in her face, and made her pick them up again, and clean and brighten them. She, however, did everything he bade her, without opposition, silently and with half-shut eyes. When the first cock crowed, the manikin carried her back to the royal palace, and laid her in her bed.

Next morning when the princess arose, she went to her father, and told him that she had had a very strange dream. "I was carried through the streets with the rapidity of lightning," said she, "and taken into a soldier's room, and I had to wait upon him like a servant, sweep his room, clean his boots, and do all kinds of menial work. It was only a dream, and yet I am just as tired as if I really had done everything." "The dream may have been true," said the king; "I will give thee a piece of advice. Fill thy pocket full of peas, and make a small hole in it, and then if thou art carried away again, they will fall out and leave a track in the streets." But unseen by the king, the manikin was standing beside him when he said that, and heard all. At night when the sleeping princess was again carried through the streets, some peas certainly did fall out of her pocket, but they made no track, for the crafty manikin had just before scattered peas in every street there was. And again the princess was compelled to do servant's work until cockcrow.

Next morning the king sent his people out to seek the track, but it was all in vain, for in every street poor children were sitting, picking up peas, and saying, "It must have rained peas, last night." "We must think of something else," said the king; "keep thy shoes on when thou goest to bed, and before thou comest back from the place where thou art taken, hide one of them there, I will soon contrive to find it." The black manikin heard this plot, and at night when the soldier again ordered him to bring the princess, revealed it to him, and told him that he knew of no expedient to counteract this stratagem, and that if the shoe were found in the soldier's house it would go badly with him." "Do what I bid thee," replied the soldier, and again this third night the princess was obliged to work like a servant, but before she went away, she hid her shoe under the bed.

Next morning the king had the entire town searched for his daughter's shoe. It was found at the soldier's, and the soldier himself, who at the entreaty of the dwarf had gone outside the gate, was soon brought back, and thrown into prison. In his flight he had forgotten the most valuable things he had, the blue light and the gold, and had only one ducat in his pocket. And now loaded with chains, he was standing at the window of his dungeon, when he chanced to see one of his comrades passing by. The soldier tapped at the pane of glass, and when this man came up, said to him, "Be so kind as to fetch me the small bundle I have left lying in the inn, and I will give you a ducat for doing it." His comrade ran thither and brought him what he wanted. As soon as the soldier was alone again, he lighted his pipe and summoned the black manikin. "Have no fear," said the latter to his master. "Go wheresoever they take you, and let them do what they will, only take the blue light with you." Next day the soldier was tried, and though he had done nothing wicked, the judge condemned him to death. When he was led forth to die, he begged a last favor of the king. "What is it?" asked the king. "That I may smoke one more pipe on my way." "Thou mayst smoke three," answered the king, "but do not imagine that I will spare thy life." Then the soldier pulled out his pipe and lighted it at the blue light, and as soon as a few wreaths of smoke had ascended, the manikin was there with a small cudgel in his hand, and said, "What does my lord command?" "Strike down to the earth that false judge there, and his constable, and spare not the king who has treated me so ill." Then the manikin fell on them like lightning, darting this way and that way, and whosoever was so much as touched by his cudgel fell to the earth, and did not venture to stir again. The king was terrified; he threw himself on the soldier's mercy, and merely to be allowed to live at all, gave him his kingdom for his own, and the princess to wife.

[7]

The Friar and Boy

The father of the boy Jack had married a second time, and Jack's stepmother behaved most harshly to him, and half starved him.

> Nay, tho' his meat and drink was poor
> He had not half enough.
> Yet, if he seemed to crave for more
> His ears she straight did cuff.

His father, however, behaved kindly, and to get the lad away proposed he should look after the cows all day, taking his provision with him. One day an old man came to him and begged for food, on which Jack offered him his dinner, which the old man thankfully took and ate.

Indeed, he was so grateful that he told Jack he would give him three things, whatever he liked to choose. Jack replied:

> "The first thing I'd have thee bestow
> On me without dispute,
> Pray let it be a cunning bow,
> With which I birds may shoot."
> "Well thou shalt have a bow, my son,
> I have it here in store,
> No archer ever yet had one
> Which shot so true before.
> Take notice well of what I say.
> Such virtues are in this
> That wink or look another way
> The mark you shall not miss."

Jack also asked for a pipe, and the old man said:

"A pipe I have for thee, my son,
The like was never known,
So full of mirth and mickle joy,
That whensoe'er 'tis blown,
All living creatures that shall hear
The sweet and pleasant sound
They shan't be able to forebear
But dance and skip around."

The third thing Jack chose was, that whenever his stepmother looked crossly at him, she should, against her will, behave in a rude and unseemly manner, which was also granted.

The old man left him; and at evening Jack took the cattle home, and as he went, he tried his pipe with wonderful effect.

His cows began to caper then,
The bulls and oxen too,
And so did five and twenty men
Who came this sight to view,
Along the road he piping went,
The bulls came dancing after,
Which was a fit of merriment,
That caused a deal of laughter.
For why, a friar in his gown
Bestrides the red cow's back,
And so rides dancing thro' the town,
After this young wag Jack.

He found his father at home, and telling him how he had disposed of his dinner, the good man handed him a capon; at which his stepmother frowned, and, to her great disgust, her punishment was prompt, and she had to retire, Jack bantering her. She vowed vengeance, and

A friar whom she thought a saint,
Came there to lodge that night;
To whom she made a sad complaint,
How Jack had shamed her quite.
Said she, "For sweet St. Francis sake,
Tomorrow in the field,
Pray thrash him till his bones you break
No show of comfort yield."

The friar went the next morning to give Jack his thrashing, but Jack begged him not to be angry, and he would show him something; so he took his bow and shot a pheasant, which fell in a thorn bush. The friar ran to secure the bird, and when well in the bush, Jack played his pipe, with woeful effects as regards the friar, who in his involuntary dancing got literally torn to pieces, till he begged Jack:

"For good St. Francis sake,
Let me not dancing die."

He naturally told his pitiful tale when he reached Jack's father's house, and the father asked him if it were true, and if so, to play the pipe and make them dance. The friar had already experienced the sensation, and

The friar did quake for fear
And wrung his hands withal.
He cried, and still his eyes did wipe,
"That work kills me almost;
Yet if you needs must hear the pipe,
Pray bind me to a post."

This was done; the pipe struck up, and everyone began their involuntary dance, to the delight of the father and the great disgust of the stepmother and the friar, who

was almost dead,
While others danced their fill.
Against the post he banged his head
For he could not stand still.
His ragged flesh the rope did tear,
And likewise from his crown,
With many bangs and bruises there
The blood did trickle down.

The lad led them all into the street, where everyone joined in the mad scene, until his father asked him to stop. Then the friar summoned him before the proctor, and the gravity of the court was disturbed by Jack's playing his pipe at the proctor's request. All had to dance, nor would Jack desist until he had a solemn promise that he should go free.

[8]

The Serpent's Stone

In the reign of a certain king there lived a proud and oppressive seneschal. Now, near the royal palace was a forest well stocked with game; and by the direction of this person various pits were dug there, and covered with leaves, for the purpose of entrapping the beasts. It happened that the seneschal himself went into this forest, and with much exaltation of heart exclaimed internally, "Lives there a being in the empire more powerful than I am?" This braggart thought was scarcely formed, ere he rode upon one of his own pitfalls and immediately disappeared. The same day had been taken a lion, a monkey, and a serpent. Terrified at the situation into which fate had thrown him, he cried out lustily, and his noise awoke a poor man called Guido, who had come with his ass into that forest to procure firewood, by the sale of which he got his bread. Hastening to the mouth of the pit, he was promised great wealth if he would extricate the seneschal from his perilous situation. "My friend," answered Guido, "I have no means of obtaining a livelihood except by the faggots which I collect: if I neglect this for a single day, I shall be thrown into the greatest difficulties." The seneschal reiterated his promises of enriching him; and Guido went back to the city and returned with a long cord which he let down into the pit and bade the seneschal bind it round his waist. But before he could apply it to the intended purpose, the lion leaped forward and seizing upon the cord, was drawn up in his stead. Immediately exhibiting great signs of pleasure, the beast ran off into the wood. The rope again descended, and the monkey, having noticed the success of the lion, vaulted above the man's head and shaking the cord, was in like manner set at liberty, and hurried off to his haunts. A third time the cord was let down, and the serpent twining around it, was drawn up, gave signs of gratitude and escaped. "Oh, my good friend," said the seneschal, "the beasts are gone; now draw me up quickly, I pray you." Guido complied, and afterward succeeded in drawing up his horse, which the seneschal instantly mounted and rode back to the palace. Guido returned home; and his wife, observing that he had come without wood, was very dejected and inquired the cause. He related what had occurred, and the riches he was to receive for his service. The wife's countenance brightened.

Early in the morning her husband went to the palace. But the seneschal denied all knowledge of him and ordered him to be whipped for his presumption. The porter executed the directions and beat him so severely that he left him half dead. As soon as Guido's wife understood this, she saddled their ass and brought him home in a very infirm state. The sickness which ensued consumed the whole of their little property; but as soon as he had recovered, he returned to his usual occupation in the wood. Whilst he was thus employed, he beheld afar off ten asses laden with packs, and a lion following close on them, pursuing the path which led toward Guido. On looking narrowly at this beast, he remembered that it was the same which he had freed from its imprisonment in the pit. The lion signified with his foot that he should take the loaded asses and go home. This Guido did, and the lion followed. On arriving at his own door, the noble beast fawned upon him, and wagging his tail as if in triumph, ran back to the woods. Guido caused proclamation to be made in different churches that, if any asses had been lost, the owners should come to him; but no one appearing to demand them, he opened the packages and to his great joy discovered them full of money. On the second day Guido returned to the forest but forgot an iron instrument to cleave the wood. He looked up and beheld the monkey whose liberation he had effected; and the animal, by help of teeth and nails, accomplished his desires. Guido then loaded his asses and went home. The next day he renewed his visit to the forest; and sitting down to prepare his instrument, discerned the serpent whose escape he had aided, carrying a stone in its mouth of three colors: on one side white, on another black, and on the third red. It opened its mouth and let the stone fall into Guido's lap. Having done this, it departed. Guido took the stone to a skillful lapidary, who had no sooner inspected it than he knew its virtues, and would willingly have paid him a hundred florins for it. But Guido refused; and by means of that singular stone obtained great wealth and was promoted to a military command. The emperor having heard of the extraordinary qualities which it possessed desired to see it. Guido went accordingly; and the emperor was so struck by its uncommon beauty, that he wished to purchase it at any rate; and threatened, if Guido refused compliance, to banish him the kingdom.

"My lord," answered he, "I will sell the stone; but let me say one thing—if the price be not given, it shall be presently restored to me." He demanded three hundred florins, and then, taking it from a small coffer, put it into the emperor's hands. Full of admiration, he exclaimed, "Tell me where you procured this beautiful stone." This he did; and narrated from the beginning the seneschal's accident and subsequent ingratitude. He told how severely he had been injured by his command; and the benefits he had received from the lion, the monkey, and the serpent. Much moved at the recital, the emperor sent for the seneschal and said, "What is this I hear of thee?" He was unable to reply. "O wretch!" continued the emperor, "monster of ingratitude! Guido liberated thee from the most imminent danger, and for this thou hast nearly destroyed him. Dost thou see how even irrational things have rendered him good for the service he performed? But thou hast returned evil for good. Therefore I deprive thee of thy dignity, which I will bestow upon Guido; and I further adjudge you to be suspended on a cross." This decree infinitely rejoiced the noblemen of the empire; and Guido, full of honors and years, ended his days in peace.

[9]

The Chaste Mates

The Emperor Gallus employed a singularly skillful carpenter in the erection of a magnificent palace. At that period a certain knight lived who had a very beautiful daughter; and who, perceiving the extraordinary sagacity of the artificer, determined to give him the lady in marriage. Calling him, therefore, he said, "My good friend, ask of me what you will; so that it be possible, I will do it, provided you marry my daughter." The other assented, and the nuptial rites were celebrated accordingly. Then the mother of the lady said to the carpenter, "My son, since you have become one of our family, I will bestow upon you a curious shirt. It possesses this singular property, that as long as you and your wife are faithful to each other, it will neither be rent, nor worn, nor stained. But if—which Heaven forbid!—either of you prove unfaithful, instantly it will lose its virtue." The carpenter, very happy in what he heard, took the shirt and returned great thanks for the gift.

A short time afterward, the carpenter being sent for to superintend the building of the emperor's palace, took with him the valuable present which he had received. He remained away from home until the structure was complete; and numbers, observing how much he labored, admired the freshness and spotless purity of his shirt. Even the emperor condescended to notice it, and said to him, "My master, how is it that in despite of your laborious occupation and the constant use of your shirt, it still preserves its color and beauty?"

"You must know, my lord," said he, "that as long as my wife and I continue faithful to each other, my shirt retains its original whiteness and beauty; but if either of us forget our matrimonial vows, it will sully like any other cloth."

A soldier, overhearing this, thought within himself, "If I can, I will make you wash your shirt." Wherefore, without giving any cause of suspicion to the carpenter, he secretly hastened to his house and solicited his wife to dishonor. She received him with an appearance of pleasure, and seemed to be entirely influenced by the same feelings. "But," added she, "in this place we are exposed to observation; come with me and I will conduct you into a private chamber." He followed her, and closing the door, she said, "Wait here awhile; I will return presently." Thus she did every day, all the time supplying him only with bread and water. Without regard to his urgency, she compelled him to endure this humiliating treatment; and before long, two other soldiers came to her from the emperor's court with the same evil views. In like manner, she decoyed them into the chamber and fed them with bread and water.

The sudden disappearance, however, of the three soldiers gave rise to much inquiry; and the carpenter on the completion of his labors received the stipulated sum and returned to his own home. His virtuous wife met him with joy, and looking upon the spotless shirt, exclaimed, "Blessed be God! our truth is made apparent—there is not a single stain upon the shirt." To which he replied, "My beloved, during the progress of the building, three soldiers, one after another, came to ask questions about the shirt. I related the fact, and since that time nothing has been heard of them." The lady smiled and said, "The soldiers respecting whom you feel anxious thought me a fit subject for their improper solicitation and came hither with vilest intent. I decoyed them into a remote chamber, and have fed them with bread and water." The carpenter, delighted with this proof of his wife's fidelity, spared their lives and liberated them; and he and his wife lived happily for the rest of their lives.

[10]

Little Annie, the Goose Girl

Once on a time there was a king who had so many geese he was forced to have a lassie to tend them and watch them; her name was Annie, and so they called her "Annie the goose girl." Now you must know there was a king's son from England who went out to woo; and as he came along Annie sat herself down in his way.

"Sitting all alone there, you little Annie?" said the king's son.

"Yes," said little Annie, "here I sit and put stitch to stitch and patch on patch. I'm waiting today for the king's son from England."

"Him you mustn't look to have," said the prince.

"Nay, but if I'm to have him," said little Annie, "have him I shall, after all."

And now limners were sent out into all lands and realms to take the likenesses of the fairest princesses, and the prince was to choose among them. So he thought so much of one of them, that he set out to seek her, and wanted to wed her, and he was glad and happy when he got her for his sweetheart.

But now I must tell you this prince had a stone with him which he laid by his bedside, and that stone knew everything, and when the princess came little Annie told her, if so be she'd had a sweetheart before, or didn't feel herself quite free from anything which she didn't wish the prince to know, she'd better not step on that stone which lay by the bedside.

"If you do, it will tell him all about you," said little Annie.

So when the princess heard that, she was dreadfully downcast, and she fell upon the thought to ask Annie if she would get into bed that night in her stead and lie down by the prince's side, and then when he was sound asleep, Annie should get out and the princess should get in, and so when he woke up in the morning he would find the right bride by his side.

So they did that, and when Annie the goose girl came and stepped upon the stone the prince asked:

"Who is this that steps into my bed?"

"A maid pure and bright," said the stone, and so they lay down to sleep; but when the night wore on the princess came and lay down in Annie's stead.

But next morning, when they were to get up, the prince asked the stone again: "Who is this that steps out of my bed?"

"One that has had three bairns," said the stone.

When the prince heard that, he wouldn't have her, you may know very well; and so he packed her off home again, and took another sweetheart.

But as he went to see her, little Annie went and sat down in his way again.

"Sitting all alone there, little Annie, the goose girl?" said the prince.

"Yes, here I sit, and put stitch to stitch, and patch on patch; for I'm waiting today for the king's son from England," said Annie.

"Oh! you mustn't look to have him," said the king's son.

"Nay, but if I'm to have him, have him I shall, after all"; that was what Annie thought.

Well, it was the same story over again with the prince; only this time, when his bride got up in the morning, the stone said she'd had six bairns.

So the prince wouldn't have her either, but sent her about her business; but still he thought he'd try once more if he couldn't find one who was pure and spotless; and he sought far and wide in many lands, till at last he found one he thought he might trust. But when he went to see her, little Annie the goose girl had put herself in his way again.

"Sitting all alone there, you little Annie, the goose girl?" said the prince.

"Yes, here I sit, and put stitch to stitch, and patch on patch; for I'm waiting today for the king's son from England," said Annie.

"Him you mustn't look to have," said the prince.

"Nay, but if I'm to have him, have him I shall, after all," said little Annie.

So when the princess came, little Annie the goose girl told her the same as she had told the other two, if she'd had any sweetheart before, or if there was anything else she didn't wish the prince to know, she mustn't tread on the stone that the prince had put at his bedside; for, said she: "It tells him everything."

The princess got very red and downcast when she heard that, for she was just as naughty as the others, and asked Annie if she would go in her stead and lie down with the prince that night; and when he was sound asleep, she would come and take her place, and then he would have the right bride by his side when it was light next morning.

Yes! they did that. And when little Annie the goose girl came and stepped upon the stone, the prince asked: "Who is this that steps into my bed?"

"A maid pure and bright," said the stone; and so they lay down to rest.

Farther on in the night the prince put a ring on Annie's finger, and it fitted so tight she couldn't get it off again; for the prince saw well enough there was something wrong, and so he wished to have a mark by which he might know the right woman again.

Well, when the prince had gone off to sleep, the princess came and drove Annie away to the pigsty, and lay down in her place. Next morning, when they were to get up, the prince asked: "Who is this that steps out of my bed?"

"One that's had nine bairns," said the stone.

When the prince heard that, he drove her away at once, for he was in an awful rage; and then he asked the stone how it all was with these princesses who had stepped on it, for he couldn't understand it at all, he said.

So the stone told him how they had cheated him, and sent little Annie the goose girl to him in their stead.

But as the prince wished to have no mistake about it, he went down to her where she sat tending her geese, for he wanted to see if she had the ring too, and he thought, if she has it, 'twere best to take her at once for my queen.

So when he got down he saw in a moment that she had tied a bit of rag round one of her fingers, and so he asked her why it was tied up.

"Oh! I've cut myself so badly," said little Annie the goose girl.

So he must and would see the finger, but Annie wouldn't take the rag off. Then he caught hold of the finger; but Annie, she tried to pull it from him, and so between them the rag came off, and then he knew his ring.

So he took her up to the palace, and gave her much fine clothes and attire, and after that they held their wedding feast; and so little Annie the goose girl came to have the king of England's son for her husband after all, just because it was written that she should have him.

XIII

MALADIES AND REMEDIES

In folktales one frequently encounters curious diseases and strange cures. A witch can cause one to fall sick by her magic image or evil eye. A girl has a mysterious malady because a toad swallowed a strand of her hair and hopped off to his hole. The remedy is to find and kill the toad. A king must touch a scrofulous person to effect a cure, for it was believed in some lands that scrofula, or a similar affliction, was caused by violating a royal taboo, such as eating from a king's dishes. In parts of Natal it is still believed that a king's touch will cure palsy. It was generally believed for a long time (and some believe it today) that the cause of disease was the presence of a demon in the body or afflicted part. When the medicine man conjured the demon out of the sick person, he regularly sent it into the body of another person or an animal. This superstition accounts for, at least in part, the belief that a disease could be transferred as a unit, leaving not a trace behind as it took up its habitation elsewhere. According to this theory, to cure a cold, give it to someone else or pass it on to a scapegoat. The second selection in this section describes a "disembodied" but visible disease in transit seeking new lodgings.

"Contagion" is from the *Gesta Romanorum*, ed. 1824, and "Laying the Plague" is from Hugh Miller's *Scenes and Legends of the North of Scotland*, 1874. "The Poor Frog, or Transferring a Disease," "Magdalen and the Pins," "The Hag and the Earl of Derby," and "The King's Evil" are from *The Gentleman's Magazine Library*, 1884.

[1]

Contagion

In the kingdom of a certain prince there were two knights, one of whom was avaricious and the other envious. The former had a beautiful wife whom everyone admired and loved. But the spouse of the latter was ugly and disagreeable. Now the envious knight had a piece of land adjoining the estate of his covetous neighbor, of which the last exceedingly desired possession. He made him many offers, but the envious person invariably refused to sell his inheritance for silver or gold. At last, in the envy of his soul, he meditated how to destroy the beauty of the wife of the covetous knight, and offered him the land on condition of enjoying his wife for one night. The covetous wretch immediately assented; and bade his wife submit herself to his will. This diabolical contract adjusted, the envious knight instantly infected himself with St. Anthony's Fire and communicated the disease to the lady, for which he assigned the following reason. He said that, being filled with envy at the beauty and grace which he observed in his neighbor's wife, while his own was so deformed and hateful, he had resolved to remove the disparity. The lady wept exceedingly and related to her husband what had happened. This troubled him, but he bethought himself of a remedy. "As yet," said he, "no symptoms of the disorder are perceptible. At a short distance from hence there is a large city, and in it a university. Go there; stand in the public way and entice every passer-by to you. By this means you will free yourself from the distemper."

The lady did as she was directed; and the emperor's son, passing by, fell violently in love with her. Afraid to infect a person so near the throne, she resisted his advances and informed him that she suffered from the Rose. This, however, altered not the feelings of the young man; and accordingly the disease of the woman adhered to him. Ashamed of what had befallen, and at the same time fearful of discovery, he went to his mistress and abode with her. This circumstance she stated to her husband, and he, much troubled, set his bedchamber in order, and there the prince dwelt in the strictest seclusion, attended upon only by the lady. Here he continued seven years.

It chanced in the seventh year that there was an intolerable heat, and the sick man had a vessel of wine standing by his side, designed to refresh his exhausted spirits. At this moment a serpent came out of the garden, and, after bathing itself in the vessel, lay down at the bottom. The prince, awaking from sleep, under the influence of an excessive thirst, took up the vessel and drank; and without knowing it, swallowed the serpent. The creature, finding itself thus unexpectedly imprisoned, began to gnaw his bowels so grievously as to put the prince to inconceivable anguish. The lady greatly compassionated him; and indeed, for three days he was an object of pity. On the fourth, however, an emetic being administered, he vomited and cast up, together with the inward disease, the serpent which had tormented him. Immediately the pain ceased, and little by little the St. Anthony's Fire left him. In seven days his skin was as free from the disorder as the skin of a child; and the lady, much delighted, clothed him in sumptuous apparel and presented him a beautiful war horse, on which he returned to the emperor. He was received with all honor, and after his father's death ascended the throne, and ended his days in peace.

[2]

Laying the Plague

In a central part of the churchyard of Nigg there is a rude undressed stone, near which the sexton never ventures to open a grave. A wild apocryphal tradition connects the erection of this stone with the times of the quarantine fleet which eighty or a hundred years ago lay in the port of Cromarty. The plague, as the story goes, was brought to the place by one of the vessels, and was slowly flying along the ground, disengaged from every vehicle of infection, in the shape of a little yellow cloud. The whole country was alarmed, and groups of people were to be seen on every eminence, watching with anxious horror the progress of the little cloud. They were relieved, however, from their fears and the plague by an ingenious man of Nigg, who, having provided himself with an immense bag of linen, fashioned somewhat in the manner of a fowler's net, cautiously approached the yellow cloud, and with a skill which could have owed nothing to previous practice, succeeded in enclosing the whole of it in the bag. He then secured it by wrapping it up carefully, fold after fold, and fastening it down with pin after pin; and as the linen was gradually changing, as if under the hands of a dyer, from white to yellow, he consigned it to the churchyard, where it has slept ever since.

[3]

The Poor Frog, or Transferring a Disease

Blairsville Joint School Library
Blairsville, Pa.

The daughter of a Worcestershire farmer had suffered long under a sad disease which wasted her strength and had brought her nearly to the grave. The anxious father had consulted every medical practitioner of note the country round, and had sought at Gloucester that certainty of relief which the high talents of the medical profession so naturally promised. A large glandular swelling on one side of her neck drained from her the whole strength of life. And still no relief was found: it was pronounced incurable. At this time a cunning man of high reputation presented himself and proposed the experiment of a charm, which, under similar circumstances, had been universally successful. He examined the part minutely and left the patient, requiring neither the exhibition of medicine nor attention to diet. Nature was to be his only handmaid. Now comes the extraordinary fact. He caught a frog, no matter where; and with his knife inflicted a wound on that part of its neck corresponding exactly with the seat of the disease on the patient's neck, and then suffered the animal to escape. "If," said he, "it lives, the disease will gradually waste away and your daughter recover. But if the creature dies in consequence of this injury, there is then no hope; the malady will continue to increase, and a painful, though it may be a lingering, death will be the certain consequence."

Now Nature triumphed and the charm worked! The swelling went down and the farmer's daughter recovered her health. The cunning man had accomplished what the learned physicians said was impossible.

[4]

Magdalen and the Pins

Magdalen Holyday was the daughter of poor honest persons, Phineas and Martha Holyday, of the parish of Rendham, near Framlingham. She was eighteen, unmarried, and servant maid to Mr. Simon Jones, minister of the Parish of Saxmunham, with whom she had dwelt for the space of three years and upward, and was esteemed by all the neighbors as a civil, well-behaved young woman and of good conduct above her years. She was sweet and civil in her speech, and painstaking in her religion; so that she was well respected of all in the said parish, old and young. Except for a defect in the color of her hair, she was a very fair and comely person. Her stature was moderate and her disposition cheerful. No reproach was ever thrown upon her, save that some few of the Gospelers would taunt her, that being handmaid to a minister of the Church, she would frequent wakes and fairs at Whitsuntide, and saint days and holy days. But they could not throw anything in her teeth which they would, as she always went in company with her brother, aunts, or other sober people of good repute, who could keep scandal from her door. Her family did not like Oliver Cromwell, nor any of his ordinances, but were true and faithful to King Charles, of blessed memory, though they were but poor folk.

Now Magdalen Holyday had in her youth been touched of the king for the evil when he came into the Associated Counties. But since that she had always preserved her health, so that the rose-blush in her cheek and the milky snow on her forehead were known to all. But to come to my story. It happened on Monday, in Lammas, 1672, about noon, as she was carrying in dinner. No one was in the parlor but the parson, his wife, and their eldest daughter, Rebecca. On a sudden, just as Magdalen had placed a suet dumpling on the board, she uttered a loud shriek, as if she were distraught, and stooping down as in great pain, said she felt a pricking as of a large pin in the upper part of her leg, but she did not think that any such thing could be there. Yet on ungartering her hose, she felt a pin had got there under the skin, yet not drawing blood nor breaking the skin, nor making any hole or sign, and she could hardly feel the head of it with her finger. And from that time it continued tormenting her with violent drawing pains all the day and night. As this continued without abatement, Mistress Jones, by advice of the minister, sent for the assistance of two apothecaries, one a surgeon of great repute, who had studied under the great Hondius at Frankfort, and the other a real son of Galen. After examining the part, and above and below at sufficient distance, both declared they could see no sign of the said pin. But on her constant and confident assertion that there was a pin, they made an incision but could find none.

Magdalen now told them that a few days before this had happened to her, an old woman came to the door and begged a pin of her. But she did not give her a pin, and the old woman muttered something, but she did not suspect her then.

The poor girl was tormented ceaselessly, both by night and day, for if she slept her sleep was troubled with dreams and wicked apparitions. Sometimes she saw something like a mole run into her bed; sometimes she saw a naked arm held over her. And so was this poor maid thus tormented by evil spirits in spite of all godly prayers and ringing of church bells.

Now two doctors, Anthony Smith and Samuel Kingston, took her in hand. First they made a decoction of southern wood, mugwort vervain, famed for expelling demons. This they made her drink.

Then they anointed the part with an embrocation made of dog's grease, bear's fat, capon's grease, four and twenty slips of mistletoe, cut in pieces and powdered small with gum of Venice turpentine. This they had corked tightly in a vial and exposed for nine days to the sun till it formed into a green balsam. The afflicted part was anointed with this for the space of three weeks' time, during which, instead of amendment, the poor patient daily got worse, and vomited, not without constant shrieks or gruntling, the following substances: parings of nails, bits of spoons, triangular pieces of brass, crooked pins, bodkins, lumps of red hair, broken egg shells, parchment shavings, a hen's leg bone, 1,002 worms, pieces of glass, bones like the great teeth of a horse, aluminous matter, and saltpeter. When the doctors had well nigh given up, at length relief was found. Magdalen brought up, with violent retching, a whole row of pins stuck on blue paper! And then the doctors joyfully perceived that their potent drugs had wrought the designed cure. They comforted her and declared that she had subdued her bitter foe.

Since then she has been perfectly well. She married the steward of Sir John Heveningham and bore him four healthy children. Whether her strange sickness was inflicted upon her by the said old woman, an emissary of Satan, or whether it was meant wholesomely to rebuke her for frequenting wakes, May dances and Candlemas fairs, and such like pastimes, is still a question.

[5]

The Hag and the Earl of Derby

On April 16, 1594, the Earl of Derby was taken with a strange sickness. The cause of this was thought by his physicians to be partly a surfeit and partly a most violent distempering himself with vehement exercise, taken from days together in the Easter week. But he himself believed it to be the work of a witch.

The first of April before the earl fell sick, a woman requested him to give or assign her a dwelling place near him, so that she might from time to time speedily reveal to him such things as God revealed to her for his good. As her request was thought to no purpose, it was refused.

On the fourth of April he dreamed that his wife was dangerously sick, and being sorely troubled by the vision, he suddenly cried out and started from his bed, calling for help. Half asleep, he sought for her about the chamber, but being fully awaked, was comforted because he found her well.

On the fifth of April, in his chamber at Kronstey about six o'clock at night, there appeared suddenly a tall man with a ghostly and threatening countenance, who twice or thrice seemed to cross him as he was passing through the chamber. And when he came to the same part of the chamber where the shadow appeared, he felt sick at his stomach. And yet Goborne, one of his secretaries attending then upon him, saw nothing, a fact which amazed the earl. The same night he dreamed he was in fighting stabbed to the heart twice or thrice. Also wounded in many other parts of his body.

About midnight, April 10, one Master Halsall found an image of wax in the earl's bedchamber. The hair on the wax image was like the earl's hair, and it was twisted through the belly of the effigy from the navel to the secrets. And the image was spotted. Afterward spots appeared on the earl's sides and belly. This image was hastily cast into the fire by Master Halsall before it was viewed, because he thought by burning it, as he said, he should relieve his lord from witchcraft and burn the witch who so much tormented his lord. But it fell out contrary to his love and affection, for after the melting of the wax figure, the earl declined more and more.

The doctors were called in. They gave him a glyster to draw the course of the humors downward, and had some success. Also they got good results from a gentle infusion of rhubarb and manna in a draught of chicken broth. On the twelfth of April, one Jane, a witch, demanded of Mr. Goborne whether the earl felt any pain in his lower parts, and that very same night his water stopped up of a sudden, to the astonishment of all. The next day all means were used to rectify this condition—glysters, drinks, plasters, fomentations, oils, poultices, even a catheter—but with no favorable results.

Meanwhile Sir Edward Filton and other justices examined certain witches. Sir Edward reported that one of them—doubtless, Jane—being bidden to say the Lord's Prayer, said it well. But being conjured in the name of Jesus that if she had bewitched the earl, she would not be able to say the same, she never could repeat the petition "Forgive us our trespasses"; no, not even when it was repeated to her.

In all the time of his sickness the earl often took bezoar stone and unicorn's horn. Although these and some other remedies seemed to help him a little, he insisted that the doctors labored in vain, because he was certainly bewitched. He fell twice into a trance, not being able to move head, hand, or foot. And shortly before he expired, he cried out against all witches and witchcraft, reposing his only hope of salvation upon the merits of the Christian God.

[6]

The King's Evil

One Christopher Lovel, residing in the city of Bristol where he got his living by labor, was extremely afflicted for many years with the king's evil, and such a flow of the scrofulous humor, that though it found a vent by five running sores about his breast, neck, and arms, there was such a tumor on one side of his neck, as left no hollow between his cheek and the upper part of his left shoulder, and forced him to keep his head always awry. The young man was reduced by the virulence of the humor to the lowest state of weakness; appeared a miserable object in the eyes of all the inhabitants of that populous city; and having for many years tried all the remedies which the art of physic could administer, without receiving any benefit, resolved at last to go abroad to be touched. He had an uncle in the place, who was an old seaman and carried him from Bristol at the end of August, 1716, along with him to Cork in Ireland, where he put him on board a ship that was bound to St. Martin's in the isle of Rhee.

From thence Christopher made his way first to Paris, and thence to the place where he was touched, in the beginning of November following, by the eldest lineal descendant of a race of kings, who had indeed, for a long succession of ages, cured that distemper by the royal touch. But this descendant and next heir of their blood had not, at least at that time, been crowned or anointed. The usual effect, however, followed: from the moment that the man was touched and invested with the narrow ribbon, to which a small piece of silver was pendant, according to the rites prescribed in the office appointed by the church for that solemnity, the humor dispersed insensibly, his sores healed up, and he recovered strength daily, till he arrived in perfect health in the beginning of January following at Bristol, having spent only four months and some few days in this voyage. There it was, and in the week preceding St. Paul's fair, that I saw the man in his recovered vigor of body, without any remains of his complaint, but what were to be seen in the red scars then left upon the five places where the sharp humor had found a vent, but which were otherwise entirely healed and as sound as any other part of his body.

Dr. Lane, an eminent physician in the place, whom I visited on my arrival, told me of this cure as the most wonderful thing that ever happened; and pressed me as well to see the man upon whom it was performed, as to talk about his case with Mr. Samuel Pye, a very skillful surgeon, and I believe still living in that city; who had tried in vain for three years together to cure the man by physical remedies. I had an opportunity of doing both; and Mr. Pye, after dining together, carrying me to the man, I examined and informed myself fully of all particulars, relating as well to his illness as his cure; and found upon the whole, that if it is not to be deemed miraculous, it at least deserved the character, given it by Dr. Lane, of being one of the most wonderful events that has ever happened. There are abundance of instances of the cure of the king's evil by the touch of our English princes in former times, mentioned by Tucker in his book on that subject: and it is observable that the author was himself an infidel on that head, till convinced of his mistake by the late learned Mr. Anstis, garter-king-of-arms, who furnished him with those proofs out of the English records, which attest the facts, and are printed in that treatise. But I am apt to think there never was an instance in which the distemper had prevailed to a higher degree, or the surprising cure of it was known to such infinite multitudes of people, as in the case of Christopher Lovel.

Notes

I Otherworld and Transformed Lovers

1. "The Serpent Woman." It is believed in parts of Spain that an evil woman must become a snake at night for a certain number of years, and that if such a woman bites a person, the cure is extremely difficult. In our story the effect of the Serpent Woman's touching Don Luis's wrist is as deadly as a serpent's bite. To kiss a Poison Maiden like the one in the *Gesta Romanorum* (Tale XI) is fatal. Her bite and her perspiration are deadly, and she also kills by fixing her gaze upon someone, i.e. she has the evil eye.

2. "Melusina." As in the similar "Sir Launfal" and "Undine," the mortal loses his mate because he violates a taboo. Because of her mother's curse Melusina became a serpent from the waist downward every Saturday until she should marry a man who would promise never to see her on that day, and keep his promise. Jean d'Arras makes Melusina a good Christian; she is married by a bishop and he blesses the nuptial bed. However, Otherworld wives are usually antagonistic to Christianity. For example, when the husband of the Otherworld wife in the English romance "Richard Cœur de Lyon" tried to force her to hear Mass, she took two of her children by the hand, sailed right out through the church roof, and never was seen again.

Brantôme mentions the supernatural protection given by Melusina to the Castle of Lusignan and the terror of the neighbors on hearing her shrieks and wailings when the castle was leveled by the brutal Duc de Montpensier. They often saw her in the bloom of female beauty, but with a dragon's tail, hovering over the castle or bathing in a rill which washed its walls. She always screamed when death or disaster was about to strike any of her descendants. In other words, she became a banshee.

3. "The Forty He-goats" belongs to the Cupid-and-Psyche cycle. The fine Norse tale of "East o' the Sun and West o' the Moon" is another interesting version. In this last the poor man's youngest daughter (as usual in folktales) marries a prince who has been transformed into a white bear by his stepmother, a witch. The couple live in a rich castle, and at night the prince reassumes his human shape. But the bride violates a taboo and reveals to her mother that she has never seen her spouse after he has gone to bed. The mother tells her that he is probably an ugly troll. When the girl lights a candle to see if this is so (and violating another taboo) three drops of hot tallow fall on the prince and wake him. Now he must leave her, and she must search long and undergo great hardships before she finds him. Then for a while she is a Forgotten Fiancée but finally succeeds in making her prince recognize her and in besting the long-nosed princess who was her rival. "Hans, the Hedgehog" and "The Donkey" in the Grimms' *Household Tales* are similar to our story.

Transformation by immersion in water often occurs in folktales. A man may lose his sex or become an animal or god, or even a werewolf, by swimming a stream or plunging into a magic spring or pool. Notice that the princess does not recognize her husband until he emerges from the water.

4. "The Weaver Who Impersonated Vishnu" has many analogues. Once the belief that the gods make love to mortals is admitted, the way is prepared for impostors to impersonate amorous deities and deceive women. One parent of many a hero belonged to the Otherworld, or was supposed to. Godefroy of Bouillon descended from a swan maiden, Plato's mother was impregnated by the spirit of Apollo, and Merlin's father was an incubus. The magician Nectanebus made Olympias believe that the god Ammon would appear to her, and disguising himself as that deity, he gained admission to her bedchamber and begot Alexander.

The tale of "Paulina and Anubis," told by Josephus, is on this theme. When the chaste wife Paulina would not listen to his improper proposals, Mundus employed an evil woman who knew that Paulina was very much given to the worship of Isis to bribe a priest to tell her that Anubis was in love with her and commanded her to come to him in the temple of Isis. As Paulina's husband did not object and she herself felt greatly flattered, she went, but it was Mundus, not Anubis, who embraced her in the dark temple. She supposed that her partner was Anubis until Mundus himself several days later told her how he had tricked her. Then she rent her garments and reported to her husband and to the emperor Tiberius how she had been beguiled. Tiberius banished Mundus, crucified the evil woman and guilty priests, and had the temple of Isis demolished.

The connection of this tale with the most famous of these stories, the fabliau about the false angel Gabriel in the *Decameron* (4th day, 2nd tale), is obvious.

5. "Tannhäuser and Venus" belongs to the Otherworld-Lover type. It has become Christianized and localized. The hero of the old poem, "Thomas of Ercildoune," has been called the Scottish Tannhäuser. Because the Queen of Elfland granted him her favors, he had to accompany her to Fairyland. Their journey to the Otherworld, the visions of Heaven, Hell, etc., and the familiar Fairyland taboos of food and speech turn up again in the closely related ballad, "Thomas Rymer." The Queen of Elfland brought Thomas Rymer back from Fairyland to avoid his being taken by the Devil as a "teind" or tithe; and on parting she gave him the power of prophesying. Mention of paying a "teind" to Hell is also found in the famous ballad "Tam Lin," which also depicts an Otherworld love. Tam was captured by the Queen of Fairies but became tired of living with her. His mortal sweetheart, following faithfully his directions, pulled him off his horse and held on to him while he turned from snake to bear to lion, then to hot iron and coal of fire, and finally to his proper shape. Thus the power which the Queen of the Fairies had over Tam was broken.

II Birth

1. "The Apple Tree" is related to the Griselda story and other tales of persecuted wives. In some of the stories of the girl with severed hands, the girl mutilates herself to discourage the incestuous love of her father. Conception caused by an apple tree is not unusual, for many myths connect this tree with generation and birth. Magic springs and fountains of youth are of frequent occurrence in folktales. It is very likely that in the original versions of this

story the servant maid based her accusation on the fact that the wife had borne twins. In some of the variants a jealous queen-mother accuses the heroine, who has borne twins, of having given birth to puppies, whereupon the poor mother wanders off with her children.

2. "Legend of Margaret, Countess of Henneberg." The countess in this local legend is punished for believing that twin births prove that the mother is guilty of adultery. Similarly in Marie de France's well-known "Lay of the Ash Tree" (*Lai le Frene*) the sharp-tongued lady accuses the mother who gave birth to twins of being unfaithful to her husband. "Everyone will understand," she says, "that two men fathered the two babies, and the fact that one of the men was not her legal mate is a disgrace to both her and her husband." Formerly the mother of twins and the children were often killed or banished. Sometimes they fled and founded a city. Rome is said to have been founded thus.

3. "The Girl Born with a Serpent around her Neck." There is an old Hindu tale about a woman who bore twins, a boy and a cobra. The cobra was kind and helpful, telling his mother how to avoid the effects of snakebite. The third story of the third night in Straparola's *Notti* is similar to our story, but a cruel stepmother takes the place of the Bluebeard in our tale. She orders Blanchebelle abandoned in a forest after the poor girl had had her hands cut off and her eyes snatched out. The serpent, after restoring her hands and eyes by means of herbs gathered in the woods, becomes a beautiful princess. In some of the Hindu variants of the Dog Gellert story, the mongoose and the child it saves from the snake are brothers.

4. "The Beast with Seven Heads." In this story the fish is clearly the father of the boys, pups, and colt. Because of their common origin, when one of these is in peril the father's blood signals the fact by boiling. This demonstrates the basis for the Life-Token motif, that is, things once in contact are ever afterward in magical contact, and whatever happens to one is felt by the others. Similarly precious stones change color, a fountain becomes muddy, etc. to indicate that danger, sickness, or death threatens the person who gave the jewels or who had drunk from the fountain. In the Grimms' "The Gold Children," a story similar to ours, two golden lilies which sprang from parts of the fish buried in the ground are life tokens of the two golden boys who were born after the fisherman's wife ate two pieces of the golden fish. Many of the motifs in our story can be found in stories about Perseus and Andromeda, as well as in "The Two Brothers" and "The Dragon Slayers."

5. "Hercules is Born." According to tradition, Alcmena bore twins. The story goes that on the night she expected her husband Amphitryon to return home from the war, Jupiter in the guise of Amphitryon appeared and begot Hercules. To have more time for his love-making the god made the night three times longer than normal. After he had gone, the real husband arrived and begot Iphicles. Jupiter's infidelity made Juno hate both Alcmena and Hercules, and she had two reasons for retarding the birth of the latter. She wished to kill Alcmena and also to rob Hercules of the high station his divine father had planned for him. In the last Juno succeeded. The delay of Hercules' birth caused Eurystheus to be born first, and he became ruler by virtue of a foolish promise Juno had tricked Jupiter into making.

In the ballad "Willie's Lady" a "vile rank witch" who hated her son's wife tries to kill her by retarding her baby's birth. The witch is tricked into revealing her spells—witch knots and combs in the lady's hair, a bush of woodbine hung in the house, and a goat or fox tethered under the bed—by being shown a wax baby which she takes to be the child whose birth she was trying to prevent.

III Adventures of the Soul

1. "The Egyptian Brothers" was discovered in 1852 in a papyrus dating from about 1250 B.C. but is much older than this. It is connected with the Osiris myth, which is related in turn to that of Attis, the Phrygian Adonis. The chaste shepherd Attis fled from evil, mutilated himself, and died under the tree with which he was identified. Later he came to life again. His mother was a virgin and became pregnant from placing a ripe pomegranate or almond in her bosom. Bata's becoming a bull was doubtless due to the cult of the Apis bull of Memphis. Like the sacrifice of the sacred ram of Thebes, the slaying of Apis is an example of the periodic slaying of sacred animals, and, of course, the blood of such an animal must not be allowed to fall to the ground. The Lilith-like wife of Bata wished to eat the bull's liver because this organ was supposed to be the seat of the soul.

This story is of great interest to the folklorist because it contains many folktale motifs of the kind which was formerly thought to have originated in India and made their way to Europe about the tenth century A.D. or later. But this story existed long before that and shows that Egypt as well as India possessed folktales and with similar motifs. Among these motifs are shape-shifting, resuscitation by replacing the heart, aromatic hair causing love, Potiphar's wife, advice from speaking animals, obstacle flight, life tokens, separable soul, water of life, plant from blood of slain person, speaking tree, and impregnation by swallowing.

2. "The King Who Lost His Body." Among the many tales more or less like this are those of King Nanda and Indradatta in the *Ocean of Story*, Prince Fadl-Allah in the *Arabian Nights*, and Solomon and Asmodeus in the *Talmud*. In the last Solomon entrusts his ring (power, soul) to one of his wives. The evil spirit Asmodeus, stealing it from her, assumes Solomon's form and drives the naked king into the streets of Jerusalem, where the people scorn him. Asmodeus usurps the throne but cannot bear to wear the ring with the Incommunicable Name graven on it. So he casts it into the sea. Solomon, now a scullion in the palace, finds the ring in the belly of a fish. Regaining his power, he banishes Asmodeus, and, having been purged of excessive pride by his sobering experience, rules as a good king should. Also belonging to this type are the story of Jovinian in the *Gesta Romanorum* and Longfellow's well-known *King Robert of Sicily*.

3. "The Giant Whose Life Was Hidden in an Egg" is a version of the Separable-Soul type. In this type the character who hides his soul away is nearly always wicked, and sometimes he is supernatural, often being a giant. He runs away with a woman and forces her to live with him. The woman's lover or husband comes to the rescue. On the way he befriends some animals, and they promise their aid. Now it is the task of the woman to worm the giant's secret from him. Before he reveals where he has hidden his soul, he lies to her twice about it. Finally he tells her where it is, and her mate with the help of the animals finds the egg or parrot, or whatever contains the soul, and destroys it. If, as often, the giant's soul is in his hair, or in a particular lock or hair-string, the hero cuts it off. Immediately the giant loses his strength

and dies. Notice that in the most famous of these stories, "Sampson and Delilah," the roles are changed. Sampson becomes the hero and Delilah the villain. But Sampson still lies twice before he tells her where his strength is.

4. "The Young King of Easaidh Ruadh." A version of the same type as told by a blind fiddler of Islay named James Wilson. The main story is preceded by an account of the hero's gambling with a magician and winning his daughter and favorite horse but losing the third time and being set a difficult task. The helpful animals in the Grimms' "Crystal Ball," also about a separable soul, assist the hero because he is their brother. In other stories of this type animals help because the hero has made a just division of food or has fed them, but in our story their motivation is not clear. The word "gruagach" generally means maiden, but in our story seems to mean "giant-magician."

5. "Chundun Rajah." A notable version of the Separable-Soul theme. The Peris, which are of Persian origin and belong to the genii or jinn, were at first evil but as time passed became benign and guided human souls to Paradise. In folktales a person's life may depend upon a talisman or necklace which he wears, and it is a common belief that good fortune or even life will depart if the necklace or similar magic object is removed from the wearer's neck. In our story we see reflected the traditional idea that death is similar to sleep, swoon, or trance. In general, it is believed that the soul (or one of the souls) remains in or near the body until it is completely decomposed. To get rid of a vampire, its body is burned. In fairy tales especially one finds a great reluctance to take death (except for villains) as final and permanent. Often paraphrases for death, such as metamorphoses or petrifaction, are used.

6. "The Pretty Witch's Lover." As the young man's soul (life, strength) is in his blood, he revives when he eats the sausage and gets his blood back. The Roman *striga* was often described as sucking blood. The clove flower is a witch herb used in sorcery. The blood as the vehicle of the soul is often saved in some way, even drunk. For instance, in the ballad "The Three Ravens" the fallow deer, a maiden transformed, lifted the head of her slain lover and "kist the wounds that were so red."

7. "Godfather Death." In Breton myth the Ankou, herald of death and driver of the spectral cart which receives the bodies of the dead, lives in a palace lit with candles, each candle representing a human life. At night Ankou blows out such candles as he sees fit. In some versions of "Godfather Death" the godson prolongs his life by tricking Death. By turning the bed around he confuses Death, or by asking for and getting time to finish the Lord's Prayer, he never comes to the end of it. The idea of life being bound up with candles, torches, or lamps occurs frequently in folklore. The burning lamp hanging over the cask containing the chopped-up body of Virgilius, the necromancer, probably has some such meaning.

8. "The Singing Bone." In the related ballad, "The Twa Sisters," one sister drowns another. In some versions a part of the drowned girl's body is fitted into a musical instrument. In others the instrument itself is made from the body. In either case the instrument plays and reveals the murder and murderer. In the Norse versions this takes place at the wedding of the evil sister and the dead girl's betrothed. In "The Juniper Tree" a boy is slain by his stepmother and eaten by his unwitting father. A half-sister buries the bones under the juniper tree, and a bird, the reincarnation of the boy, sings a song about his

murder. After giving his sister a ring and his father some slippers, the bird drops a millstone upon his stepmother, killing her. Then the bird becomes a boy again.

IV Fairies, Ogres, and the Like

1. "The Green Children." A version based on the accounts of the historians William of Newburgh (1136–1200) and Ralph of Coggeshall, who died about 1227.

2. "Fairy Ointment." Of course, Dame Goody was really a midwife, and the fairy father called her to deliver his wife, not to be a baby-sitter. It is believed that women who go to Fairyland and assist a fairy mother at childbirth bring eternal good luck upon themselves and their families. In Iran it is believed that if a mixture made of an ant's egg and a fly's brain, dried and powdered, is rubbed upon the eyelids, it will enable anyone to see the jinn.

3. "A Fairy's Child." A Breton version of the changeling motif. A changeling is the ugly ill-tempered offspring of fairy or elf left in place of a human baby which was stolen while unguarded or before it was baptized. The changeling's mother, it was supposed, would bring back the stolen child and take her brat away if the latter was made to laugh, or if it was treated either with great cruelty or great fondness. Or if placed on the beach where the incoming tide would catch it, the fairies, rather than see it drown, would take it away and restore the stolen child. Or the changeling might be passed backward through an opening in the trunk of a tree (birth in reverse) and left in the forest for a while. If on returning the humans found that the exchange had been made, they plunged the child nine times in a stream to rid him of the fairy taint.

"The child and the Fiddle" in B. Hunt's *Folk Tales of Breffny*, 1912, tells of a strange eighteen-month-old child who divided his time between whimpering and fiddling. When the man of the house saw him fiddling, he cried, "Let you be off out of this, or I'll throw you at the back of the fire, for you are no right thing at all." At this the brat fled, leaving his fiddle behind. When the good man threw the instrument on the burning turf, he discovered that it was no real fiddle at all, only an old bog stick rotten with age.

4. "On Fairy Time" illustrates the extraordinary rapid flight of time which is one of the most striking features of the Otherworld of fairies and their kin.

5. "Childe Rowland." The Scandinavian story of Burd Ellen's abduction by trolls and rescue by her brother (doubtless related to the Bluebeard cycle) is here fused with an Irish tale of a girl who suddenly vanishes as she was running around a church "widershins." Of Celtic origin also are the two herdsmen and the henwife—paralleled by the giant herdsman often encountered by Irish heroes on entering Fairyland—and, of course, Merlin, the enchanter. "Childe Rowland" is a typical product of the English Middle Ages.

6. "The Elfin Millers." An interesting literary version of a local legend.

7. "Pipi Menou and the Flying Women" is a Breton version of the Swan-Maiden type. In some versions the maiden's father, often an ogre, sets the hero some difficult tasks. In others the maiden succeeds in finding her enchanted feather envelope, which her lover had hid, and flies away, and he has difficulty in recovering her. Swan-Maiden stories are found all over the world.

8. "The Nix of the Millpond." As in "Nix Nought Nothing" a boy is unwittingly promised to an Otherworld creature. The giant's daughter helps Nix

Nought Nothing escape, and in our story the faithful wife, assisted by a wise old woman, rescues the hero. The fear of being dragged into the water by a nixie, or the like, is doubtless partly founded on the belief that it is dangerous to let one's reflection fall on some waters since it might be seized from below and the person's soul drawn down into the depths.

9. "The Black Rock Mermaid." Belief in the mermaid is widespread. The sight of one of these sea-dwelling female creatures usually presages a storm or disaster. She often lures people to destruction. To speak to her before she can utter anything, and then seize her girdle or cap, gives a person power over her. There are many stories about mermaids marrying mortals.

10. "The Cat on the Dovrefell." In some versions of this humorous tale the role of the trolls is played by a single skrattel.

V Devils and a Giant

1. "The Devil a Lawyer." In this type the Devil helps the hero, who has been dishonestly used, and appears as an advocate in court.

2. "The Devil and His Grandmother." This tale belongs to the Devil's Riddle type. The Devil often loses his prey. In one tale he grants a ripe old sinner's request not to take him until the candle burns out. The sinner promptly smothers the candle flame between the pages of a Bible and so triumphs over the Evil One. In another tale the Devil is persuaded to climb a tree. His man immediately cuts a cross on the tree trunk, and now the Devil cannot climb down until he has made concessions.

3. "Fearless John." A version of the Youth-Who-Wanted-to-Know-What-Fear-Is story. The magic objects play an important role. In some other versions all or part of our Devil's role is played by a dragon or by a hobgoblin which haunts a château. There is great variety in the means of trying to cause John to feel fear. He spends a night in a cemetery or under a gallows; he is attacked by ghost cats, or he is shaved by a ghostly barber. Finally he learns what fear is when eels are put down his back while he is asleep, or from seeing his shadow or having a fish jump onto his breast, or from a basketful of gudgeons wiggling down his spine.

4. "Of a Haunted Chamber in St. Mary's Abbey, York." The "ape" in this story is a privy ghost or demon. Ghosts and demons, it was thought, were especially likely to haunt uninhabited or malodorous places. In Talmudic times privies were located in the fields at some distance from houses and therefore were considered to be especially dangerous. Besides they were evil smelling. The privy-goer often made a loud noise by rattling nuts in a jar. Or he repeated some of the special incantations to get the protection of the guardian angels. A story is told about a rabbi who wore his phylacteries in a demon-infested privy to frighten off the evil spirits. A knight in the *Cent Nouvelles Nouvelles* (Tale LXX) is attacked by a privy demon and after a terrific struggle emerges victorious because, as he said, he continually called to mind the powerful holy words of the sacrament of baptism.

5. "Nix Nought Nothing." Among the many entertaining motifs here perhaps the most interesting are those of the Obstacle Flight, which some scholars think is based on the fear of the dead, and the Forgotten Fiancée, which often includes the "sale-of-bed" incident wherein the rival bride sells the heroine per-

mission to sleep with the bewitched hero. As he is drugged, she does not succeed in making him recognize her until the third night.

6. "The Giant That Was a Miller." An English version of the old folktale that was given literary treatment by Homer in the famous tale about Polyphemus. Our story has lost one of the traditional motifs, that is, the hero's assuming the name of "No Man" and so causing a misunderstanding when the giant calls for help. And Homer's ram, under whose belly Ulysses concealed himself, is here a dog.

VI Werewolves and Some Other Animals

1. "Werewolves." The transformation of man into wolf was generally thought to be brought about through sorcery, but it could also result from a pact with the Devil or be the consequence of an ecclesiastical malediction. As is obvious from this account, werewolves are ferocious creatures. However, in some of the famous literary treatments of the theme, the reader is asked to sympathize with the werewolf, and he is shown in a much more favorable light. Indeed, the real hero of the romance of *William of Palerme*, c. 1350, is the werewolf. Although the spell of a wicked stepmother made him a wolf in shape, his noble actions showed that he had the heart and soul of a noble knight. The villain of Marie de France's *Lai du Bisclavaret* is an unfaithful wife who hid her werewolf husband's clothes and so kept him in wolf's form so that she could marry again without fear of interference. Finally both these good werewolves regained human form.

2. "Niceros and the Werewolf." Jean Bodin in *Demonomania* gives Pliny's account of the family of Antaeus. According to this, a member of this family was annually chosen by lot and led to the shore of a lake. He undressed, hung his clothes on an oak, swam the lake, and then fled into the wilderness where he was transformed into a wolf. There he lived with other wolves for nine years. If during this time he saw no man, he returned to the lake, swam over it, reassumed human shape, and returned home. For successfully passing this ordeal nine years were added to his life.

Perhaps concepts related to the scapegoat and to the periodic slaying of a king have influenced this story of the Antaeus family. One of the methods werewolves and other transformed men take to shift their shape is swimming a stream or lake.

3. "Werewolves in Leon." The relation between the skin covering and the form beneath it is close and vital. It appears that the magic skin of wolf or fox or hyena, or the feather envelope of the swan maiden causes the transformation into wolf, swan, etc. Just as the swan maiden has to remain a woman in form until she finds and dons her feathers, in some stories the werewolf remains a wolf until he can find the clothes he had taken off to don the magic girdle, or covering made of wolfskin, or skin of a hanged man which transformed him. He usually shifts to human form at daybreak. When he does this, he must put the wolfskin, etc. in a warm safe place, for whatever happens to it happens to him—a fine example of sympathetic magic. If the skin freezes, the man freezes. If it becomes hot, as it did when one werewolf hid his skin in an oven, he is roasted.

4. "The Ungrateful Snake." This fable is a literary version of the Ungrateful-Serpent-Returned-to-Captivity type. In some variants other animals take the

role of the snake. Virgilius, the necromancer, tricked the demon into returning into his hole just as the fox does the serpent in our story.

5. "The Sole." A typical Because story or etiological tale.

6. "Why the Bear Is Stumpy-tailed." A famous Because story.

VII Vampires

1. "The Two Corpses." Apparently the vampire stretched out on the table in the chapel was a new one and had not yet been buried.

2. "The Warlock." The moujik was a wizard and on death became a vampire. Of course, he was powerless before the cross. Ralston points out that the money in the coffin seems an improbable incident and thinks that perhaps in the original version the warlock may have turned into a heap of gold.

3. "The Shoemaker of Breslow." The fresh appearance of the corpse of this suicide when disinterred indicates that he was a vampire, and the mark on his great toe, like the Devil's mark on a witch, seems to show that he had been a wizard in league with His Satanic Majesty.

4. "The Coffin Lid." It is believed that when the wooden stake is driven through the heart of a vampire, the body will writhe in agony but forever afterward lie still. In Surinam Negro belief the vampire is a woman who shifts her shape into animal form at night and prowls around looking for a human whose blood she can drink. One way to catch her is to sprinkle pepper on the sloughed-off skin and so making it too painful to put on again.

5. "The Soldier and the Vampire." Here the vampire shows that he is a drawer of blood. The aspen tree was thought sacred in ancient heathen days. Wishing rods were made from it in Germany, and the Bretons say that Christ's cross was made of aspen wood.

6. "The Dead Witch." The demon enters the witch's corpse, or rather her skin, probably intending to become a vampire.

VIII More Ghosts

1. "Evan Kermenou, Man of His Word." This is a version of the Grateful-Dead-Man story which begins with a rescued princess and does not use the motifs of the Monster in the Bridal Chamber or the Serpent Maiden. Here the princess is rescued from a dragon, not from slavery or robbers as commonly. However, the picture which brings recognition, the casting of the hero overboard, the dividing in half of the child (or winnings), etc. occur about as usual. The faithful wife's question about the old key and the new key is a popular motif and turns up in many other tales.

Another notable treatment of the Grateful-Dead-Man theme is the Middle English tale of *Sir Amadace.*

2. "The Book of Tobit." At base this is the Grateful-Dead-Man story combined with the Monster-in-the-Bridal-Chamber motif. When the kind man marries the often-widowed princess, the Grateful Dead Man saves the bridegroom's life by killing the serpent which had been creeping from her mouth and strangling her husbands. But this base is considerably modified in "The Book of Tobit." The angel Raphael is substituted for the Grateful Dead Man, and the corpse-burying kind man is doubled, becoming both Tobit and Tobias—

the first burying the corpse and the second marrying the perilous widow. The strangling serpent becomes Asmodeus, the king of the demons and the destroyer of marital happiness.

3. "Poltergeist." The poltergeist is a noisy racketing ghost, usually invisible, but always making a great nuisance of himself. He throws stones, pulls off bedclothes, presses down upon sleepers, sets fires, disturbs coffins in burial vaults and makes mysterious sounds. Usually after a while he takes his malicious self away.

4. "The Ghost with the Black and Blue Mark." The wound that is inflicted on the witch or werewolf while in animal form reappears in the corresponding part of the body when human form is reassumed. Similarly the ghost's contusion appears on the corpse in our story.

5. "Laying a Greek Ghost." Notice that Arignotus considers an incantation in the Egyptian tongue stronger than one in Greek. In folklore the older the language, the more powerful the incantation.

6. "Laying an English Ghost." To lay a ghost was not always easy or safe. The father of the poet James Thomson, it is said, died "under the oppression of diabolical malignity," having rashly undertaken to lay the celebrated Woolie Ghost. As the parson, attempting to lay a spirit that haunted a house at Homersfield in Suffolk, read the prayer book, the ghost read too and kept one line ahead of him. This made the good man's efforts futile. However, when the parson began again, one of the family released two pigeons, and as the ghost stopped to look at them, the good man got ahead of him and the job was done. The ghost was never seen again.

7. "The Spectral War Horse." There are many legends about the ghosts of slain warriors rising from their battlefield graves and fighting again.

8. "The Banshee's Wail." The banshee is a female ghost or fairy which gives notice of the impending death of a member of a family by keening, clapping of hands, and bloodcurdling shrieks. Here, as often, she is invisible. When she can be seen, she is a snake-woman like Melusina, or a beautiful maiden, or a gaunt woman with long white floating hair and clad in a cloak or a shroud. Sometimes she sits wailing under a tree which has been struck by lightning. Occasionally she appears at a ford and washes the bloody garments of the person or persons about to die. Frequently she is the ghost of the castoff mistress of a former lord of the castle. She is a family spirit, and quite often, as here, she names the person who is about to expire.

IX Witches and Wizards

1. "The Story of Telephron, the Student." A story of witchcraft and communication with the spirits of the dead. A good illustration of the importance of the name in incantations. The reluctance of the dead man to be "brought back to the duties of a momentary existence" resembles Samuel's attitude when he was raised by the Witch of Endor on the eve of Saul's disastrous engagement with the Philistines: I Sam. 28.

2. "The Enchanted Goatskins." Locks of hair, nail parings, clothing—anything that has been in contact with the person to be affected by the magic spell—are essential ingredients in love potions and similar witches' brews. They are also used in image magic and wherever contact magic is brought into play.

3. "The Witch of Treva." Witches often transformed themselves into cats and hares. Formerly the Irish killed all hares they found among the cows on May Day, supposing the hares to be witches with designs on the butter supply. The dead witch often becomes a vampire, especially if a cat or some other animal jumps or flies over the corpse before it is buried.

4. "The Witch Cat." A witch once detected or stripped of disguise can no longer be a witch. For one thing, her name could be used in magic directed against her. The shaved cat becomes the hairless woman because injuries, etc. suffered by the animal form remain when the human form is reassumed.

5. "The Bewitched Buttermilk." The hot iron that burned the buttermilk under the wizard's spell brands the wizard's back. It is believed in Lancashire that one way to break a witch's spell is to make an oatmeal cake in which the bewitched person's urine has been mixed and on which the (supposed) witch's name has been inscribed. Then the cake is slowly burned. This forces the witch to come to the house and take off the spell. Otherwise she would be burned to death.

6. "Hagridden." Farmers who fear that their horses might be ridden by witches keep them away by nailing a horseshoe over the stable door, by hanging some broom over the rack, or by placing a self-bored stone near the stalls. The self-bored stone is also a charm against nightmares and the evil eye.

7. "Virgilius, the Necromancer." Many motifs from classical myths and ancient tales attached themselves to Virgil when in the Middle Ages he became Virgilius, the necromancer. His releasing the demon is like the tale of the "Fisherman and the Genie" in the *Arabian Nights.* The "word" on the board confining this spirit must have been magic and its function similar to that of Solomon's Seal (Star of David) which barred the egress of bottle imps or genii in Arabian stories. Virgilius's bronze fly reminds one of both Apollonius Tyaneus's brazen fly, which kept the flies out of Byzantium, and Moses's brazen serpent in *Exodus*, which stayed the plague of serpents. There are similarities between the myth of Medea and Virgilius's unsuccessful attempt to rejuvenate himself. Medea, plotting the death of Peleas, chopped up an old ram, boiled the pieces in a kettle and drew forth a lamb. When Peleas's daughters tried the same magical operation on their father, they were unable to bring him back to life.

Some of the feats of the Breton magician, Doctor Coathalec (in F. M. Luzel's *Contes Populaires de Basse-Bretagne*, 1887) are like those of Virgilius. For instance, he also tried to make himself immortal. However, the police interfered and the judge threw the bottle containing the embryonic doctor against the wall. And thus the magician met his end. Once the doctor lost his shadow to the Devil; but he got along very well without it. Magicians were supposed to be able to live without shadows and also to make them project in any direction.

8. "Friar Bacon." Note that this powerful wizard was benevolent and at bottom religious. The brazen head was his most notable experiment but just as extraordinary was his raising of Julian the Apostate's spirit.

X Saints and Sinners

1. "The Legend of Saint George." Although the beginnings are lost in the mists of obscurity, the legend of Saint George grew and became glorious. It

answered a need of the Christian fighting men of the Middle Ages. Saint George became patron of England, Aragon, Portugal, and the Slovenes. At first George was apparently an obscure soldier who testified to his Christian faith before Diocletian and was put to death at Nicomedia A.D. 303. But as no authentic account of his martyrdom could be found, the Council of Nicæa placed his legend among the Apocryphal books. George had been brought up by his mother at Lydda on the coast of Joppa, and it was here that Perseus was supposed to have rescued Andromeda from the monster. So Perseus the killer of dragons and the remover of barrenness from women fused with the saint and became part of the legend. Saint George, the martyr, not only gave miraculous assistance to the arms of the Christians under Godfrey of Bouillon but also killed dragons and rescued maidens. And he could give children to barren women. His relics were just as highly prized as Thomas of Canterbury's shirt, a snippet of which would facilitate childbirth.

2. "Piers Shonks, the Dragon Killer of Hertfordshire." A tomb, supposed to be that of Piers Shonks, who died in 1086, is in the wall of the church at Brent Pelham.

3. "Saint Romuald." The saint has magic powers and benefits his district dead or alive.

4. "Doctor Faustus." This is a chapbook version of the story. According to an old account, about the middle of the fifteenth century a goldsmith of Metz named John Fust or Faust came to Paris with a number of printed Bibles. He sold these as copies written by hand. The uniformity of the supposed manuscripts astonished everyone and was considered a supernatural feat. The red ink with which the Bibles were embellished was thought to be Faust's blood, and he was, therefore, accused of being in league with the Devil.

Theophilus, who lived in Asia Minor in the sixth century, sealed the parchment he gave to the Devil in blood. His story is a forerunner of the Faust legend. Theophilus, who had been dismissed from his office, wanted it back and enlisted the services of a Jewish magician. The day after he signed the pact with the Devil, he got his position back. Then for seven years Theophilus lived a riotous life. However, feeling his end draw near, for forty days and forty nights he fasted and prayed to the Virgin. She tore the bond from the Devil and laid it upon the breast of the repentant sinner as he lay asleep in the church.

5. "The Wandering Jew." The poem on which this version is based was popular in France just after the Wandering Jew was supposed to have passed through Brussels on April 22, 1774. The Wandering Jew is called either Cartophilus, or Joseph Laquedem, or Ahasuerus. The story is a migratory legend.

6. "The *Flying Dutchman*, or Vanderdecken's Message Home." The phantom ship called the *Flying Dutchman* is seen in bad weather off the Cape of Good Hope. It bears a press of sail when other ships, from stress of weather, are unable to show an inch of canvas. To see her is considered by mariners the worst possible of omens.

There is a legend of a hellish crew which were stricken by the plague because of some heinous crime they had committed on their ship, which was laden with great treasure. These desperate men sailed from port to port asking for help and offered all their ill-gotten wealth for it, but were excluded from every harbor for fear of the contagion that was devouring them.

This is a possible basis for our story, but most of the versions give the cause of the punishment by endless wandering as the rash oath of the ship's captain, a passionately determined man. He swore during a heavy storm that he would round the Cape in spite of God or Devil, or be damned.

Other famous wrongdoers punished in similar fashion are Peter Rugg, the missing man, who wanders about New England trying to find Boston and is called the Storm Breeder; Al Samiri, the Israelite who made the Golden Calf; Herne the Hunter, who haunts Windsor Forest; and the Grand Veneur, whose story, like some of the others mentioned here, is related to the Wild-Hunt cycle. The Grand Veneur, or chief huntsman, is a specter which hunts in the forest of Fontainebleau. Once, it is said, Henry the Fourth heard the Grand Veneur's dogs baying and his huntsmen blowing their horns. The king ordered the Count de Soissons to see what it was. The count accordingly advanced toward the sound. Suddenly a tall black man appeared in a thicket, cried out, "Do you hear me?" and vanished.

7. "The Beggar's Curse." Crowds of beggars appear at the Breton Pardons, days of celebration which are partly Christian and partly survival of the Druidical Feasts of the Dead. As beggars are thought to be under the special protection of the Deity, no one should fail to show them due consideration or withhold alms, particularly during Pardons. "The Beggar's Curse," like "The *Flying Dutchman*" and "The Wandering Jew," punishes the transgressor by imposing the dread ordeal of long wandering.

XI The Power of the Name and of Magic Words

1. "Tom Tit Tot," known also as "Rumpelstilzchen" and "Titeliture." The basis is as follows: a fairy or troll, or the like, hoping to get a person in his power, offers to help him or her with a task. But the person discovers the Otherworld helper's name just in the nick of time, and this, as was agreed at the start, cancels all obligations. So the imp or elf loses his victim.

2. "Ra and Isis." This old myth is a fine example of name magic—and contact magic as well.

3. "The Golem." Name magic can create a Frankenstein monster.

4. "The Golem of Prague." Virgilius, the necromancer, had a servant somewhat like Rabbi Loew's Joseph. According to some versions, it was Rabbi Loew's custom late Friday afternoon to remove the charm that activated Joseph in order that his golem might rest on the Sabbath. Forgetting to do this on one occasion, the rabbi had to chase after him. Catching him in front of the synagogue, the rabbi quickly removed the charm and poor Joseph instantly crumbled into dust. But in Poland Rabbi Jaffe's golem was created especially to light fires and do other chores forbidden to Jews on the Sabbath. Once, letting his zeal get out of hand, this golem set fire to almost everything combustible he could find.

5. "Simeli Mountain." A story of the Open-Sesame type. An authentic part of European folklore although doubtless originating in the *Arabian Nights*. The magic words "open sesame" vary in different versions but never entirely lose all resemblance to the original formula: e.g., the "Semsi mountain, open!" of our story. Sesame, it will be remembered, is one of the magic plants which supposedly crack open mountains.

XII The Evil Eye and Things Charged with Magic

1. "Afraid of the Evil Eye." Today the evil eye is doubtless the widest spread of all superstitions, being believed in the city as well as in the country. Notice in the story the crucifix and the sign of the cross being used as counter-charms.

2. "Old Madge's Spell." In magical practice everywhere fire and smoke protects, cleanses, and cures. In Iran, for instance, the victim of the evil eye envelops his head in smoke coming from burning myrtle leaves, frankincense, and wild rue seeds while an incantation is repeated. This brings a cure. In our story it is most important that the smoke should come from furze belonging to the witch, for the chief aim is to force her to take off the spell. There are many ways to force a witch to come to the home of her victim and do this. One is to burn horse intestines. Another is to take some of the bewitched person's urine and put it in a bottle along with three pins, three needles, and three nails and a little salt. When the bottle is corked and set before the fire, the witch will find it very difficult to make water. She will have to come to this house and take off the spell to get relief.

The deadening of Old Madge's eyes in our story plainly points to the basis of the superstition of the evil eye—that is, the belief that there is an evil spirit in the eyes of certain envious and dangerous persons which discharges a powerful malign glance. Not very long ago a mother in Philadelphia killed her own daughter to "drive out" the demon she saw in her eyes.

Among the many protective charms against the evil eye are the "*mano fica*," the sign of the horn, the horseshoe, spitting, and the use of menstruous blood. Calandrin in the *Decameron* (8th day, 3rd story) is duped into thinking himself invisible until he reaches home and his wife, setting her eyes on him, begins to scold. The jesters, who have been playing with his credulity, now tell him that he ought to know that women *dans leurs temps critique* cause all magic to lose its force.

3. "The Wax Image." A fine example of image magic. A backfiring of a spell on its maker, as in our story, is strictly according to the laws of magic. If a spell is "discharged" and for some reason or other does not take effect upon the intended victim, it boomerangs upon the conjuring magician. It is dangerous to release magic force that does not accomplish its purpose: e.g., when the presumptuous sextons in "The Golem of Prague" continued with their futile attempts to reanimate the golem, an epidemic broke out and killed a thousand persons. In Iran a cowry shell which resembles an eye is used as a charm to protect from the evil eye. Such a shell is called "eye-cracker" because it is believed it casts back the evil upon the fascinator and causes his eye to crack.

Those who practice image magic usually mutter an appropriate incantation, naming the person to be harmed. Some place the image in water running toward the east. The body of the victim wastes away as the water wears away the clay image. If the image is discovered before it has done its business, it loses its power and the intended victim recovers. Pins, thorns, and rusty nails thrust into the vital parts of an image cause a long painful death. A fire kindled under an image causes the victim to waste away with a fever. To kill a witch by shooting at an image, one must use a silver bullet.

4. "The Hand of Glory at the Old Spital Inn." Directions on how to make this sinister charm can be found in the thirteenth-century *Marvellous Secrets of Little Albert*. Having cut off the left hand or foot of a person who died

in an abnormal way (on the gallows or in childbed), pickle it and dry it. Place in its palm a candle made with the fat of a hanged man or unchristened child, combined with virgin wax and Lapland sesame. The last ingredient enables the Hand of Glory to burst open locks. When the candle (sometimes the fingers) is lighted no sleeper in a house to be robbed can awake. Often the robber repeats an incantation for good measure. Only milk or blood will extinguish the baleful flames. The mandrake (mandragora, *main de gloire*), which grows under a gallows from the droppings of a hanged man's blood (or brains), is supposed to be able to do the same work as the Hand of Glory. It is likely, therefore, that the latter borrowed its name from the French *main de gloire*.

5. "The Insulted Spring." A fine example of animism. There were, of course, magic springs long before the Christian era. The well-dressing ceremonies of today are survivals of the simple nature worship of an earlier time. Indeed, man has always believed that living water had the power of healing, granting wishes, and answering prayers. In Pagan times nearly every spring had its attendant nymph: in Christian times this nymph becomes a ghost that haunts the well. In numerous quest tales the hero, often with a magic helper, travels great distances to get the water of life from a magic spring or well.

6. "The Blue Light." This belongs to the type of Aladdin and His Wonderful Lamp. Like the holy relics of the Middle Ages and the Seven-League boots of folktales, the blue light is a talisman.

7. "The Friar and Boy." Magic music occurs often in folktales.

8. "The Serpent's Stone." In Tale CV of the *Gesta Romanorum* a grateful snake drops a magic stone on the king's eyes and restores his sight. The magic stone in one form or another cures diseases, gives wealth, sends out light, and makes wishes come true.

9. "The Chaste Mates." In folktale and ballad there are many criterions of chastity. In Adam Cobsam's "The Wright's Chaste Wife" (1462) the bridegroom receives a rose garland which will not fade so long as his wife is "stable." In the minstrel ballad, "The Boy and the Mantle," the magic mantle and the horn are chastity tests.

10. "Little Annie, the Goose Girl." The magic stone here performs the same function as the golden chair and the bedclothes in the ballad "Gil Brenton."

XIII Maladies and Remedies

1. "Contagion." The translator took *rubor Aegyptus* to mean leprosy, but it can just as well be taken to mean St. Anthony's Fire, i.e., erysipelas, as I have done. The story illustrates the primitive belief that a person gets rid of a disease (bad luck, fatigue, etc.) by passing it on to another person, or to an animal. After moving from one host to another, the *rubor Aegyptus* finally lodges in the serpent.

2. "Laying the Plague." Again disease is regarded as a transferable or mobile unit. The plague is laid and sent into a rock just as a demon or ghost might be.

3. "The Poor Frog, or Transferring a Disease." Interesting description of transferring a disease. Doubtless the cunning man also uttered a charm or incantation. Often a disease is first conjured or "drawn" into a vehicle or "carrier" and thence transferred to a person or animal. In Iran, for instance, a black rag

doll is placed under the pillow of a child ill with whooping cough or croup. A coin is then tucked under each corner of the mattress. After the sick child has slept upon these, the money is given to the poor to attain merit. The rag doll is now thrown into the courtyard of an Armenian or a Jewish family. The child who picks up the doll will get the whooping cough or croup and the sick child will be well. Many examples of this kind of primitive therapeutics could be given.

4. "Magdalen and the Pins." Notice it is stated here that after Charles II "touched" Magdalen, her scrofula disappeared. Doubtless the girl is supposed to be the victim of a witch's spell. The vomiting of pins, etc. suggests some connection with such stories about the Devil as the one in Belleforest's *Histoires Prodigieuses*, 1575, relating how the serving girl Constance confessed that the Devil had made her conceive. But when she gave birth, instead of a child, "nails, bits of wood, bones, stones, tow," and other strange things emerged.

5. "The Hag and the Earl of Derby." In reality the earl died because he was poisoned, but the people attributed his death to witchcraft. The story illustrates the witch's use of image magic. It is said that image magic was used in 1324 in an attempt to destroy Edward II. In 1441 the Duchess of Gloucester employed a witch and a clerk to make a lead image of Henry VI and use it magically to kill the king. Indeed, as late as 1803 the Abbé Fiard attributed the mysterious feebleness of Louis XVI to image magic.

Before Ambrose Paré found them to possess no medicinal value, bezoar stones were highly prized as an antitoxic agent. They were carried as amulets, and during a plague were rented out by the day. Unicorn's horns were also used as an antidote to poisons.

6. "The King's Evil" has a Jacobite cast, as it was the Pretender, James Stuart, then at Avignon, who touched Lovel. The Hanoverians would have nothing to do with this hoary survival. The ceremony of touching for the king's evil was usually performed in a church or chapel, and the king was assisted by a surgeon, who examined the sick, and a chaplain, who read an appropriate text. The king placed his hands on both cheeks of the sick person and said, "I touch, but God healeth." Then an angel, or other coin worth about two and one-half crowns, hung on a ribbon, was placed about the patient's neck, and he retired. It was generally believed that if the coin was lost, the disease would return.

Some believed that Bridget Bostock, the Copnall doctress, who flourished about the middle of the eighteenth century and "cured" by rubbing fasting spittle on the affected parts of her patients, was successful chiefly because she had (it was thought) preserved her virginity. The supposed magical virtue of virginity is illustrated by an old recipe for the king's evil, which runs: Let the virgin fasting lay her hand upon the sore and say, "Apollo denieth that the heat of the plague can increase, where the naked virgin quencheth it." Then the girl must spit three times upon the sore. It is believed everywhere that human saliva, especially fasting saliva, has great magical power.

M 833